Chemical Interactions: Teacher's

Contents in Brief

Teacher's Edition

See Program Component List on page ii

Student Edition

Prentice Hall Science Explorer

Series Tables of Contents

Life Science

The Nature of Science and Technology

1. What Is Science?
2. The Work of Scientists
3. Technology and Engineering

From Bacteria to Plants

1. Living Things
2. Viruses and Bacteria
3. Protists and Fungi
4. Introduction to Plants
5. Seed Plants

Animals

1. Sponges, Cnidarians, and Worms
2. Mollusks, Arthropods, and Echinoderms
3. Fishes, Amphibians, and Reptiles
4. Birds and Mammals
5. Animal Behavior

Cells and Heredity

1. Cell Structure and Function
2. Cell Processes and Energy
3. Genetics: The Science of Heredity
4. Modern Genetics
5. Changes Over Time

Human Biology and Health

1. Bones, Muscles, and Skin
2. Food and Digestion
3. Circulation
4. Respiration and Excretion
5. Fighting Disease
6. The Nervous System
7. The Endocrine System and Reproduction

Environmental Science

1. Populations and Communities
2. Ecosystems and Biomes
3. Living Resources
4. Land, Water, and Air Resources
5. Energy Resources

Earth Science

Inside Earth

1. Plate Tectonics
2. Earthquakes
3. Volcanoes
4. Minerals
5. Rocks

Earth's Changing Surface

1. Mapping Earth's Surface
2. Weathering and Soil Formation
3. Erosion and Deposition
4. A Trip Through Geologic Time

Earth's Waters

1. Earth: The Water Planet
2. Freshwater Resources
3. Ocean Motions
4. Ocean Zones

Weather and Climate

1. The Atmosphere
2. Weather Factors
3. Weather Patterns
4. Climate and Climate Change

Astronomy

1. Earth, Moon, and Sun
2. Exploring Space
3. The Solar System
4. Stars, Galaxies, and the Universe

Physical Science

Chemical Building Blocks

1. Introduction to Matter
2. Solids, Liquids, and Gases
3. Elements and the Periodic Table
4. Exploring Materials

Chemical Interactions

1. Atoms and Bonding
2. Chemical Reactions
3. Acids, Bases, and Solutions
4. Carbon Chemistry

Motion, Forces, and Energy

1. Motion
2. Forces
3. Forces in Fluids
4. Work and Machines
5. Energy
6. Thermal Energy and Heat

Electricity and Magnetism

1. Magnetism
2. Electricity
3. Using Electricity and Magnetism
4. Electronics

Sound and Light

1. Characteristics of Waves
2. Sound
3. The Electromagnetic Spectrum
4. Light

Teacher's Edition

Chemical Interactions

PRENTICE HALL Science Explorer

PEARSON
Prentice
Hall

Needham, Massachusetts
Upper Saddle River, New Jersey

ISBN 0-13-181142-8   1 2 3 4 5 6 7 8 9 10   08 07 06 05 04

Pacing Options

PRENTICE HALL

TeacherEXPRESS™
Plan • Teach • Assess

Lab zone™

SCIENCE EXPLORER offers many aids to help you plan your instruction time, whether regular class periods or block scheduling. Section-by-section lesson plans for each chapter include suggested times for Student Edition activities. TeacherExpress™ and the Lab zone™ Easy Planner CD-ROM will help you manage your time electronically.

Pacing Chart

	PERIODS	BLOCKS		PERIODS	BLOCKS
Careers: Saving the Ozone Layer	1–2	½–1	**Chapter 4 Carbon Chemistry**		
Chapter 1 Atoms and Bonding			Chapter 4 Project *Check Out the Fine Print*	Ongoing	Ongoing
Chapter 1 Project *Models of Compounds*	Ongoing	Ongoing	**1** Properties of Carbon	1–2	½–1
1 Elements and Atoms	2–3	1–1½	**2** Carbon Compounds	3–4	1½–2
2 Atoms, Bonding, and the Periodic Table	3–4	1½–2	**3** Integrating Life Science: Life With Carbon	3–4	1½–2
3 Ionic Bonds	3–4	1½–2	Chapter 4 Review and Assessment	1–2	½–1
4 Covalent Bonds	2–3	1–1½	Interdisciplinary Exploration: Soap—The Dirt Chaser	2–3	1–1½
5 Tech & Design: Bonding in Metals	1–2	½–1			
Chapter 1 Review and Assessment	1–2	½–1			
Chapter 2 Chemical Reactions					
Chapter 2 Project *Design and Build a Closed Reaction Chamber*	Ongoing	Ongoing			
1 Observing Chemical Change	3–4	1½–2			
2 Describing Chemical Reactions	2–3	1–1½			
3 Controlling Chemical Reactions	3–4	1½–2			
4 Integrating Health: Fire and Fire Safety	1–2	½–1			
Chapter 2 Review and Assessment	1–2	½–1			
Chapter 3 Acids, Bases, and Solutions					
Chapter 3 Project *Make Your Own Indicator*	Ongoing	Ongoing			
1 Understanding Solutions	3–4	1½–2			
2 Concentration and Solubility	2–3	1–1½			
3 Describing Acids and Bases	2–3	1–1½			
4 Acids and Bases in Solution	3–4	1½–2			
5 Integrating Life Science: Digestion and pH	1–2	½–1			
Chapter 3 Review and Assessment	1–2	½–1			

Research-Based and Proven to Work

As the originator of the small book concept in middle school science, and as the nation's number one science publisher, Prentice Hall takes pride in the fact that we've always listened closely to teachers. In doing so, we've developed programs that effectively meet the needs of your classroom.

As we continue to listen, we realize that raising the achievement level of all students is the number one challenge facing teachers today. To assist you in meeting this latest challenge, Prentice Hall has combined the very best author team with solid research to create a program that meets your high standards and will ensure that no child is left behind.

With Prentice Hall, you can be confident that your students will not only be motivated, inspired, and excited to learn science, but that they will also achieve the success needed in today's environment of the No Child Left Behind (NCLB) legislation and testing reform.

On the following pages, you will read about the key elements found throughout *Science Explorer* that truly set this program apart and ensure success for you and your students.

> As we continue to listen, we realize that raising the achievement level of all students is the number one challenge facing teachers today.

A Science Program Backed by Research

In developing Prentice Hall *Science Explorer*, we used research studies as a central, guiding element. Research on *Science Explorer* indicated key elements of a textbook program that ensure students' success: support for reading and mathematics in science, consistent opportunities for inquiry, and an ongoing assessment strand. This research was conducted in phases and continues today.

1. Exploratory: Needs Assessment

Along with periodic surveys concerning state and national standards as well as curriculum issues and challenges, we conducted specific product development research, which included discussions with teachers and advisory panels, focus groups, and quantitative surveys. We explored the specific needs of teachers, students, and other educators regarding each book we developed in Prentice Hall *Science Explorer*.

2. Formative: Prototype Development and Field-Testing

During this phase of research, we worked to develop prototype materials. Then we tested the materials by field-testing with students and teachers and by performing qualitative and quantitative surveys. In our early prototype testing, we received feedback about our lesson structure. Results were channeled back into the program development for improvement.

3. Summative: Validation Research

Finally, we conducted and continue to conduct long-term research based on scientific, experimental designs under actual classroom conditions. This research identifies what works and what can be improved in the next revision of Prentice Hall *Science Explorer*. We also continue to monitor the program in the market. We talk to our users about what works, and then we begin the cycle over again. The next section contains highlights of this research.

A Science Program With Proven Results

In a year-long study in 2000–2001, students in six states using Prentice Hall *Science Explorer* outscored students using other science programs on a nationally normed standardized test.

The study investigated the effects of science textbook programs at the eighth-grade level. Twelve eighth-grade science classes with a total of 223 students participated in the study. The selected classes were of similar student ability levels.

Each class was tested at the beginning of the school year using the TerraNova CTBS Basic Battery Plus, and then retested at the end of the school year. The final results, shown in the graph, show a significant improvement in test scores from the pre-test to the post-test evaluation.

• All tests were scored by CTB/McGraw-Hill, the publisher of the TerraNova exam. Statistical analyses and conclusions were performed by an independent firm, Pulse Analytics, Inc.

In Japan, Lesson Study Research has been employed for a number of years as a tool for teachers to improve their curriculum. In April 2003, Prentice Hall adapted this methodology to focus on a lesson from this edition. Our goal was to test the effectiveness of lesson pedagogy and improve it while in the program development stage. In all three classrooms tested, student learning increased an average of 10 points from the pre- to the post-assessment.

• Detailed results of these studies can be obtained at **www.PHSchool.com/research.**

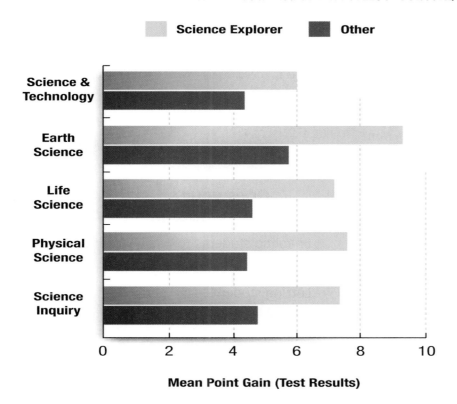

Inquiry

Foundational Research: Inquiry in the Science Classroom

"How do I know if my students are inquiring?" "If students are busy doing lots of hands-on activities, are they using inquiry?" "What is inquiry, anyway?" If you're confused, you are not alone. Inquiry is the heart and soul of science education, with most of us in continuous pursuit of achieving it with our students!

Defining Science Inquiry

What is it? Simply put, inquiry is the intellectual side of science. It is thinking like a scientist—being inquisitive, asking why, and searching for answers. The National Science Education Content Standards define inquiry as the process in which students begin with a question, design an investigation, gather evidence, formulate an answer to the original question, and communicate the investigative process and results. Since it is often difficult to accomplish all this in one class period, the standards also acknowledge that at times students need to practice only one or two inquiry components.

Understanding Inquiry

The National Research Council in Inquiry and the National Science Education Standards (2000) identified several "essential features" of classroom inquiry. We have modified these essential features into questions to guide you in your quest for enhanced and more thoughtful student inquiry.

1. *Who asks the question?* In most curricula, these focusing questions are an element given in the materials. As a teacher you can look for labs that, at least on a periodic basis, allow students to pursue their own questions.

2. *Who designs the procedures?* To gain experience with the logic underlying experimentation, students need continuous practice with designing procedures. Some labs in which the primary target is content acquisition designate procedures. But others should ask students to do so.

3. *Who decides what data to collect?* Students need practice in determining the data to collect.

4. *Who formulates explanations based upon the data?* Students should be challenged to think—to analyze and draw conclusions based on their data, not just copy answers from the text materials.

5. *Who communicates and justifies the results?* Activities should push students not only to communicate but also to justify their answers. Activities also should be thoughtfully designed and interesting so that students want to share their results and argue about conclusions.

Making Time for Inquiry

One last question—Must each and every activity have students do all of this? The answer is an obvious and emphatic "No." You will find a great variety of activities in *Science Explorer*. Some activities focus on content acquisition, and thus they specify the question and most of the procedures. But many others stress in-depth inquiry from start to finish. Because inquiry is an intellectual pursuit, it cannot merely be characterized by keeping students busy and active. Too many students have a knack for being physically but not intellectually engaged in science. It is our job to help them engage intellectually.

Michael J. Padilla, Ph.D.
Program Author of *Science Explorer*
Professor of Science Education
University of Georgia
Athens, Georgia

"Because inquiry is an intellectual pursuit, it cannot merely be characterized by keeping students busy and active."

Evaluator's Checklist

Does your science program promote inquiry by—

✔ Enabling students to pursue their own questions

✔ Allowing students to design their own procedures

✔ Letting students determine what data are best to collect

✔ Challenging students to think critically

✔ Pushing students to justify their answers

Inquiry in *Science Explorer*

Science Explorer offers the most opportunities to get students to think like a scientist. By providing inquiry opportunities throughout the program, *Science Explorer* enables students to enhance their understanding by participating in the discovery.

Student Edition Inquiry

Six lab and activity options are included in every chapter, structured from directed to open-ended—providing you the flexibility to address all types of learners and accommodate your class time and equipment requirements. As Michael Padilla notes, some activities focus on content acquisition, and thus the question and most of the procedures are specified. But many others stress in-depth inquiry from start to finish. The graph below shows how, in general, inquiry levels are addressed in the Student Edition.

Science Explorer encourages students to develop inquiry skills across the spectrum from teacher-guided to open-ended. Even more opportunities for real-life applications of inquiry are included in Science & Society, Science & Technology, Careers in Science, and Interdisciplinary Exploration features.

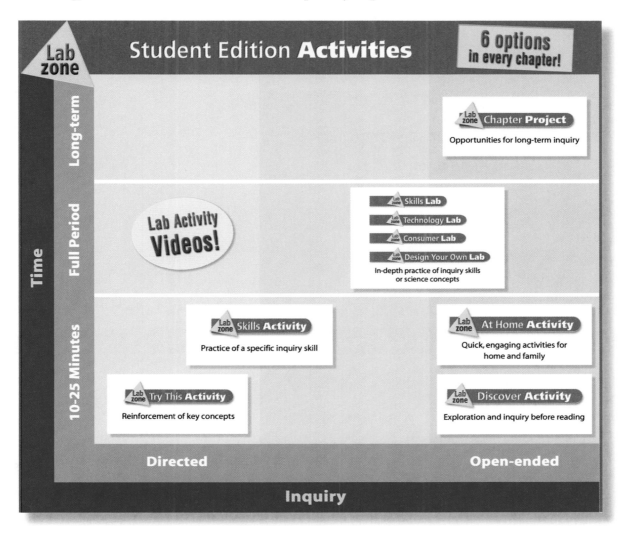

Inquiry Skills Chart

SCIENCE EXPLORER provides comprehensive teaching, practice, and assessment of science skills, with an emphasis on the process skills necessary for inquiry. This chart lists the skills covered in the program and cites the page numbers where each skill is covered.

Basic Process SKILLS			
	Student Text: Projects and Labs	Student Text: Activities	Student Text: Caption and Review Questions	Teacher's Edition: Extensions
Observing	54–55, 72–73, 135	26, 46, 84, 122, 136	144, 152	18, 50, 51, 87, 95, 126
Inferring	28–29, 110–111, 148–149	22, 33, 36, 52, 66, 86, 112, 129, 142	7, 11, 35, 42, 63, 76, 80, 89, 100, 115, 118, 152	14, 36, 49, 88
Predicting	21, 54–55, 72–73, 91, 135, 148–149	33, 94	13, 35, 42, 47, 109, 118, 152	17, 24, 62
Classifying	121	17, 48, 98, 131	42, 63, 80, 132, 134, 141, 145, 152	68
Making Models	5, 21, 45, 135	56, 58, 140	62, 67, 118	9, 23, 67, 87, 123, 124, 128, 130
Communicating	5, 21, 28–29, 45, 54–55, 72–73, 83, 90–91, 110–111, 121, 135, 148–149	11, 20, 27, 35, 39, 53, 71, 77, 79, 89, 103, 109, 115, 117, 125, 134, 138, 145, 151	65	
Measuring	110–111, 148–149			58
Calculating	72–73, 110–111	6, 52, 60, 61, 93, 96, 130	63, 97, 118	
Creating Data Tables	54–55, 72–73, 90–91, 110–111			
Graphing	21, 72–73, 90–91	33, 52	68	71
Advanced Process SKILLS			
Posing Questions			53, 152	
Developing Hypothesis		74, 126		
Designing Experiments	29, 73, 83, 90–91, 110–111, 148–149	88		

	Advanced Process SKILLS (continued)			
	Student Text: Projects and Labs	Student Text: Activities	Student Text: Caption and Review Questions	Teacher's Edition: Extensions
Controlling Variables	28–29, 83, 90–91, 110–111, 148–149			
Forming Operational Definitions		30, 104		
Interpreting Data	21, 28–29, 45, 54–55, 72–73, 110–111, 121, 148–149	12, 25, 33, 52, 69, 106, 130	14, 23, 80, 94, 96, 118	
Drawing Conclusions	29, 54–55, 72–73, 90–91, 110–111, 121, 135, 148–149	51, 52, 92, 130	42, 118, 134	51
	Critical Thinking SKILLS			
Comparing and Contrasting	5, 83		8, 11, 16, 20, 27, 35, 39, 53, 63, 89, 109, 115, 118, 134, 145	26, 31, 59, 124, 131, 137, 141
Applying Concepts		20, 35, 71, 77, 89, 109, 134	27, 39, 42, 50, 63, 71, 75, 77, 80, 89, 93, 97, 99, 103, 108, 115, 118, 130, 134, 137, 143, 152	
Interpreting Diagrams, Graphs, Photographs, and Maps			10, 14, 15, 31, 32, 34, 35, 38, 42, 49, 53, 57, 68, 85, 86, 96, 107, 113, 118, 124, 129	31, 33, 52, 59, 114, 115
Relating Cause and Effect			17, 20, 24, 27, 35, 39, 42, 70, 80, 89, 97, 114, 118, 125, 134, 152	108
Making Generalizations			27, 42, 52, 53, 71, 103, 105, 109, 128, 145	
Making Judgments			103, 145, 147	38
Problem Solving	45		37, 59, 77, 80, 109, 118, 147, 152	
	Informational Organizational SKILLS			
Concept Maps			79, 117	40, 78, 103, 116, 145, 150
Compare/Contrast Tables			41	63
Venn Diagrams			151	19, 35, 87
Flowcharts				
Cycle Diagrams				

The *Science Explorer* program provides additional teaching, reinforcement, and assessment of skills in the *Inquiry Skills Activities Book* and the *Integrated Science Laboratory Manual*.

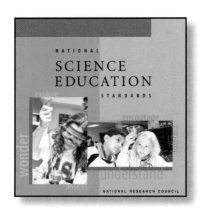

A National Look at Science Education

Project 2061 was established by the American Association for the Advancement of Science (AAAS) as a long-term project to improve science education nationwide. A primary goal of Project 2061 is to define a "common core of learning"—the knowledge and skills we want all students to achieve. Project 2061 published *Science for All Americans* in 1989 and followed this with *Benchmarks for Science Literacy* in 1993. *Benchmarks* recommends what students should know and be able to do by the end of grades 2, 5, 8, and 12. Project 2061 clearly states that *Benchmarks* is not a curriculum but a tool for designing successful curricula.

The National Research Council (NRC) used *Science for All Americans* and *Benchmarks* to develop the National Science Education Standards (NSES), which were published in 1996. The NSES are organized into six categories (Content, Teaching, Assessment, Professional Development, Program, and System) to help schools establish the conditions necessary to achieve scientific literacy for all students.

Michael Padilla, the program author of *Science Explorer,* guided one of six teams of teachers whose work led to the publication of *Benchmarks.* He also was a contributing writer of the National Science Education Standards. Under his guidance, *Science Explorer* has implemented these standards through its inquiry approach, a focus on student learning of important concepts and skills, and teacher support aligned with the NSES teaching standards.

Neither *Benchmarks* nor the NSES requires a single, uniform national curriculum, and in fact there is a great diversity nationwide in science curricula. The correlations that follow are designed to help you use the *Science Explorer* program to meet your particular curriculum needs.

Meeting the National Science Education Standards

ATOMS AND BONDING

Science as Inquiry (Content Standard A)

● **Design and conduct a scientific investigation** Students investigate what kinds of compounds produce ions in solution. *(Skills Lab—Shedding Light on Ions)*

● **Develop descriptions, explanations, predictions, and models using evidence** Students make models demonstrating how atoms bond in ionic and molecular compounds. Students investigate how the radius of an atom is related to its atomic number. *(Chapter Project; Skills Lab—Comparing Atom Sizes)*

Physical Science (Content Standard B)

● **Properties and changes of properties in matter** Elements are often called the building blocks of matter because all matter is composed of one element or a combination of two or more elements. The number of valence electrons in an atom of an element determines many properties of that element, including the ways in which the atom can bond with other atoms. Ionic bonds form as a result of the attraction between positive and negative ions. The chemical bond formed when two atoms share electrons is called a covalent bond. A metallic bond is an attraction between a positive metal ion and the electrons surrounding it. *(Chapter Project; Elements and Atoms; Atoms, Bonding, and the Periodic Table; Ionic Bonds; Skills Lab—Shedding Light on Ions; Covalent Bonds; Bonding in Metals)*

● Transfer of energy The "sea of electrons" model of solid metals explains their ability to conduct heat and electricity. *(Bonding in Metals)*

History and Nature of Science (Content Standard G)

● **History of science** Atomic theory grew as a series of models that developed from experimental evidence. Since 1869, when Mendeleev first developed the periodic table, scientists have discovered or created nearly 50 new elements. *(Elements and Atoms; Science and History)*

CHEMICAL REACTIONS

Science as Inquiry (Content Standard A)

● **Use appropriate tools and techniques to gather, analyze, and interpret data** Students investigate how temperature affects the action of the enzyme catalase. *(Skills Lab—Temperature and Enzyme Activity)*

● **Think critically and logically to make the relationships between evidence and explanations**

A National Look at Science Education (continued)

Students investigate different types of evidence of chemical reactions. (*Skills Lab—Where's the Evidence?*)

Physical Science (Content Standard B)

● **Properties and changes of properties in matter** Matter can be described in terms of two kinds of properties—physical properties and chemical properties. Many chemical reactions can be classified in one of three categories: synthesis, decomposition, or replacement. Chemists can control rates of chemical reactions by changing various factors. Fuel, oxygen, and heat are necessary to start and maintain a fire. (*Chapter Project; Observing Chemical Change; Skills Lab—Where's the Evidence?; Describing Chemical Reactions; Controlling Chemical Reactions; Skills Lab—Temperature and Enzyme Activity; Fire and Fire Safety*)

● **Transfer of energy** As matter changes, it can either absorb or release energy. All chemical reactions need a certain amount of activation energy to get started. (*Observing Chemical Change; Controlling Chemical Reactions*)

Science and Technology (Content Standard E)

● **Design a solution or product** Students design and build a closed reaction chamber. (*Chapter Project*)

Science in Personal and Social Perspectives (Content Standard F)

● **Personal health** If you know how to prevent fires in your home and what to do if a fire starts, you are better prepared to take action. (*Fire and Fire Safety*)

● **Science and technology in society** Students weigh the impact of air bag technology. (*Technology and Society*)

ACIDS, BASES, AND SOLUTIONS

Science as Inquiry (Content Standard A)

● **Design and conduct a scientific investigation** Students design an experiment to find out how to control the rate at which certain salts dissolve in water. Students experiment to see if some antacids work better than others. (*Design Your Own Lab; Consumer Lab*)

Physical Science (Content Standard B)

● **Properties and changes of properties in matter** A solution has the same properties throughout. Solubility can be used to help identify a substance because it is a characteristic property of matter. An acid is a substance that tastes sour, reacts with metals and carbonates, and turns blue litmus paper red; a base is a substance that tastes bitter, feels slippery, and turns red litmus paper blue. An acid produces hydrogen ions in water; a base produces hydroxide ions in water. Some digestive enzymes work at a low pH; for others, the pH must be high or neutral. (*Understanding Solutions; Design Your Own Lab; Concentration and Solubility; Describing Acids and Bases; Acids and Bases in Solution; Consumer Lab; Digestion and pH*)

● **Transfer of energy** Solutes lower the freezing point and raise the boiling point of a solvent. For most solids, solubility increases as the temperature increases. (*Understanding Solutions; Design Your Own Lab; Concentration and Solubility*)

Life Science (Content Standard C)

● **Structure and function in living systems** The process of digestion breaks down the complex molecules of foods into smaller molecules that can be used by the body. (*Digestion and pH*)

Science and Technology (Content Standard E)

● **Design a solution or product** Students create their own acid-base indicators. (*Chapter Project*)

Science in Personal and Social Perspectives (Content Standard F)

● **Science and technology in society** Acids and bases have many uses around the home and in industry. (*Describing Acids and Bases*)

CARBON CHEMISTRY

Science as Inquiry (Content Standard A)

● **Use appropriate tools and techniques to gather, analyze, and interpret data** Students identify carbon compounds found in different foods. Students investigate which juices contain the most vitamin C. (*Chapter Project; Consumer Lab*)

Physical Science (Content Standard B)

● **Properties and changes of properties in matter** Few atoms have the ability of carbon to bond with both itself and atoms of other elements in so many different ways. Compounds that contain carbon are called organic compounds. Carbohydrates, proteins, lipids, and nucleic acids are all organic molecules. (*Properties of Carbon; Carbon Compounds; Technology Lab; Life With Carbon*)

Life Science (Content Standard C)

● **Structure and function in living systems** The four classes of organic compounds required by living things are carbohydrates, proteins, lipids, and nucleic acids. (*Life With Carbon*)

Science and Technology (Content Standard E)

● **Understandings about science and technology** Since the first organic compound was synthesized, biologists and chemists have synthesized a number of useful compounds. (*Tech & Design in History*)

Science in Personal and Social Perspectives (Content Standard F)

● **Risks and benefits** Students weigh the risks and benefits of artificial sweeteners. (*Science and Society*)

● **Science and technology in society** Diamond, graphite, fullerenes, and nanotubes are four forms of the element carbon. (*Properties of Carbon*)

Note: To see how the benchmarks are supported by *SCIENCE EXPLORER,* go to **PHSchool.com.**

Reading Comprehension in the Science Classroom

Q&A

Q: Why are science texts often difficult for students to read and comprehend?

A: In general, science texts make complex literacy and knowledge demands on learners. They have a more technical vocabulary and a more demanding syntax, and place a greater emphasis on inferential reasoning.

Q: What does research say about facilitating comprehension?

A: Studies comparing novices and experts show that the conceptual organization of experts' knowledge is very different from that of novices. For example, experts emphasize core concepts when organizing knowledge, while novices focus on superficial details. To facilitate comprehension, effective teaching strategies should support and scaffold students as they build an understanding of the key concepts and concept relationships within a text unit.

Q: What strategies can teachers use to facilitate comprehension?

A: Three complementary strategies are very important in facilitating student comprehension of science texts. First, guide student interaction with the text using the built-in strategies. Second, organize the curriculum in terms of core concepts (e.g., the **Key Concepts** in each section). Third, develop visual representations of the relationships among the key concepts and vocabulary that can be referred to during instruction.

Nancy Romance, Ph.D.
Professor of Science Education
Florida Atlantic University
Fort Lauderdale, Florida

"Effective teaching strategies should support and scaffold students as they build an understanding of the key concepts and concept relationships within a text unit."

Reading Support in *Science Explorer*

The latest research emphasizes the importance of activating learners' prior knowledge and teaching them to distinguish core concepts from less important information. These skills are now more important than ever, because success in science requires students to read, understand, and connect complex terms and concepts.

Before students read—
Reading Preview introduces students to the key concepts and key terms they'll find in each section. The **Target Reading Skill** is identified and applied with a graphic organizer.

During the section—
Boldface Sentences identify each key concept and encourage students to focus on the big ideas of science.

Reading Checkpoints reinforce students' understanding by slowing them down to review after every concept is discussed.

Caption Questions draw students into the art and photos, helping them connect the content to the images.

After students read—
Section Assessment revisits the **Target Reading Skill** and encourages students to use the graphic organizer.

Each review question is scaffolded and models the way students think, by first easing them into a review and then challenging them with increasingly more difficult questions.

Evaluator's Checklist

Does your science program promote reading comprehension with—

✔ Text structured in an outline format and key concepts highlighted in boldface type

✔ Real-world applications to activate prior knowledge

✔ Key concepts, critical vocabulary, and a reading skill for every section

✔ Sample graphic organizers for each section

✔ Relevant photos and carefully constructed graphics with questions

✔ Reading checkpoints that appear in each section

✔ Scaffolded questions in section assessments

Math in the Science Classroom

Why should students concern themselves with mathematics in your science class?

Good science requires good data from which to draw conclusions. Technology enhances the ability to measure in a variety of ways. Often the scientist must measure large amounts of data, and thus an aim of analysis is to reduce the data to a summary that makes sense and is consistent with established norms of communication—i.e., mathematics.

Calculating measures of central tendency (e.g., mean, median, or mode), variability (e.g., range), and shape (graphic representations) can effectively reduce 500 data points to 3 without losing the essential characteristics of the data. Scientists understand that a trade-off exists between precision and richness as data are folded into categories, and so margins of error can be quantified in mathematical terms and factored into all scientific findings.

Mathematics is the language used by scientists to model change in the world. Understanding change is a vital part of the inquiry process. Mathematics serves as a common language to communicate across the sciences. Fields of scientific research that originated as separate disciplines are now integrated, such as happened with bioengineering. What do the sciences have in common? Each uses the language of mathematics to communicate about data and the process of data analysis. Recognizing this need, *Science Explorer* integrates mathematics practice throughout the program and gives students ample opportunity to hone their math skills.

Clearly, mathematics plays an important role in your science classroom!

William Tate, Ph.D.
Professor of Education and
Applied Statistics and
Computation
Washington University
St. Louis, Missouri

> "Mathematics is the language used by scientists to model change in the world."

Integrated Math Support

In the Student Edition
The math instruction is based on principles derived from Prentice Hall's research-based mathematics program.

Sample Problems, Math Practice, Analyzing Data, and a Math Skills Handbook all help to provide practice at point of use, encouraging students to Read and Understand, Plan and Solve, and then Look Back and Check.

Color-coded variables aid student navigation and help reinforce their comprehension.

In the Teacher's Edition
Math teaching notes enable the science teacher to support math instruction and math objectives on high-stakes tests.

In the Guided Reading and Study Workbook
These unique worksheets help students master reading and enhance their study and math skills. Students can create a record of their work for study and review.

Evaluator's Checklist

Does your science program promote math skills by—

✔ Giving students opportunities to collect data

✔ Providing students opportunities to analyze data

✔ Enabling students to practice math skills

✔ Helping students solve equations by using color-coded variables

✔ Using sample problems to apply science concepts

Technology and Design

Technology and Design in the Science Classroom

Much of the world we live in is designed and made by humans. The buildings in which we live, the cars we drive, the medicines we take, and often the food we eat are products of technology. The knowledge and skills needed to understand the processes used to create these products should be a component of every student's basic literacy.

Some schools offer hands-on instruction on how technology development works through industrial arts curricula. Even then, there is a disconnect among science (understanding how nature works), mathematics (understanding data-driven models), and technology (understanding the human-made world). The link among these fields of study is the engineering design process—that process by which one identifies a human need and uses science knowledge and human ingenuity to create a technology to satisfy the need. Engineering gives students the problem-solving and design skills they will need to succeed in our sophisticated, three-dimensional, technological world.

As a complement to "science as inquiry," the National Science Education Standards (NRC, 1996) call for students at all age levels to develop the abilities related to "technology as design," including the ability to identify and frame a problem and then to design, implement, and evaluate a solution. At the 5–8 grade level, the standards call for students to be engaged in complex problem-solving and to learn more about how science and technology complement each other. It's also important for students to understand that there are often constraints involved in design as well as trade-offs and unintended consequences of technological solutions to problems.

As the *Standards for Technological Literacy* (ITEA, 2000) state, "Science and technology are like conjoined twins. While they have separate identities they must remain inextricably connected." Both sets of standards emphasize how progress in science leads to new developments in technology, while technological innovation in turn drives advances in science.

Ioannis Miaoulis, Ph.D.
President
Museum of Science
Boston, Massachusetts

"Engineering gives students the problem-solving and design skills they will need to succeed in our sophisticated, three-dimensional, technological world."

Evaluator's Checklist

Does your science program promote technology and design by—

✔ Incorporating technology and design concepts and skills into the science curriculum

✔ Giving students opportunities to identify and solve technological design problems

✔ Providing students opportunities to analyze the impact of technology on society

✔ Enabling students to practice technology and design skills

Technology and Design

Technology and Design in *Science Explorer*

How often do you hear your students ask: "Why do I need to learn this?" Connecting them to the world of technology and design in their everyday life is one way to help answer this question. It is also why so many state science curricula are now emphasizing technology and design concepts and skills.

Science Explorer makes a special effort to include a technology and design strand that encourages students to not only identify a need but to take what they learned in science and apply it to design a possible solution, build a prototype, test and evaluate the design, and/or troubleshoot the design. This strand also provides definitions of technology and engineering and discusses the similarities and differences between these endeavors and science. Students will learn to analyze the risks and benefits of a new technology and to consider the tradeoffs, such as safety, costs, efficiency, and appearance.

In the Student Edition

Integrated Technology & Design Sections

Sections throughout *Science Explorer* specifically integrate technology and design with the content of the text. For example, students not only learn how seismographs work but also learn what role seismographs play in society and how people use the data that are gathered.

Technology Labs

These labs help students gain experience in designing and building a device or product that meets a particular need or solves a problem. Students follow a design process of Research and Investigate, Design and Build, and Evaluate and Redesign.

Chapter Projects

Chapter Projects work hand-in-hand with the chapter content. Students design, build, and test based on real-world situations. They have the opportunity to apply the knowledge and skills learned to building a product.

Special Features

This technology and design strand is also reflected in Technology & Society and Science & Society features as well as Technology & History timelines. These highly visual features introduce a technology and its impact on society. For example, students learn how a hybrid car differs from a traditional car.

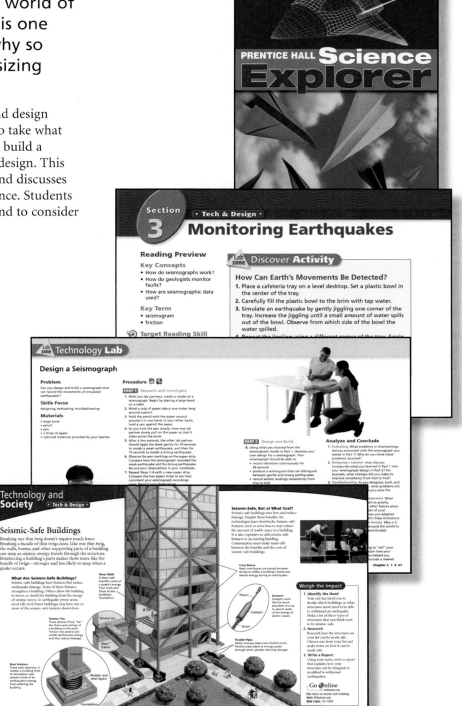

Assessment in the Science Curriculum

No Child Left Behind clearly challenges school districts across the nation to raise expectations for all students with testing of student achievement in science beginning in 2007–2008.

A primary goal of NCLB is to provide classroom teachers with better data from scientifically valid assessments in order to inform instructional planning and to identify students who are at risk and require intervention. It has been a common practice to teach a science lesson, administer a test, grade it, and move on. This practice is a thing of the past. With the spotlight now on improving student performance, it is essential to use assessment results as a way to identify student strengths and challenges. Providing student feedback and obtaining student input is a valuable, essential part of the assessment process.

Assessment is a never-ending cycle, as is shown in the following diagram. Although you may begin at any point in the assessment cycle, the basic process is the same.

An important assessment strategy is to ensure that students have ample opportunities to check their understanding of skills and concepts before moving on to the next topic. Checking for understanding also includes asking appropriate, probing questions with each example presented. This enables students and teachers to know whether the skills or concepts being introduced are actually understood.

Eileen Depka
Supervisor of Standards and Assessment
Waukesha, Wisconsin

"Meeting the NCLB challenge will necessitate an integrated approach to assessment with a variety of assessment tools."

Implement the plan with a focus on gathering and using assessment information throughout.

Use a variety of assessment tools to gain information and strengthen student understanding.

Analyze assessment results to create a picture of student strengths and challenges.

Identify strategies to achieve the target, create a plan for implementation, and choose assessments tools.

Choose a target to create a focused path on which to proceed.

IMPLEMENT   ASSESS   ANALYZE   STRATEGIZE   TARGET

Evaluator's Checklist

Does your science program include assessments that—

- ✔ Are embedded before, during, and after lesson instruction
- ✔ Align to standards and to the instructional program
- ✔ Assess both skill acquisition and understanding
- ✔ Include meaningful rubrics to guide students
- ✔ Mirror the various formats of standardized tests

Assessment in *Science Explorer*

Science Explorer's remarkable range of strategies for checking progress will help teachers find the right opportunity for reaching all their students.

The assessment strategies in *Science Explorer* will help both students and teachers alike ensure student success in content mastery as well as high-stakes test performance. A wealth of opportunities built into the Student Edition help students monitor their own progress. Teachers are supported with ongoing assessment opportunities in the Teacher's Edition and an easy-to-use, editable test generator linked to content objectives. These integrated, ongoing assessment tools assure success.

Especially to support state and national testing objectives, Prentice Hall has developed test preparation materials that model the NCLB approach.

- **Diagnostic Assessment** tools provide in-depth analysis of strengths and weaknesses, areas of difficulty, and probable underlying causes that can help teachers make instructional decisions and plan intervention strategies.

- **Progress Monitoring** tools aligned with content objectives and state tests provide ongoing, longitudinal records of student achievement detailing individual student progress toward meeting end-of-year and end-of-schooling grade level, district, or state standards.

- **Outcomes** tools that mimic state and national tests show whether individual students have met the expected standards and can help a school system judge whether it has made adequate progress in improving its performance year by year.

Caption Questions enhance critical thinking skills

Reading Checkpoints reinforce students' understanding

Scaffolded Section Assessment Questions model the way students think

Comprehensive Chapter Reviews and Assessment provide opportunities for students to check their own understanding and practice valuable high-stakes test-taking skills

Exam*View*®, Computer Test Bank CD-ROM provides teachers access to thousands of modifiable test questions in English and Spanish

Test Preparation Blackline Masters and Student Workbook include diagnostic and prescription tools, progress-monitoring aids, and practice tests that help teachers focus on improving test scores.

Section 3 Assessment

Target Reading Skill Sequencing Refer to your flowchart about seismographs as you answer Question 1.

Reviewing Key Concepts

1. a. Defining What is a seismogram?
   b. Explaining How can geologists tell apart the different types of seismic waves on a seismogram?
   c. Comparing and Contrasting Two identical seismographs are located 1,000 km and 1,200 km from an earthquake's epicenter. How would the two seismograms for the earthquake compare?

2. a. Reviewing What changes are measured by the instruments used to monitor faults?
   b. Describing How are satellites used to measure movements along a fault?
   c. Inferring A satellite that monitors a fault detects an increasing tilt in the land surface along the fault. What could this change in the land surface indicate?

3. a. Listing What are three ways in which geologists use seismographic data?
   b. Explaining How do geologists use seismographic data to make maps of faults?
   c. Making Generalizations Why is it difficult to predict earthquakes?

Writing in Science

Dialogue Geologists in Alaska have just detected an earthquake and located the earthquake's epicenter. Write a dialogue in which the geologists notify a disaster response team that will help people in the earthquake area.

Chapter 2 F ◆ 65

Standardized Test Prep

Test-Taking Tip
When answering questions about diagrams, read all parts of the diagram carefully, including title, captions, and labels. Make sure that you understand the meaning of arrows and other symbols. Determine exactly what the question asks. Then eliminate those answer choices that are not supported by the diagram.

Practice answering this question.
The diagram shows how stress affects a mass of rock in a process called
  A compression.
  B tension.
  C squeezing.
  D shearing.
The correct answer is **D** because the arrows show rock being pulled in opposite directions.

Choose the letter that best answers the question or completes the statement.

1. In a strike-slip fault, rock masses along the fault move
   A in the same direction.
   B down only.
   C together.
   D sideways past each other.

2. Stress will build until an earthquake occurs if friction along a fault is
   F decreasing.   G high.
   H low.   J changed to heat.

Use the information below and your knowledge of science to answer Questions 3 and 4.

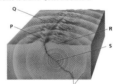

Seismic waves

3. When an earthquake occurs, seismic waves travel
   A from P in all directions.
   B from R to S.
   C from S in all directions.
   D from Q to P.

4. At point R, seismic waves from an earthquake would be
   F weaker than at P.
   G likely to cause little damage.
   H weaker than at Q.
   J likely to cause the most damage.

5. To estimate the total energy released by an earthquake, a geologist should use the
   A Mercalli scale.   B Richter scale.
   C epicenter scale.   D moment magnitude scale.

Constructed Response

6. A geologist discovers a large fault beneath a major city. Why would this information be helpful in determining earthquake risk in the area? What three safety steps should the geologist recommend?

Chapter 2 F ◆ 79

Master Materials List

SCIENCE EXPLORER offers an abundance of activity options in the Student Edition so you can pick and choose those that suit your needs. Prentice Hall has worked with Neo/SCI Corporation to develop Consumable Kits and Nonconsumable Kits that precisely match the needs of the SCIENCE EXPLORER labs. Use this Master Materials List or the Materials Ordering CD-ROM to help order your supplies. For more information on materials kits for this program, contact your local Prentice Hall sales representative or Neo/SCI Corporation at 1-800-526-6689 or www.neosci.com.

Consumable Materials

Description	Textbook Section(s)	Quantity per class	Description	Textbook Section(s)	Quantity per class
Aluminum foil, roll	2-1(Lab)	1	*Ice, bag	3-1(Lab)	1
*Ammonia cleaner, bottle	3-3(DIS), 3-4(DIS)	1	Iodine solution, 30 mL	2-3(DIS), 4-3(Lab)	1
Antacid tablet	3-4(TT)	5	*Juice, fruit	3-3(DIS), 3-4(TT), 4-3(TT)	1
*Antacid, liquid, variety	3-4(Lab)	5			
*Apple, mashed	4-2(DIS)	1	*Juice, red cabbage	3-4(DIS)	1
Baking soda, 454 g	2-1(DIS), 2-4(DIS), 3-2(SA), 3-3(DIS)	1	Knife, plastic, pkg/20	2-3(SA)	1
			Lemon juice, 60 mL	3-3(DIS), 3-4(DIS)	1
*Banana, mashed	4-2(DIS)	1	Light bulb, mini, pkg/5	1-3(Lab)	1
Beverages, variety	4-3(Lab)	5	Limewater, 500 mL	2-1(TT)	1
*Bread, crusty, loaf	3-5(DIS)	1	*Liquids, variety	3-2(DIS), 4-3(TT)	5
Candle, birthday, pkg/24	2-1(Lab), 2-4(DIS)	1	Litmus paper, blue, pkg/100	3-3(DIS), 3-4(TT)	1
Catalase, 1g	2-3(Lab)	1	Litmus paper, red, pkg/100	3-3(DIS), 3-4(TT)	1
*Coffee	3-4(TT)	1	Matches, pkg/32	2-1(Lab), 2-4(DIS)	5
Copper strip	1-3(Lab)	10	*Metal, piece, variety	1-5(DIS)	15
Copper sulfate, 30 g	2-1(Lab)	1	Methyl orange, 1g	3-4(Lab)	1
Cotton balls, pkg/100	4-2(DIS)		*Milk, gallon	4-3(DIS), 4-3(TT)	1
Cup, clear, plastic, pkg/50, 9 oz.	2-1(DIS), 2-1(TT), 2-1(Lab), 2-3(DIS), 3-1(DIS), 3-2(DIS), 3-3(DIS), 3-4(DIS), 3-4(TT), 3-4(Lab), 4-2(TT), 4-3(DIS), 4-3(Lab)	3	Modeling clay, white, 1lb.	2-1(Lab), 2-4(DIS)	1
			Oil, vegetable, 16 oz.	1-4(DIS)	1
			*Paper towel, roll	4-2(TT)	1
			*Paper, brown	4-3(TT)	5
			*Paper, white, ream	1-1(DIS), 4-1(DIS)	
Cup, paper, pkg/50, 5 oz.	4-2(DIS)	1	*Pencil	1-3(TT), 4-1(DIS)	5
*Detergent, liquid	1-4(DIS)	1	Pepper, 1.5 oz.	3-1(DIS)	1
Dropper, plastic, pkg/10	3-3(DIS), 3-4(DIS), 3-4(TT), 3-4(Lab), 4-3(TT), 4-3(Lab)	9	Petroleum jelly, packet	4-2(TT)	5
			*Pineapple, mashed	4-2(DIS)	1
Dry cell, 1.5-V	1-3(Lab)	10	Salt, 737 g	3-1(DIS), 3-1(TT), 3-1(SA), 3-1(Lab), 3-3(DIS)	1
Filter paper, 9 cm, pkg/50	2-3(Lab), 4-3(DIS)	15			
Gelatin, 1oz.	2-3(SA), 3-1(TT)	2	Salt, coarse, 500 g	1-3(TT), 3-1(Lab)	1
*Gumdrops, multi-colored	4-2(Lab)	300–400	Salt, rock, 1lb.	3-1(Lab)	1
Hydrochloric acid, 8%, 30 mL	2-1(Lab), 3-4(Lab)	1	*Soap solution	3-3(DIS)	1
Hydrogen peroxide, 8 oz.	2-3(Lab)	1	*Soda water, 1-L bottle	2-1(TT), 3-4(TT)	2

KEY: **CP:** Chapter Project; **DIS:** Discover; **SA:** Skills Activity; **TT:** Try This; **Lab:** Skills, Consumer, Design Your Own, & Technology & Design
* items school supplied

Quantities based on five groups of six students per class.

Master Materials List

Consumable Materials (continued)

Description	Textbook Section(s)	Quantity per class	Description	Textbook Section(s)	Quantity per class
Sodium carbonate, 30 mL	2-1(Lab)	1	Sugar, 454 g	1-3(Lab), 2-1(CP), 2-1(Lab)	1
Sodium chloride, 100 g	1-3(Lab)	1	*Tea	3-4(TT)	1
*Solids, variety	3-2(DIS)	5	Thread, spool	1-3(TT)	1
*Solute, variety	3-1(SA)	5	Toothpick, pkg/250	4-2(Lab)	1
Spoon, plastic, pkg/25	1-3(Lab), 2-1(DIS), 2-1(Lab), 2-3(DIS), 3-1(DIS), 3-1(Lab), 3-2(DIS), 3-2(SA)	1	Vinegar, 500 mL	2-1(DIS), 2-4(DIS), 3-3(DIS), 4-3(DIS)	2
Spoon, large	2-4(DIS)	5	Vitamin C tablet, 1000 mg	2-3(DIS), 4-3(Lab)	2
Starch, 2 g	4-3(Lab)	1	*Water, distilled	1-3(Lab)	1
			*Wintergreen candy	4-2(DIS)	5

Nonconsumable Materials

Description	Textbook Section(s)	Quantity per class	Description	Textbook Section(s)	Quantity per class
Alligator clips	1-3(Lab)	40	Graduated cylinder, polypropylene, 10 mL	2-1(Lab)	5
*Apron, safety	2-1(TT), 2-3(DIS), 3-4(TT)	30	Graduated cylinder, polypropylene, 100 mL	1-3(Lab), 3-1(DIS), 3-1(Lab), 3-2(SA), 4-3(DIS)	5
*Balance	2-2(TT), 3-1(SA), 3-1(Lab)	5	*Hot plate	3-1(SA), 3-1(Lab)	5
Beaker, glass, 100 mL	3-1(TT)	5	Jar, clear, plastic, 250 mL, with lid	1-3(TT), 1-4(DIS)	5
Beaker, polypropylene, 250 mL	1-3(Lab), 2-3(Lab), 2-4(DIS), 3-1(Lab), 3-2(SA)	5	Nut, hex, pkg/25	2-2(TT)	1
			*Periodic table	1-2(DIS), 1-2(SA), 1-2(Lab), 1-3(SA)	5
Bolt, round head, pkg/25	2-2(TT)	1	pH color chart	3-4(TT)	1
*Calculator	1-1(DIS), 1-2(Lab)	5	Rack, test tube	3-1(Lab)	5
Checkers, pkg/24	1-3(DIS)	5	Rubber stopper, #4, solid	3-1(Lab)	25
*Coins, variety	2-2(DIS)	120	Rubber stopper, 1-hole	2-3(Lab)	5
Container, plastic, narrow	4-3(DIS)	10	Ruler, 15 cm, pkg/10	1-1(DIS), 1-2(Lab), 2-3(SA)	1
*Dime	1-1(DIS)	5	Socket, mini	1-3(Lab)	5
Drawing compass	1-2(Lab)	5	Stirring rod	1-3(TT), 3-1(Lab)	5
Dropper bottle, 30 mL	2-1(Lab)	5	*Stopwatch	2-3(Lab), 3-1(Lab)	5
Flashlight, pen	3-1(TT)	5	Test tube, 25 X 150 mm	2-3(Lab), 3-1(Lab)	30
Forceps, plastic	2-3(Lab)	5	Thermometer, 12", alcohol, -10°C to 110°C	3-1(SA), 3-1(Lab)	5
Funnel	4-3(DIS)	10	Tongs	2-1(Lab)	5
*Goggles, safety	2-1(DIS), 2-1(TT), 2-3(DIS), 2-4(DIS), 3-4(TT)	30	Wire, copper, insulated, 25 m	1-3(Lab)	1

KEY: CP: Chapter Project; **DIS:** Discover; **SA:** Skills Activity; **TT:** Try This; **Lab:** Skills, Consumer, Design Your Own, & Technology & Design
  * items school supplied

Quantities based on five groups of six students per class.

Chemical Interactions

Book-Specific Resources

Student Edition
Interactive Textbook
Teacher's Edition
All-in-One Teaching Resources
Color Transparencies
Guided Reading and Study Workbook
Student Edition on Audio CD
Discovery Channel Video
Lab Activity Video
Consumable and Nonconsumable Materials Kits

Program Print Resources

Integrated Science Laboratory Manual
Computer Microscope Lab Manual
Inquiry Skills Activity Books
Progress Monitoring Assessments
Test Preparation Workbook
Test-Taking Tips With Transparencies
Teacher's ELL Handbook
Reading in the Content Area

Program Technology Resources

TeacherExpress™ CD-ROM
Interactive Textbook
Presentation Pro CD-ROM
ExamView®, Computer Test Bank CD-ROM
Lab zone™ Easy Planner CD-ROM
Probeware Lab Manual With CD-ROM
Computer Microscope and Lab Manual
Materials Ordering CD-ROM
Discovery Channel DVD Library
Lab Activity DVD Library
Web Site at PHSchool.com

Spanish Print Resources

Spanish Student Edition
Spanish Guided Reading and Study Workbook
Spanish Teaching Guide With Tests

Cover
Spectacular fireworks and golden, roasted marshmallows both result from chemical reactions.

Acknowledgments appear on page 198, which constitutes an extension of this copyright page.

PEARSON

Prentice Hall

ISBN 0-13-115097-9

2 3 4 5 6 7 8 9 10   08 07 06 05 04

Program Authors

Michael J. Padilla, Ph.D.
Professor of Science Education
University of Georgia
Athens, Georgia

Michael Padilla is a leader in middle school science education. He has served as an author and elected officer for the National Science Teachers Association and as a writer of the National Science Education Standards. As lead author of Science Explorer, Mike has inspired the team in developing a program that meets the needs of middle grades students, promotes science inquiry, and is aligned with the National Science Education Standards.

Ioannis Miaoulis, Ph.D.
President
Museum of Science
Boston, Massachusetts

Originally trained as a mechanical engineer, Ioannis Miaoulis is in the forefront of the national movement to increase technological literacy. As dean of the Tufts University School of Engineering, Dr. Miaoulis spearheaded the introduction of engineering into the Massachusetts curriculum. Currently he is working with school systems across the country to engage students in engineering activities and to foster discussions on the impact of science and technology on society.

Martha Cyr, Ph.D.
Director of K–12 Outreach
Worcester Polytechnic Institute
Worcester, Massachusetts

Martha Cyr is a noted expert in engineering outreach. She has over nine years of experience with programs and activities that emphasize the use of engineering principles, through hands-on projects, to excite and motivate students and teachers of mathematics and science in grades K–12. Her goal is to stimulate a continued interest in science and mathematics through engineering.

Book Authors

David V. Frank, Ph.D.
Head, Department of
Physical Sciences
Ferris State University
Big Rapids, Michigan

John G. Little
Science Teacher
St. Mary's High School
Stockton, California

Steve Miller
Science Writer
State College, Pennsylvania

Contributing Writers

Linda Blaine
Science Teacher
Millbrook High School
Raleigh, North Carolina

Mary Sue Burns
Science Teacher
Pocahontas County
High School
Dunmore, West Virginia

Thomas L. Messer
Science Teacher
Foxborough Public Schools
Foxborough, Massachusetts

Thomas R. Wellnitz
Science Teacher
The Paideia School
Atlanta, Georgia

Consultants

Reading Consultant

Nancy Romance, Ph.D.
Professor of Science
Education
Florida Atlantic University
Fort Lauderdale, Florida

Mathematics Consultant

William Tate, Ph.D.
Professor of Education and
Applied Statistics and
Computation
Washington University
St. Louis, Missouri

Reviewers

Tufts University Content Reviewers

Faculty from Tufts University in Medford, Massachusetts, developed *Science Explorer* chapter projects and reviewed the student books.

Astier M. Almedom, Ph.D.
Department of Biology

Wayne Chudyk, Ph.D.
Department of Civil and Environmental Engineering

John L. Durant, Ph.D.
Department of Civil and Environmental Engineering

George S. Ellmore, Ph.D.
Department of Biology

David Kaplan, Ph.D.
Department of Biomedical Engineering

Samuel Kounaves, Ph.D.
Department of Chemistry

David H. Lee, Ph.D.
Department of Chemistry

Douglas Matson, Ph.D.
Department of Mechanical Engineering

Karen Panetta, Ph.D.
Department of Electrical Engineering and Computer Science

Jan A. Pechenik, Ph.D.
Department of Biology

John C. Ridge, Ph.D.
Department of Geology

William Waller, Ph.D.
Department of Astronomy

Content Reviewers

Paul Beale, Ph.D.
Department of Physics
University of Colorado
Boulder, Colorado

Jeff Bodart, Ph.D.
Chipola Junior College
Marianna, Florida

Michael Castellani, Ph.D.
Department of Chemistry
Marshall University
Huntington, West Virginia

Eugene Chiang, Ph.D.
Department of Astronomy
University of California – Berkeley
Berkeley, California

Charles C. Curtis, Ph.D.
Department of Physics
University of Arizona
Tucson, Arizona

Daniel Kirk-Davidoff, Ph.D.
Department of Meteorology
University of Maryland
College Park, Maryland

Diane T. Doser, Ph.D.
Department of Geological Sciences
University of Texas at El Paso
El Paso, Texas

R. E. Duhrkopf, Ph.D.
Department of Biology
Baylor University
Waco, Texas

Michael Hacker
Co-director, Center for Technological Literacy
Hofstra University
Hempstead, New York

Michael W. Hamburger, Ph.D.
Department of Geological Sciences
Indiana University
Bloomington, Indiana

Alice K. Hankla, Ph.D.
The Galloway School
Atlanta, Georgia

Donald C. Jackson, Ph.D.
Department of Molecular Pharmacology, Physiology, & Biotechnology
Brown University
Providence, Rhode Island

Jeremiah N. Jarrett, Ph.D.
Department of Biological Sciences
Central Connecticut State University
New Britain, Connecticut

David Lederman, Ph.D.
Department of Physics
West Virginia University
Morgantown, West Virginia

Becky Mansfield, Ph.D.
Department of Geography
Ohio State University
Columbus, Ohio

Elizabeth M. Martin, M.S.
Department of Chemistry and Biochemistry
College of Charleston
Charleston, South Carolina

Joe McCullough, Ph.D.
Department of Natural and Applied Sciences
Cabrillo College
Aptos, California

Robert J. Mellors, Ph.D.
Department of Geological Sciences
San Diego State University
San Diego, California

Joseph M. Moran, Ph.D.
American Meteorological Society
Washington, D.C.

David J. Morrissey, Ph.D.
Department of Chemistry
Michigan State University
East Lansing, Michigan

Philip A. Reed, Ph.D.
Department of Occupational & Technical Studies
Old Dominion University
Norfolk, Virginia

Scott M. Rochette, Ph.D.
Department of the Earth Sciences
State University of New York, College at Brockport
Brockport, New York

Laurence D. Rosenhein, Ph.D.
Department of Chemistry
Indiana State University
Terre Haute, Indiana

Ronald Sass, Ph.D.
Department of Biology and Chemistry
Rice University
Houston, Texas

George Schatz, Ph.D.
Department of Chemistry
Northwestern University
Evanston, Illinois

Sara Seager, Ph.D.
Carnegie Institution of Washington
Washington, D.C.

Robert M. Thornton, Ph.D.
Department of Biology
University of California
Davis, California

John R. Villarreal, Ph.D.
College of Science and Engineering
The University of Texas – Pan American
Edinburg, Texas

Kenneth Welty, Ph.D.
School of Education
University of Wisconsin–Stout
Stout, Wisconsin

Edward J. Zalisko, Ph.D.
Department of Biology
Blackburn College
Carlinville, Illinois

Teacher Reviewers

David R. Blakely
Arlington High School
Arlington, Massachusetts

Jane E. Callery
Two Rivers Magnet Middle
School
East Hartford, Connecticut

Melissa Lynn Cook
Oakland Mills High School
Columbia, Maryland

James Fattic
Southside Middle School
Anderson, Indiana

Dan Gabel
Hoover Middle School
Rockville, Maryland

Wayne Goates
Eisenhower Middle School
Goddard, Kansas

Katherine Bobay Graser
Mint Hill Middle School
Charlotte, North Carolina

Darcy Hampton
Deal Junior High School
Washington, D.C.

Karen Kelly
Pierce Middle School
Waterford, Michigan

David Kelso
Manchester High School Central
Manchester, New Hampshire

Benigno Lopez, Jr.
Sleepy Hill Middle School
Lakeland, Florida

Angie L. Matamoros, Ph.D.
ALM Consulting, INC.
Weston, Florida

Tim McCollum
Charleston Middle School
Charleston, Illinois

Bruce A. Mellin
Brooks School
North Andover, Massachusetts

Ella Jay Parfitt
Southeast Middle School
Baltimore, Maryland

Evelyn A. Pizzarello
Louis M. Klein Middle School
Harrison, New York

Kathleen M. Poe
Fletcher Middle School
Jacksonville, Florida

Shirley Rose
Lewis and Clark Middle School
Tulsa, Oklahoma

Linda Sandersen
Greenfield Middle School
Greenfield, Wisconsin

Mary E. Solan
Southwest Middle School
Charlotte, North Carolina

Mary Stewart
University of Tulsa
Tulsa, Oklahoma

Paul Swenson
Billings West High School
Billings, Montana

Thomas Vaughn
Arlington High School
Arlington, Massachusetts

Susan C. Zibell
Central Elementary
Simsbury, Connecticut

Safety Reviewers

W. H. Breazeale, Ph.D.
Department of Chemistry
College of Charleston
Charleston, South Carolina

Ruth Hathaway, Ph.D.
Hathaway Consulting
Cape Girardeau, Missouri

Douglas Mandt, M.S.
Science Education Consultant
Edgewood, Washington

Activity Field Testers

Nicki Bibbo
Witchcraft Heights School
Salem, Massachusetts

Rose-Marie Botting
Broward County Schools
Fort Lauderdale, Florida

Colleen Campos
Laredo Middle School
Aurora, Colorado

Elizabeth Chait
W. L. Chenery Middle School
Belmont, Massachusetts

Holly Estes
Hale Middle School
Stow, Massachusetts

Laura Hapgood
Plymouth Community
Intermediate School
Plymouth, Massachusetts

Mary F. Lavin
Plymouth Community
Intermediate School
Plymouth, Massachusetts

James MacNeil, Ph.D.
Cambridge, Massachusetts

Lauren Magruder
St. Michael's Country
Day School
Newport, Rhode Island

Jeanne Maurand
Austin Preparatory School
Reading, Massachusetts

Joanne Jackson-Pelletier
Winman Junior High School
Warwick, Rhode Island

Warren Phillips
Plymouth Public Schools
Plymouth, Massachusetts

Carol Pirtle
Hale Middle School
Stow, Massachusetts

Kathleen M. Poe
Fletcher Middle School
Jacksonville, Florida

Cynthia B. Pope
Norfolk Public Schools
Norfolk, Virginia

Anne Scammell
Geneva Middle School
Geneva, New York

Karen Riley Sievers
Callanan Middle School
Des Moines, Iowa

David M. Smith
Eyer Middle School
Allentown, Pennsylvania

Gene Vitale
Parkland School
McHenry, Illinois

Contents

Chemical Interactions

Reference Section

VIDEO

Enhance understanding through dynamic video.

Preview Get motivated with this introduction to the chapter content.

Field Trip Explore a real-world story related to the chapter content.

Assessment Review content and take an assessment.

Web Links

Get connected to exciting Web resources in every lesson.

SCi NSTA
LINKS Find Web links on topics relating to every section.

Active Art Interact with selected visuals from every chapter online.

Planet Diary® Explore news and natural phenomena through weekly reports.

Science News® Keep up to date with the latest science discoveries.

Experience the complete text-book online and on CD-ROM.

Activities Practice skills and learn content.

Videos Explore content and learn important lab skills.

Audio Support Hear key terms spoken and defined.

Self-Assessment Use instant feedback to help you track your progress.

Activities

Saving the Ozone Layer

Inquiry and Photochemistry

Working scientist Dr. Mario Molina investigates the effect of pollution on the ozone layer. This article shows how he uses curiosity, persistence, reasoning, and relating cause and effect as key elements of scientific inquiry. While chemical reactions are studied elsewhere in this book, students need not have any previous knowledge of those concepts to understand this real-world application of scientific inquiry.

Build Background Knowledge

Help students understand the relationship between the ozone layer and aerosols. Ask: **What do you know about the ozone layer?** (Sample answer: It is a layer in the atmosphere. It has a hole in it.) Point out the aerosol spray can in the photograph on the next page. Ask: **Why should people stop using aerosol spray cans?** (Sample answer: They release pollutants that harm the ozone layer.)

Introduce the Career

Before students read the article, let them read the title, examine the pictures, and read the captions on their own. Then ask: **What questions came into your mind as you looked at these pictures?** (Sample questions: What is the ozone layer? Why do we need to save the ozone layer? Do we know how to save it? How can a hole in the ozone layer over Antarctica affect people in the United States? What might happen to us if we did nothing to protect the ozone layer?) Point out to students that just as they had questions about what they were seeing, scientists too have questions about what they observe.

Dr. Mario Molina uses a mass spectrometer to analyze chemical reactions.

Saving the Ozone Layer

As a child growing up in Mexico, long before he won a Nobel prize in Chemistry, Mario Molina enjoyed experimenting with science. "I was always interested in chemistry sets or toy microscopes. With the microscope in front of me, I'd take a piece of lettuce, put it in water, and let it rot and really stink. To see the life teeming in a drop of water—that for me was fascinating. Even then I realized it would be great if I could become a research scientist."

What Mario wanted to do, he decided, was "actually use science for things that affect society." Mario Molina began by looking at the chemicals people put into the air.

Career Path

Mario Molina was born in Mexico City, Mexico. He received a B.S. from Universidad Autónoma de México, and a Ph.D. from the University of California at Berkeley. In 1995, Mario Molina, Sherwood Rowland, and Paul Crutzen won the Nobel prize in Chemistry for their work on chlorofluorocarbons (CFCs) and the ozone layer. From 1989 to 2004, Mario was a professor at the Massachusetts Institute of Technology in Cambridge, Massachusetts. He is now a professor in the Department of Chemistry and Biochemistry at the University of California, San Diego.

x ◆ L

Background

Facts and Figures Chemistry is the study of properties of materials, such as their structure and composition. Chemists also study how different materials interact and how adding or removing energy from materials changes them.

Photochemistry is one branch of chemistry. Scientists in this branch study how chemicals are affected by visible light and other forms of electromagnetic radiation, such as ultraviolet rays. Photochemists also study how radiation from the sun causes ozone to be formed. Another branch of chemistry includes organic chemistry. Organic chemists study carbon-containing compounds. They may be concerned with such things as developing new medicines or synthetic materials.

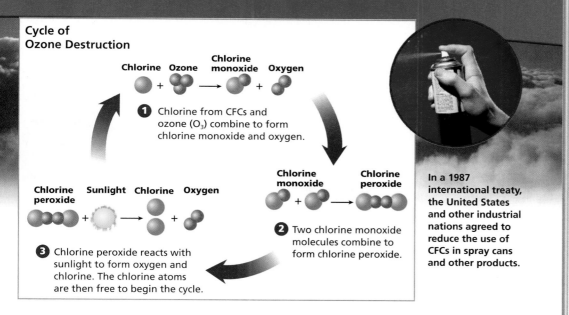

Cycle of Ozone Destruction

Chlorine + Ozone → Chlorine monoxide + Oxygen

1 Chlorine from CFCs and ozone (O_3) combine to form chlorine monoxide and oxygen.

Chlorine monoxide → Chlorine peroxide

2 Two chlorine monoxide molecules combine to form chlorine peroxide.

Chlorine peroxide + Sunlight → Chlorine + Oxygen

3 Chlorine peroxide reacts with sunlight to form oxygen and chlorine. The chlorine atoms are then free to begin the cycle.

In a 1987 international treaty, the United States and other industrial nations agreed to reduce the use of CFCs in spray cans and other products.

Talking With **Dr. Mario Molina**

Asking Simple Questions

In the early 1970s, one of Dr. Molina's co-workers, Sherwood Rowland, heard about a group of compounds called chlorofluorocarbons, or CFCs. CFCs were used in air conditioners, refrigerators, and aerosol spray cans. But they leaked into the air. "It is something that is not natural, but is now in the atmosphere all over the planet," says Mario. What happens to these compounds in the air, Rowland and Molina wondered, and what do they do to the air?

"We didn't know ahead of time if CFCs were doing damage or not," Mario explains. "So what we did was study what was going on. We learned that CFCs aren't changed much down near Earth. But we expected that if they got high enough in the atmosphere, solar radiation would destroy them."

Radiation is how energy from the sun reaches Earth. Ultraviolet (UV) rays, a form of radiation, break compounds apart and change them. "Above a certain altitude, everything falls apart. We had to learn how high CFCs went and how long it took them to get there. Then we asked: What does it mean that CFCs are up there?"

A Protective Shield in the Sky

In his laboratory, Dr. Molina studied how ultraviolet light changes CFCs. "It became clear that these molecules would be destroyed by UV rays in the stratosphere—the upper atmosphere, where the ozone layer is. At the time, I didn't even know what the ozone layer was."

Mario Molina learned fast. The ozone layer is a thin layer of the atmosphere that contains ozone, a form of oxygen. The ozone blocks out UV rays from the sun. UV rays would be dangerous to living things if they reached Earth's surface.

Dr. Molina learned something very disturbing. When the sun's rays break CFCs apart, chlorine forms. A chain of chemical changes that destroys ozone then begins. "Very small amounts of CFCs can have very big effects on ozone."

L ◆ 1

Background

Use Maps Direct students to examine the satellite images. Ask: **What part of world are these images showing?** *(Antarctica in the Southern Hemisphere)* **In what year was a hole in the ozone layer clearly visible?** *(1986)* **How has the size of the hole in the ozone layer changed over time?** *(It has grown larger.)*

Build Inquiry Skills Give students practice in identifying cause and effect using the depletion of the ozone layer as an example. Ask: **Where is the hole in the ozone layer forming?** *(Over Antarctica)* **Where are people using aerosols and equipment that leak CFCs?** *(Sample answer: In the United States and Europe)* Ask: **How are the actions of people in one part of the world affecting the ozone layer in another part of the world?** *(Sample answer: The hole in the ozone layer is caused by CFCs, which enter the atmosphere when people from all over the world use products or equipment containing CFCs.)* **What are other examples of local actions that could cause global harm?** *(Sample answer: Burning fuels that increase greenhouse gases, causing global warming)*

Research Invite students to learn more about the different layers of the atmosphere. Specifically, have students find out what the stratosphere is and how it relates to the ozone layer. You may want students to diagram the layers of Earth's atmosphere and write a short description of the characteristics of each layer.

Changes in the Antarctic Ozone Layer, 1979–2001

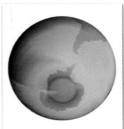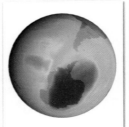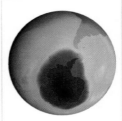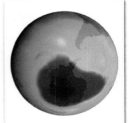

In 1979, thinning of the ozone layer was barely visible.

In 1986, a hole in the ozone layer was clearly visible.

In 1994, the hole in the ozone layer was expanding.

In 2001, the damage to the ozone layer was greatly increased.

These images of the South Pole, taken by satellite between 1979 and 2001, show a hole developing in the ozone layer of the atmosphere.

← More ozone   Less ozone →

A Scary Prediction Comes True

Mario Molina and his co-workers made a frightening prediction. If CFCs can reach the stratosphere, they will eventually damage the protective ozone layer. Other scientists thought Mario Molina was wrong or exaggerating. But more and more evidence came in. Researchers sent balloons up into the stratosphere with scientific instruments to measure chlorine formed by CFCs. They found that CFCs were in the stratosphere and that the sun's rays were breaking them down.

Was the ozone layer being hurt? Yes. Over Antarctica, there was an "ozone hole," an opening in the ozone layer. The hole lets in harmful radiation from the sun. "That was a surprise to us and to everybody. It was a very large effect that we hadn't predicted. Some scientists thought the ozone hole was natural, but we thought it was caused by CFCs. We checked it out by doing experiments from Antarctica. In a couple of years it became very clear that this hole was a result of the CFCs."

Scientist and Speaker

Dr. Molina now had to convince people to stop making and using CFCs. "The effect over Antarctica was so large that it was easy to measure and test. But similar effects exist everywhere. As scientists we had to inform the public and the government. If you're convinced that you're right and that something dangerous is going to happen, you need to risk speaking out."

Mario Molina went to the U.S. Senate and to other governments. He was able to show how UV radiation was causing damage. "There was damage to some crops, damage to growing fish, damage that we can already see and measure today."

Finally, the world listened. Through the United Nations, an agreement was signed by most industrial nations to stop using CFCs by the year 1995.

2 ◆ L

Background

Facts and Figures The ozone layer is not very dense. If all the ozone molecules that make up the ozone layer were compressed at Earth's surface, they would form a layer about as thick as a pie crust.

In 1987, 24 countries signed an agreement called the Montreal Protocol that calls for gradually phasing out and eventually ending the production of many CFCs. Now, over 150 countries have agreed to these goals.

"Greenhouse effect" is a term that describes how the atmosphere keeps Earth warm. Greenhouse gases include carbon dioxide, methane, and water vapor. In 1997, 160 nations agreed to the Kyoto Protocol. This agreement commits industrialized countries to reduce emissions of six greenhouse gases to below 1990 levels by 2012.

Chlorine Levels in the Atmosphere 1960–2100

— Predicted levels without controls
— Actual levels with controls
-- - Predicted levels with controls
○ Antarctica ozone hole begins to form

The graph above shows that the level of chlorine in the atmosphere would have increased rapidly if controls on CFCs had not been passed. With controls in place, the amount of chlorine in the atmosphere should gradually decrease to levels in the light blue region of the graph. The ozone hole should then close.

In the laboratory, Mario and a graduate student investigate chemical reactions that affect the atmosphere.

Work Still to Do

"Everybody has to work together," chemist Molina says. He has done more than his share. He gave $200,000 of his Nobel prize money to help train scientists from Latin America and other developing countries. "There is a need to understand our planet, and we need very good minds to work on these problems. There are big challenges out there," he says with a confident smile, "but fortunately the science is fascinating."

Writing in Science

Career Link Mario says, "If you're convinced that you're right . . . you need to risk speaking out." After conducting a scientific investigation, a scientist's job is to communicate the results of the research. Suppose you are a scientist whose research is controversial. In a paragraph, describe the steps you might follow to convince other scientists, citizens, and governments to take action based on your research.

Go Online
PHSchool.com
For: More on this career
Visit: PHSchool.com
Web Code: cgb-2000

Analyze Data Have students examine the graph on this page. Ask: **What does this graph show?** (*Actual and predicted chlorine levels in the atmosphere between 1960 and 2100*) **What data is given on the x-axis?** (*Time in years*) **What is the responding variable?** (*Chlorine levels*) **When was the Antarctica ozone hole found?** (*About 1979*) **When did the actual chlorine level separate from the predicted chlorine level?** (*About 1998*) **When are chlorine levels in the atmosphere predicted to be lower than 2 parts per billion?** (*About 2040*)

Research Students may confuse the "greenhouse effect," or global warming with ozone depletion. Emphasize that these are two different phenomena with different causes. Encourage students to learn more about global warming and compare its causes with the causes of ozone depletion.

Writing in Science

Writing Mode Persuasion
Scoring Rubric
4 Exceeds criteria; includes a concise, grammatically correct paragraph with precise details that completely describe the steps a scientist might follow to convince other people to take action
3 Meets criteria
2 Includes sketchy details and/or minor errors
1 Paragraph is incomplete and/or has serious errors

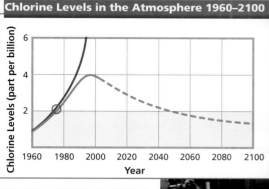

Go Online
PHSchool.com
For: More on this career
Visit: PHSchool.com
Web Code: cgb-2000

Students can research this career and others that are related to the study of chemistry.

Chapter at a Glance

 **Chapter Project** *Models of Compounds*

Technology

Local Standards

Video Preview

 Teaching Resources

- Chapter Project Teacher Notes, pp. 38–39
- Chapter Project Student Overview, pp. 40–41
- Chapter Project Student Worksheets, pp. 42–43
- Chapter Project Scoring Rubric, p. 44

Section 1

Elements and Atoms

3 periods
1 1/2 blocks

L.1.1.1 Explain why elements are sometimes called the building blocks of matter.

L.1.1.2 Describe how atomic theory developed and changed.

PHSchool.com

Section 2

Atoms, Bonding, and the Periodic Table

3 periods
1 1/2 blocks

L.1.2.1 Explain how the reactivity of elements is related to valence electrons in atoms.

L.1.2.2 State what the periodic table tells you about atoms and the properties of elements.

active art

Video Field Trip

Section 3

Ionic Bonds

4 periods
2 blocks

L.1.3.1 Describe ions, and explain how they form bonds.

L.1.3.2 Explain how the formulas and names of ionic compounds are written.

L.1.3.3 Identify the properties of ionic compounds.

Section 4

Covalent Bonds

3 periods
1 1/2 blocks

L.1.4.1 State what holds covalently bonded atoms together.

L.1.4.2 Identify the properties of molecular compounds.

L.1.4.3 Explain how unequal sharing of electrons occurs and how it affects molecules.

Section 5

Bonding in Metals

2 periods
1 block

L.1.5.1 Describe how metal atoms are bonded in solid metal.

L.1.5.2 Explain how metallic bonding results in useful properties of metals.

Review and Assessment

Test Preparation

 Teaching Resources

- Key Terms Review, p. 86
- Transparency L15
- Performance Assessment Teacher Notes, p. 93
- Performance Assessment Scoring Rubric, p. 94
- Performance Assessment Student Worksheet, p. 95
- Chapter Test, pp. 96–99

Video Assessment

Go Online
PHSchool.com

Test Preparation
Blackline Masters

Chapter Activities Planner

For more activities

LAB ZONE Easy Planner CD-ROM

Student Edition	Inquiry	Time	Materials	Skills	Resources
Chapter Project	Open-ended	Ongoing (2–3 weeks)	**All in One Teaching Resources** See p. 38	Making models, comparing and contrasting, communicating	**Lab zone Easy Planner** **All in One Teaching Resources** Support pp. 38–39
Section 1					
Discover Activity, p. 6	Guided	10 minutes	Dime or other small round object, metric ruler, calculator	Calculating	**Lab zone Easy Planner**
Section 2					
Discover Activity, p. 12	Guided	10 minutes	Periodic table	Interpreting data	**Lab zone Easy Planner**
Skills Activity, p. 17	Directed	10 minutes	Periodic table	Classifying	**Lab zone Easy Planner**
At-Home Activity, p. 20	Guided	Home		Applying concepts	**Lab zone Easy Planner**
Skills Lab, p. 21	Guided	30 minutes	Drawing compass, metric ruler, calculator, periodic table of the elements (Appendix D)	Making models, graphing, interpreting data	**Lab zone Easy Planner** **Lab Activity Video** **All in One Teaching Resources** Skills Lab: *Comparing Atom Sizes*, pp. 58–60
Section 3					
Discover Activity, p. 22	Guided	15 minutes	12 red checkers, 12 black checkers	Inferring	**Lab zone Easy Planner**
Skills Activity, p. 25	Directed	15 minutes	Periodic table, Figure 16	Interpreting data	**Lab zone Easy Planner**
Try This Activity, p. 26	Directed	15 minutes for setup, 3 minutes a day for 3 days	15 cm thread, coarse salt such as kosher salt or sea salt, jar or cup, pencil, hot tap water, stirring rod or spoon	Observing	**Lab zone Easy Planner**
Skills Lab, pp. 28–29	Guided	40 minutes	Conductivity probe or 2 dry cells (1.5 V) with small light bulb and socket and 4 lengths of wire with alligator clips on both ends, 2 copper strips, distilled water, small beaker, small plastic spoon, sodium chloride, 100-mL graduated cylinder, sucrose, additional materials	Controlling variables, interpreting data, inferring	**Lab zone Easy Planner** **Lab Activity Video** **All in One Teaching Resources** Skills Lab: *Shedding Light on Ions*, pp. 69–72
Section 4					
Discover Activity, p. 30	Guided	10 minutes	Small jar with tight-fitting top, water, vegetable oil, liquid detergent	Forming operational definitions	**Lab zone Easy Planner**
At-Home Activity, p. 35	Guided	Home		Applying concepts	**Lab zone Easy Planner**
Section 5					
Discover Activity, p. 36	Guided	10 minutes	Small pieces of three different metals	Inferring	**Lab zone Easy Planner**

Section 1 Elements and Atoms

 2–3 periods 1–1 1/2 blocks

Objectives

L.1.1.1 Explain why elements are sometimes called the building blocks of matter.

L.1.1.2 Describe how atomic theory developed and changed.

Local Standards

Key Terms

• matter • element • compound • mixture • atom • scientific theory • model
• electrons • nucleus • protons • energy level • neutrons

Preteach

Build Background Knowledge

Students recall what they already know about elements and atoms from previous science courses.

 **Discover Activity** *How Far Away Is the Electron?* L2

Targeted Print and Technology Resources

All in One Teaching Resources

L2 Reading Strategy Transparency L1: Outlining

◉ **Presentation-Pro CD-ROM**

Instruct

The Building Blocks of Matter Compare and contrast compounds and mixtures and relate them to elements.

Atomic Theory and Models Use questioning to guide students in understanding why atoms are represented by models.

Targeted Print and Technology Resources

All in One Teaching Resources

L2 Guided Reading, pp. 47–48
L2 Transparencies L2, L3

PHSchool.com Web Code: cgd-2011

◉ **Student Edition on Audio CD**

Assess

Section Assessment Questions

 Have students use their completed outlines to answer the questions.

Reteach

Students name the particles making up atoms and identify their locations and electric charges.

Targeted Print and Technology Resources

All in One Teaching Resources

• Section Summary, p. 46
L1 Review and Reinforce, p. 49
L3 Enrich, p. 50

Section 2 Atoms, Bonding, and the Periodic Table

 2–3 periods 1–1 1/2 blocks

Local Standards

Objectives

L.1.2.1 Explain how the reactivity of elements is related to valence electrons in atoms.

L.1.2.2 State what the periodic table tells you about atoms and the properties of elements.

Key Terms

• valence electrons • electron dot diagram • chemical bond • symbol • atomic number • period • group • family • noble gas • halogen • alkali metal

---

Preteach

Build Background Knowledge

Students use a familiar analogy to understand why it is important for elements to be organized.

 Discover Activity *What Are the Trends in the Periodic* L2 *Table?*

Targeted Print and Technology Resources

All in One Teaching Resources

L2 Reading Strategy: Building Vocabulary

◉ **Presentation-Pro CD-ROM**

Instruct

Valence Electrons and Bonding Introduce electron dot diagrams to help students visualize valence electrons and understand their role in bonding.

The Periodic Table Guide students in learning how to use the periodic table by asking them to locate information in Figure 10.

 **Skills Lab** *Comparing Atom Sizes* L2

Targeted Print and Technology Resources

All in One Teaching Resources

L2 Guided Reading, pp. 53–55
L2 Transparencies L4, L5
L2 Skills Lab: Comparing Atom Sizes, pp. 58–60

📼 **Lab Activity Video/DVD**
Skills Lab: *Comparing Atom Sizes*

www.SciLinks.org Web Code: cgp-1032

◉ **Student Edition on Audio CD**

Assess

Section Assessment Questions

Have students use their completed definitions of key terms to answer the questions.

Reteach

Students identify properties of different types of elements, including noble gases, halogens and alkali metals.

Targeted Print and Technology Resources

All in One Teaching Resources

• Section Summary, p. 52
L1 Review and Reinforce, p. 56
L3 Enrich, p. 57

4D

Section 3 **Ionic Bonds**

 3–4 periods 1 1/2–2 blocks

Objectives

L.1.3.1 Describe ions and explain how they form bonds.

L.1.3.2 Explain how the formulas and names of ionic compounds are written.

L.1.3.3 Identify the properties of ionic compounds.

Key Terms

• ion • polyatomic ion • ionic bond • ionic compound • chemical formula
• subscript • crystal

Local Standards

Preteach

Build Background Knowledge

Students recall what they have learned about electrons and electrical charge as a review of what they need to know to understand ions and ionic bonds

 Discover Activity *How Do Ions Form?* L2

Targeted Print and Technology Resources

 **Teaching Resources**

L2 Reading Strategy Transparency L6: Previewing Visuals

⊙ **Presentation-Pro CD-ROM**

Instruct

Ions and Ionic Bonds Introduce common ions that students will see throughout the book.

Chemical Formulas and Names Explain how chemical formulas reflect the composition of ionic compounds.

Properties of Ionic Compounds Have students compare and contrast different ionic compounds to infer their shared properties.

 Skills Lab *Shedding Light on Ions* L2

Targeted Print and Technology Resources

Teaching Resources

L2 Guided Reading, pp. 63–66
L2 Transparencies L7, L8
L2 Skills Lab: *Shedding Light on Ions*, pp. 69–72

📼 **Lab Activity Video/DVD**
Skills Lab: *Shedding Light on Ions*

PHSchool.com Web Code: scn-1213

⊙ **Student Edition on Audio CD**

Assess

Section Assessment Questions

 Have students use their completed graphic organizers of questions and answers to answer the questions.

Reteach

Students describe properties of ionic compounds.

Targeted Print and Technology Resources

Teaching Resources

• Section Summary, p. 62
L1 Review and Reinforce, p. 67
L3 Enrich, p. 68

Section 4 Covalent Bonds

 2–3 periods 1–1 1/2 blocks

Objectives

Local Standards

L.1.4.1 State what holds covalently bonded atoms together.
L.1.4.2 Identify the properties of molecular compounds.
L.1.4.3 Explain how unequal sharing of electrons occurs and how it affects molecules.

Key Terms

- covalent bond • molecule • double bond • triple bond • molecular compound
- polar bond • nonpolar bond

Preteach

Build Background Knowledge

Students recall that atoms can form bonds by sharing electrons.

 **Discover Activity** *Can Water and Oil Mix?* **L2**

Targeted Print and Technology Resources

All in One Teaching Resources
L2 Reading Strategy Transparency L9: Asking Questions

⊙ **Presentation-Pro CD-ROM**

Instruct

How Covalent Bonds Form Introduce covalent bonds by comparing and contrasting them with ionic bonds, with which students are already familiar.

Molecular Compounds Use a graphic organizer to summarize important points about molecular compounds and their properties.

Unequal Sharing of Electrons Use the familiar example of water to explain why some molecules are polar.

Targeted Print and Technology Resources

All in One Teaching Resources
L2 Guided Reading, pp. 75–77
L2 Transparencies L10, L11, L12
www.SciLinks.org Web Code: scn-1214

⊙ **Student Edition on Audio CD**

Assess

Section Assessment Questions

Have students use their completed graphic organizers of questions and answers to answer the questions.

Reteach

Students define or describe and give examples of the key terms.

Targeted Print and Technology Resources

All in One Teaching Resources
- Section Summary, p. 74
L1 Review and Reinforce, p. 78
L3 Enrich, p. 79

Section 5 Bonding in Metals

 1–2 periods 1/2–1 block

ABILITY LEVELS
L1 Basic to Average
L2 For All Students
L3 Average to Advanced

Objectives

L.1.5.1 Describe how metal atoms are bonded in solid metal.

L.1.5.2 Explain how metallic bonding results in useful properties of metals.

Key Terms

• metallic bond • alloy • ductile • malleable

Local Standards

Preteach

Build Background Knowledge

Students name common objects containing metal and infer properties of metals based on the objects.

 **Discover Activity** *What Do Metals Do?* L2

Targeted Print and Technology Resources

All in One Teaching Resources

L2 Reading Strategy Transparency L13: *Relating Cause and Effect*

⊙ **Presentation-Pro CD-ROM**

Instruct

Metallic Bonding Use Figure 29 to help students understand the nature of metallic bonds.

Metallic Properties Explain how the properties of metals depend on the nature of metallic bonds.

Targeted Print and Technology Resources

All in One Teaching Resources

L2 Guided Reading, pp. 82–83
L2 Transparency L14

www.SciLinks.org Web Code: scn-1215

⊙ **Student Edition on Audio CD**

Assess

Section Assessment Questions

Have students use their completed graphic organizers relating cause and effect to answer the questions.

Reteach

Students name properties of metals and describe an example of each property.

Targeted Print and Technology Resources

All in One Teaching Resources

• Section Summary, p. 81
L1 Review and Reinforce, p. 84
L3 Enrich, p. 85

Go Online

NSTA-PDLINKS

For: Professional development support
Visit: www.SciLinks.org/PDLinks
Web Code: scf-1210

Professional Development

Section 1 **Elements and Atoms**

Atomic Models and Quantum Physics The development of quantum theory by Max Planck and Albert Einstein in the early 1900s had an important influence on models of the atom. Quantum theory postulates that energy, like matter, can be divided into discrete particles. A particle of energy is called a *quantum*. Quantum theory revolutionized physics. The first physicist to apply quantum theory to atomic structure was Niels Bohr in 1913. He addressed a problem raised by Ernest Rutherford's earlier atomic model, in which electrons travel around a central, positively charged nucleus. As electrons circle the nucleus, they should accelerate and radiate energy. As a result, they should become less energetic and fall into the nucleus. Bohr hypothesized that electrons could circle the nucleus without losing energy if they maintained a certain orbit, or energy level, which he calculated using quantum theory.

Although Bohr's hypothesis was essentially correct, it could not explain many observations of the actual behavior of atoms and electrons. In the 1920s, quantum mechanics was developed and applied to atomic structure. Several physicists, notably Werner Heisenberg and Erwin Schrödinger, developed the theory that matter could behave like waves as well as particles. They applied this theory to the motion of electrons and formulated the electron cloud model of the atom. This model is represented in the figure below.

**Electron Cloud Model of
Heisenberg and Schrödinger**

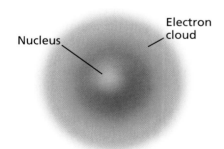

Nucleus

Electron cloud

The electron cloud model confirmed Bohr's hypothesis of electrons orbiting the nucleus in energy levels. However, in the electron cloud model, electrons are not viewed as being in a particular place in a fixed orbit. Instead, electrons are seen as being spread out over a region, to create a cloud of negative electric charge. The region in which electrons of a certain energy are likely to be found is called an orbital. According to this model, electrons can never be located with absolute certainty, but only with a certain statistical probability. In the figure, the shading shows the probability of finding an electron at a given distance from the nucleus. In 1927, Heisenberg generalized this result as a scientific principle, called the *uncertainty principle*.

Address Misconceptions

Students who know that atoms contain smaller particles may be confused when atoms are called the smallest particles of elements. For a strategy for overcoming this misconception, see **Address Misconceptions** in Section 1, *Elements and Atoms*.

Help Students Read

Using Prior Knowledge
Bohr's Atomic Model

Strategy Guide students in using prior knowledge to better understand section concepts, such as Bohr's atomic model. Use leading questions to elicit the relevant knowledge from students.

Example
1. Have students read about Bohr's atomic model in the text and study the diagram of the model in Figure 6.
2. Point out the comparison made in the text between Bohr's model and the solar system.
3. Ask students to identify which parts of the solar system represent the nucleus and electrons in Bohr's model.
4. Have students explain how electrons in Bohr's model are like the planets in the solar system.

See Section 1, *Elements and Atoms*, for a script applying the Using Prior Knowledge strategy with students.

Section 2 Atoms, Bonding, and the Periodic Table

Transition Metals in the Periodic Table In the periodic table, elements are classified as metals, metalloids, and nonmetals. Group 1 and Group 2 metals are the alkali metals and alkaline earth metals, respectively. These two groups of metals are discussed in the greatest detail in the text. Many of the remaining metals in the periodic table are called *transition metals*. They fall in Groups 3–12 and consist of 30 elements in three families, with atomic numbers 21–30, 39–48, and 71–80. Like other metals, transition metals have such properties as the ability to conduct heat and electricity, malleability, ductility, and luster. Transition metals also generally form bonds with negative ions, and the compounds that result are typically brightly colored. In addition, transition metals tend to be magnetic and to have high densities and melting points. Some transition metals are used in manufacturing as catalysts. For example, iron (Fe) catalyzes the reaction between hydrogen and nitrogen that produces ammonia. Some transition metals also play important roles in living things. Iron is an important component of vertebrate blood, binding with oxygen and allowing blood to carry oxygen throughout the body.

Two series of metals in the periodic table, the lanthanide series (elements 57–70) and the actinide series (elements 89–102), branch off after Group 2 in Periods 6 and 7. They often are called *inner transition metals*. They are also part of a somewhat larger group of metals known as *rare earth metals*. The lanthanide series is named for the element lanthanum, and all the elements in the series have about the same physical and chemical properties as lanthanum. For example, all the lanthanides, like lanthanum itself, are about as reactive as calcium. The actinide series is named for the element actinium, and actinide elements share properties with actinium. Most of the actinides are radioactive and unstable, and only a few are found in Earth's crust. Some of the others have been synthesized in small quantities.

Section 3 Ionic Bonds

Formation of Ions and Ionic Bonds A neutral atom, or group of atoms, can gain or lose one or more electrons to become an ion. Ions are positive or negative in electrical charge, depending on whether electrons are gained or lost. A positive ion, or cation, results when electrons are lost, and a negative ion, or anion, results when electrons are gained. The table shows some common ions and their charges. Other common ions are listed in Figure 16 in *Atoms and Bonding*. In both tables, cations are listed first, followed by anions.

Ions and Their Charges

Name	Formula
iron (II), or ferrous	Fe^{2+}
iron (III), or ferric	Fe^{3+}
copper (I), or cuprous	Cu^{+}
copper (II), or cupric	Cu^{2+}
hydronium	H_3O^{+}
hydroxide	OH^{-}
bromide	Br^{-}
nitrite	NO_2^{-}
chlorate	ClO_3^{-}
silicate	SiO_4^{4-}

The formation of ions is called *ionization*. It can occur in a variety of ways. For example, ions can be formed by bombarding atoms with high-speed particles, ultraviolet radiation, or X-rays. This method causes certain electrons to gain sufficient energy to break free of their atoms. High temperatures and electric currents are other ways that some substances can be ionized. Ions also result when atoms gain or lose electrons in the formation of ionic bonds. When a metal bonds with a nonmetal, for example, the metal's valence electrons are attracted to the nonmetal, resulting in the formation of positive and negative ions. An example is the ionic bonding of sodium and chlorine. In this reaction, which is illustrated in the text, chlorine attracts sodium's single valence electron, creating positive sodium ions and negative chloride ions.

Solids made of ions usually consist of groups of cations and anions, having an overall change of zero, rather than as individual molecules. The groups arrange themselves in a three-dimensional crystal structure. In the crystal, each ion is attracted most strongly to the oppositely charged ions closest to it. However, it is also attracted, to a lesser extent, to all the oppositely charged ions throughout the crystal.

Section 4 Covalent Bonds

Covalent Bonds and Polarity A covalent bond forms when two atoms share one or more pairs of electrons. Sharing electrons allows each atom to have a completed outer shell and become stable. The protons in the nuclei of the atoms and the shared electrons are mutually attracted to each other and hold the atoms together in a unit called a *molecule.*

The only completely covalent bonds are bonds between two identical atoms, such as two chlorine atoms, Cl_2, as shown in the figure below. Otherwise, most covalent bonds consist of electron pairs that are shared unequally to some degree. This is because atoms of different elements have different degrees of attraction for electrons. If this difference in attraction is pronounced, the atom that attracts the shared electrons more strongly will be slightly negative and the other atom will be slightly positive. This type of covalent bond is called a *polar covalent bond.* The bonds between hydrogen and oxygen in water are examples of polar covalent bonds. Within each water molecule, oxygen attracts the shared electrons more strongly than does hydrogen, so oxygen has a slightly negative charge and hydrogen a slightly positive charge (represented in the diagram below by the lower case Greek letter delta).

Covalent Molecules

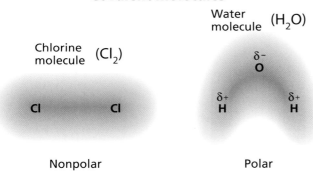

Chlorine molecule (Cl_2)

Nonpolar

Water molecule (H_2O)

Polar

The ability of an atom to attract electrons in a bond is called *electronegativity.* The stronger an atom pulls electrons, the higher its electronegativity. Elements on the right side of the periodic table (except for the noble gases) are the most electronegative, and elements on the left side of the table are the least electronegative. Fluorine, for example, is much more electronegative than potassium.

Section 5 Bonding in Metals

Properties of Metals Most metals share a number of physical properties and chemical properties as a result of metallic bonding. Physical properties of metals include the ability to conduct heat and electricity, a crystal structure, luster, malleability, ductility, opaqueness, hardness, tensile strength, elasticity, and fatigue resistance. The first five properties are described in the textbook. Opaqueness and hardness are self-explanatory. Tensile strength means resistance to breaking; elasticity is the ability to return to the original shape after being deformed; and fatigue resistance is the ability to withstand repeated stresses.

Chemical properties of metals include the ability to react easily by losing electrons and forming positive ions. Many metals combine with oxygen when exposed to moist air and become corroded. For example, iron combines with oxygen in moist air to form rust. Most metals also combine with nonmetals to form salts, such as sodium chloride.

Although generally similar in these ways, metals can differ greatly from one another. For example, most metals form cubic crystals, but some metals form crystals with more complex shapes. Metals also exhibit a wide range of melting points. The lowest melting point for a metal is −39°C (mercury) and the highest is about 3400°C (tungsten). Similarly, there is a wide range of electrical conductivity within the metals. Bismuth has the lowest electrical conductivity and silver the highest. In terms of hardness, chromium is the hardest and cesium the softest. Gold is especially ductile and malleable, aluminum is one of the best conductors of heat, and copper has great tensile strength. One of the least dense metals is sodium, which floats on water. One of the most dense is lead. Cesium and lithium are readily oxidized like iron, whereas silver and gold are not.

Chapter

1

Atoms and Bonding

Chapter Preview

Interactive Textbook

Each water molecule in this computer model consists of two hydrogen atoms (clear) bonded to one oxygen atom (red).

4 ◆ L

Chapter Project L3

Objectives
This Chapter Project will give students a chance to make models of atoms and to demonstrate how they bond in ionic and molecular compounds. After completing this Chapter Project, students will be able to
- make models of atoms and compounds
- compare and contrast ionic and covalent bonds
- communicate to their classmates what their models show

Skills Focus
Making models, comparing and contrasting, communicating

Project Time Line 2–3 weeks

All in One Teaching Resources
- Chapter Project Teacher Notes
- Chapter Project Worksheet 1
- Chapter Project Worksheet 2
- Chapter Project Scoring Rubric

Developing a Plan
Students can begin the project by previewing the part of the chapter that describes atoms. Then, they can decide what materials they will use to construct their models. Allow students several days to create their models of atoms. After they have read the parts of the chapter describing ionic and covalent bonds, they can make models of both types of compounds using their model atoms. Give students a day or two to prepare their presentations and additional time as needed to deliver their presentations to the class.

Possible Materials
Provide a wide variety of materials from which students can choose. Some possibilities are listed below. Encourage students to suggest and use other materials as well.
- Fruits, vegetables, gumdrops, marshmallows, and/or clay can be used to represent atoms.
- Tape, toothpicks, pipe cleaners, and/or paper clips can be used to connect "atoms" and represent bonds.
- Markers can be used to draw valence electrons on the models, or small objects such as raisins or grains of rice can be attached to represent valence electrons.
- A ball-and-stick modeling kit is recommended for launching the project.

Atoms and Bonding

Show the Video Preview to introduce elements, atoms, and bonding. Discussion question: **What are some properties of gold?** *(Gold has a low melting point, does not oxidize, and is fairly soft.)*

Lab zone™ Chapter Project

Models of Compounds

In this chapter, you will learn how atoms of elements react with one another to form compounds. When they form compounds, the atoms become chemically bonded to each other. In this project, you will create models of chemical compounds.

Your Goal To make models demonstrating how atoms bond in ionic compounds and in molecular compounds

To complete the project, you must
● select appropriate materials to make models of atoms
● indicate the number of bonds each atom forms
● use your model atoms to compare compounds that contain ionic bonds with compounds that contain covalent bonds
● follow the safety guidelines in Appendix A

Plan It! Brainstorm with some classmates about materials you can use to represent different atoms and chemical bonds. Look ahead in the chapter to preview ionic and covalent bonding. Think about how you will show that ionic and covalent bonding are different. You may need to find some small, but highly visible, objects to represent electrons. Be ready to display your models and explain what they show.

Chapter 1 L ◆ 5

Performance Assessment

The Chapter Project Scoring Rubric will help you evaluate how well students complete the Chapter Project. You may want to share the scoring rubric with your students so they will know what is expected. Students will be assessed on
● the appropriateness of the materials they select to make models of atoms and compounds
● how correctly they have modeled the structures of atoms and compounds
● how accurately their models show the differences between ionic and covalent bonding
● the thoroughness and organization of their presentations

Students can keep their presentation notes in their portfolios. Portfolio

Launching the Project

If possible, use a ball-and-stick modeling kit to demonstrate molecular modeling. Show students how different elements are represented by differently colored balls and how chemical bonds, including multiple bonds, are represented by dowels. Ask: **Using the modeling kit, how can you tell molecules of one compound from molecules of another compound?** *(By the different elements and types of bonds represented)* Give students a chance to read about the project. Answer any questions they may have. If students will be working in groups, divide them into groups now. Limit groups to no more than three students to ensure that each student has an opportunity to participate.

Objectives

After this lesson, students will be able to
L.1.1.1 Explain why elements are sometimes called the building blocks of matter.
L.1.1.2 Describe how atomic theory developed and changed.

Target Reading Skill 🔄

Outlining Explain that using an outline format helps students organize information by main topic, subtopic, and details.

Answers

Elements and Atoms
  I.   The building blocks of matter
       A. Elements, compounds, and mixtures
       B. Particles of elements
 II.   Atomic theory and models
       A. Dalton's atomic theory
       B. Thomson and smaller parts of atoms
       C. Rutherford and the nucleus
       D. Bohr's model
       E. A cloud of electrons
       F. The modern atomic model

All in One Teaching Resources

• Transparency L1

Preteach

Build Background Knowledge L2

Elements and Atoms

Most students will have some familiarity with elements and atoms from previous science courses. Guide them in recalling what they already know. Ask: **What are some examples of elements?** (*Sample answers: Oxygen, hydrogen, carbon, gold*) **What is an atom?** (*The smallest particle of an element*) Challenge students to describe or sketch what they think the structure of an atom is like. Accept all reasonable representations. Tell students they will learn more about elements and atoms in this section.

Reading Preview

Key Concepts
• Why are elements sometimes called the building blocks of matter?
• How did atomic theory develop and change?

Key Terms
• matter • element
• compound • mixture • atom
• scientific theory • model
• electrons • nucleus • protons
• energy level • neutrons

🔄 Target Reading Skill

Outlining An outline shows the relationship between main ideas and supporting details. As you read, make an outline about elements and atoms. Use the red headings for the main ideas and the blue headings for the supporting ideas.

Elements and Atoms
I. The building blocks of matter
A. Elements, compounds, and mixtures
B.
II. Atomic theory and models
A.
B.

Lab zone Discover **Activity**

How Far Away Is the Electron?

1. On a piece of paper, make a small circle no bigger than a dime. The circle represents the nucleus, or center, of an atom.
2. Measure the diameter of the circle in centimeters.
3. Now predict where the outer edge of this model atom would be. For example, would the outer edge be within the edges of the paper? Your desk? The classroom? The school building?

Think It Over

Calculating The diameter of an actual atom can be 100,000 times the diameter of its nucleus. Calculate the diameter of your model atom. How close was your prediction in Step 3 to your calculation? (*Hint:* To understand the scale of your answer, change the units of measurement from centimeters to meters.)

If you take a quick look around you, you will see many examples of matter. Buildings made of wood or steel, forks and spoons made of metal, your clothing, water, the air you breathe, and all living things are matter. **Matter** is anything that has mass and takes up space. But what is matter made of? More than 2,000 years ago, the ancient Greeks believed that all matter was made up of four elements—air, earth, fire, and water. Not until much later did scientists begin to realize that matter was composed of many different elements.

The Building Blocks of Matter

Elements are the simplest pure substances, and they cannot be broken down into any other substances. You are already familiar with many elements. Aluminum, iron, copper, lead, oxygen, chlorine, neon, and helium are a few you might know. But how are elements related to the many other materials you find in your world? **Elements are often called the building blocks of matter because all matter is composed of one element or a combination of two or more elements.**

Lab zone Discover **Activity**

Skills Focus Calculating

Materials dime or other small round object, metric ruler, calculator

Time 10 minutes

Tip Remind students that the diameter of a circle is represented by a straight line that passes through the center of the circle.

L1 Expected Outcome Students will probably predict that the outer edge of the model atom is near the edge of their paper or desk.

Think It Over If a dime is used to represent the nucleus, it has a diameter of 1.75 cm. An atom with this size nucleus would be 175,000 cm, or 1,750 m, in diameter.

Elements, Compounds, and Mixtures Elements usually exist in combination with other elements in the form of compounds. A **compound** is a pure substance made of two or more elements that are combined chemically in a specific ratio. For example, sodium chloride (table salt) from underground mines or from seawater is always 39.3 percent sodium and 60.7 percent chlorine by mass.

Elements can also mix with other elements *without* combining chemically. The air you breathe, for example, consists mostly of nitrogen gas and oxygen gas that are separate substances. A **mixture** is two or more substances—elements, compounds, or both—that are in the same place but are not chemically combined. Air, soil, wood, gasoline, concrete, and orange juice are a few of the many mixtures in your world.

Particles of Elements If elements are the simplest forms of matter, do you wonder what the smallest piece of an element is? If you cut a copper wire in half over and over again, could you keep cutting it forever? Or would you reach a point where you have the smallest possible piece of copper?

Again, the first people to think about this question were the ancient Greeks. Around the year 430 B.C., a Greek philosopher named Democritus proposed the idea that matter is formed of small pieces that could not be cut into smaller parts. He used the word *atomos*, which means "uncuttable," for these smallest possible pieces. In modern terms, an **atom** is the smallest particle of an element. The Greek idea of atoms had to wait about 2,000 years before it became accepted.

Reading Checkpoint: **How is a compound different from an element?**

For: More on atomic structure
Visit: PHSchool.com
Web Code: cgd-2011

FIGURE 1
Kinds of Matter
Matter may consist of elements, compounds, or mixtures.
Inferring What other mixture besides sand is present, but not visible, in the photo?

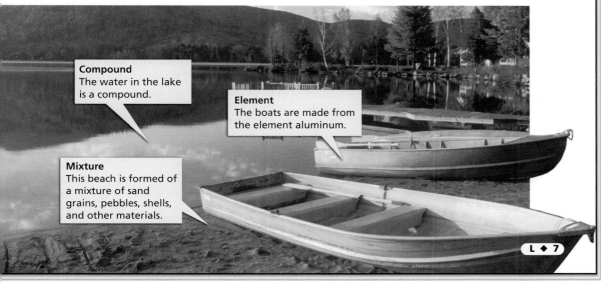

Compound
The water in the lake is a compound.

Element
The boats are made from the element aluminum.

Mixture
This beach is formed of a mixture of sand grains, pebbles, shells, and other materials.

L ◆ 7

Differentiated Instruction

English Learners/Beginning Comprehension: Modified Cloze L1
Create a paragraph that includes the boldface sentence and sentences containing boldface terms on these two pages. Omit key terms, and give students a list of the terms. Show students how to fill in the blanks. Then, have them complete the sentences using words from the list. **learning modality: verbal**

English Learners/Intermediate Comprehension: Modified Cloze L2 Give students the same paragraph as in the Beginning strategy, but include some wrong choices in the list of terms. Show students how to fill in the blanks, and then have them complete the sentences. **learning modality: verbal**

The Building Blocks of Matter

Teach Key Concepts L2
Elements, Compounds, and Mixtures

Focus Compare and contrast compounds and mixtures and relate them to elements.

Teach Draw a Venn diagram showing that both compounds and mixtures are made up of two or more elements, but only in compounds are the elements combined chemically in specific ratios.

Apply Ask: **Is air a compound or mixture?** *(Mixture)* **learning modality: visual**

Address Misconceptions L2
Smallest Particles of Elements

Focus Students familiar with subatomic particles may be confused when atoms are called the smallest particles of elements.

Teach Say that atoms can be broken into smaller parts, but, unlike whole atoms, the smaller parts are not unique to each element.

Apply Explain that atoms of different elements can share electrons to form chemical bonds. **learning modality: verbal**

For: More on atomic structure
Visit: PHSchool.com
Web Code: cgd-2011

Students can review atomic structure in an online interactivity.

Independent Practice L2
All in One Teaching Resources
• Guided Reading and Study Worksheet: *Elements and Atoms*

○ **Student Edition on Audio CD**

Monitor Progress L2

Oral Presentation Call on students to define the key terms on these pages.

Answers
Figure 1 Air

Reading Checkpoint: A compound is a pure substance made of two or more elements. An element is the simplest pure substance.

Atomic Theory and Models

Teach Key Concepts L2
Atomic Models

Focus Tell students that scientists use models to study atoms.

Teach Explain that scientists have relied on models to help them understand atoms because atoms are too tiny to be observed directly. As scientists learned more about how atoms behave, they modified their models. Have students scan the headings on these two pages. Then, ask: **Who developed the earliest model of the atom?** *(Dalton)* **Who developed the first model that included smaller particles of atoms?** *(Thomson)* **Who developed the first model that included the nucleus?** *(Rutherford)*

Apply Ask: **In general, how do you think models of atoms have changed through time?** *(Sample answer: They represented parts of atoms, not just atoms as a whole.)* **learning modality: visual**

All in One **Teaching Resources**
- Transparency L2

Use Visuals: Figure 2 L2
Dalton's Atomic Theory

Focus Have students look at Dalton's model in Figure 2.

Teach Point out that Dalton's idea that atoms were like smooth, hard balls was too simple. Dalton's other ideas about atoms, however, are still accepted with few changes. Have students read the list of Dalton's ideas about atoms.

Apply Tell students that the mass of oxygen is about 16. Ask: **Would you expect any other element have a mass of 16?** *(No, because according to Dalton's theory, atoms of different elements have different masses.)* **learning modality: verbal**

FIGURE 2
Dalton Model
Dalton thought that atoms were like smooth, hard balls that could not be broken into smaller pieces.

Summary of Dalton's Ideas

- All elements are composed of atoms that cannot be divided.
- All atoms of the same element are exactly alike and have the same mass. Atoms of different elements are different and have different masses.
- An atom of one element cannot be changed into an atom of a different element. Atoms cannot be created or destroyed in any chemical change, only rearranged.
- Every compound is composed of atoms of different elements, combined in a specific ratio.

FIGURE 3
Thomson Model
Thomson suggested that atoms had negatively charged electrons embedded in a positive sphere. **Comparing and Contrasting** *How is Thomson's model different from Dalton's?*

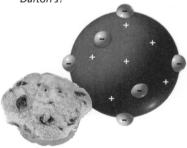

8 ◆ L

Atomic Theory and Models

The ancient Greeks did not prove the existence of atoms because they did not do experiments. In science, ideas are just ideas unless they can be tested. The idea of atoms began to develop again in the 1600s. This time, people did do experiments. As a result, atomic theory began to take shape.

A **scientific theory** is a well-tested idea that explains and connects a wide range of observations. Theories often include **models**—physical, mental, visual, and other representations of an idea to help people understand what they cannot observe directly. **Atomic theory grew as a series of models that developed from experimental evidence. As more evidence was collected, the theory and models were revised.**

Dalton's Atomic Theory Using evidence from many experiments, John Dalton, an English chemist, began to propose his atomic theory and model for atoms. The main ideas of Dalton's theory are summarized in Figure 2. With only a few changes, Dalton's atomic theory is still accepted today.

Thomson and Smaller Parts of Atoms Through a series of experiments around the start of the twentieth century, scientists discovered that atoms are made of even smaller parts. In 1897, another British scientist, J. J. Thomson, found that atoms contain negatively charged particles. Yet, scientists knew that atoms themselves had no electrical charge. So, Thomson reasoned, atoms must also contain some sort of positive charge.

Thomson proposed a model like the one in Figure 3. He described an atom that consisted of negative charges scattered throughout a ball of positive charge—something like raisins or berries in a muffin. The negatively charged particles later became known as **electrons.**

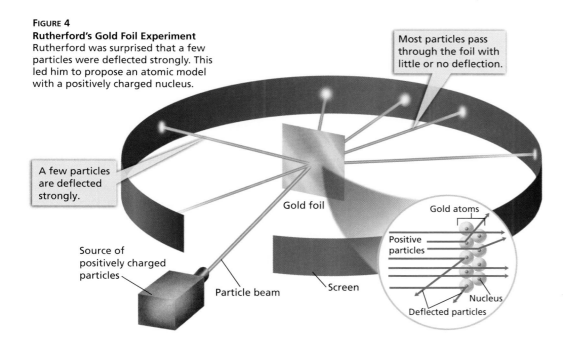

FIGURE 4
Rutherford's Gold Foil Experiment
Rutherford was surprised that a few particles were deflected strongly. This led him to propose an atomic model with a positively charged nucleus.

Most particles pass through the foil with little or no deflection.

A few particles are deflected strongly.

Source of positively charged particles

Particle beam

Gold foil

Screen

Gold atoms

Positive particles

Nucleus

Deflected particles

Rutherford and the Nucleus In 1911, one of Thomson's students, Ernest Rutherford, found evidence that countered Thomson's model. In an experiment diagrammed in Figure 4, Rutherford's research team aimed a beam of positively charged particles at a thin sheet of gold foil. They predicted that, if Thomson's model were correct, the charged particles would pass right through the foil in a straight line. The gold atoms would not have enough positive charge in any one region to strongly repel the charged particles.

Rutherford's team observed that most of the particles passed through the foil undisturbed, as expected. But, to their surprise, a few particles were deflected strongly. Since like charges repel each other, Rutherford inferred that an atom's positive charge must be clustered in a tiny region in its center, called the **nucleus** (NOO klee us). Those particles that were deflected strongly had been repelled by a gold atom's nucleus.

Scientists knew from other experiments that electrons had almost no mass. Therefore, they reasoned that nearly all of an atom's mass must also be located in the tiny, positively charged nucleus. In Rutherford's model of the atom, the atom was mostly empty space with electrons moving around the nucleus in that space. Later, Rutherford named the positively charged particles in the nucleus of an atom **protons.**

FIGURE 5
Rutherford Model
According to Rutherford's model, an atom was mostly empty space. Electrons moved around a small, positively charged nucleus in the center of the atom.

Chapter 1 L ◆ 9

Help Students Read

Using Prior Knowledge Refer to the Content Refresher in this chapter, which provides guidelines for applying the Using Prior Knowledge strategy.

Guide students in using their prior knowledge of the solar system to understand Bohr's atomic model. Have students read the paragraph about Bohr's model and look at the diagram of the model in Figure 6. Point out that Bohr's model is compared in the text to planets orbiting the sun. Ask: **If the solar system represents an atom, which part of the atom does the sun represent?** *(Nucleus)* **Which parts of the atom do the planets represent?** *(Electrons)* **How are the electrons in Bohr's model like planets in the solar system?** *(They move around the nucleus in specific orbits.)* Explain that the orbit of an electron in Bohr's model is determined by how much energy the electron has.

Visualizing an Electron Cloud

Materials electric or battery-operated fan

Time 5 minutes

Focus Use a fan to help students visualize how electrons fill the space around the nucleus in the cloud model of electrons.

Teach Show students that when the fan is off, they can clearly distinguish each blade. Then, turn on the fan and ask: **How would you describe the blades?** *(Sample answer: They are just a blur.)*

Apply Ask: **How are the electrons in a "cloud" of electrons like the blades of the fan?** *(Electrons in a cloud move in such a way around the nucleus that it is impossible to identify their positions.)* **learning modality: visual**

Bohr's Model In 1913, Niels Bohr, a Danish scientist and a student of both Thomson and Rutherford, revised the atomic model again. Bohr showed that electrons could have only specific amounts of energy, leading them to move in certain orbits. The series of orbits in Bohr's model resemble planets orbiting the sun or the layers of an onion.

A Cloud of Electrons In the 1920s, the atomic model changed again. Scientists determined that electrons do not orbit the nucleus like planets. Instead, electrons can be anywhere in a cloudlike region around the nucleus. A region around the nucleus in which electrons of the same energy are likely to be found is called an **energy level.** The lowest-energy electrons are in an energy level near the nucleus that can hold only 2 electrons. Higher-energy electrons are in larger energy levels farther from the nucleus. These larger energy levels can hold 8 or more electrons.

The Modern Atomic Model In 1932, British scientist James Chadwick discovered another particle in the nucleus of atoms. His discovery completed the modern atomic model. This new particle was hard to detect because it has no electrical charge even though it has nearly the same mass as a proton. Because the particle was electrically neutral, it was called a **neutron.**

FIGURE 6
Later Atomic Models

Through the first part of the twentieth century, atomic models continued to change.
Interpreting Diagrams How does the cloud model differ from the modern atomic model?

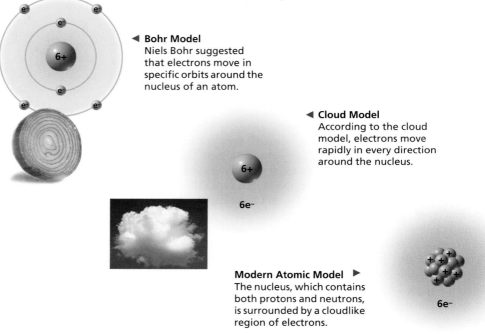

◄ **Bohr Model**
Niels Bohr suggested that electrons move in specific orbits around the nucleus of an atom.

◄ **Cloud Model**
According to the cloud model, electrons move rapidly in every direction around the nucleus.

Modern Atomic Model ►
The nucleus, which contains both protons and neutrons, is surrounded by a cloudlike region of electrons.

New research continues to provide data that support this model of a small nucleus surrounded by a cloudlike region of electrons. The nucleus contains protons and neutrons that together make up nearly all of an atom's mass. The only exception is the nucleus of the hydrogen atom, which usually consists of a single proton. A cloud of electrons made of a series of energy levels occupies most of the volume of an atom.

If you did the Discover activity at the beginning of this section, you learned that the size of an atom can be 100,000 times the size of its nucleus. To get a sense of the scale of an atom, look back at the answer you calculated if the nucleus were the size of a dime. An electron in your model atom could be more than 1,700 meters away!

All the atoms of a single element have the same number of protons. But different elements have different numbers of protons. For example, all hydrogen atoms have only one proton, and all carbon atoms have six protons. Atoms have no overall electric charge because each atom has the same number of electrons as protons. As you will read in Section 2, the number of electrons is key in explaining why different elements have different properties.

 What are neutrons, and where in an atom are they found?

Figure 7
Size of an Atom
If the nucleus of an atom were the size of a pencil eraser on home plate of this baseball field, its electrons could be farther away than the outfield.

Section 1 Assessment

Target Reading Skill Outlining Use the information in your outline about elements and atoms to help you answer the questions below.

Reviewing Key Concepts

1. a. **Defining** What is matter? What is an element?
   b. **Explaining** Why are elements called the building blocks of matter?
   c. **Inferring** Water is a compound. Does water contain elements? Explain.
2. a. **Reviewing** In general, why did atomic theory change with time?
   b. **Describing** Describe Bohr's model of the atom. What specific information did Bohr contribute to scientists' understanding of the atom?
   c. **Comparing and Contrasting** How is the modern atomic model different from Bohr's model? Why did scientists revise Bohr's model?

Writing in Science

Persuasive Letter Write a letter that Thomson might have sent to another scientist explaining why an atom must contain positive charges as well as negative charges. The letter should also explain why Thomson proposed the atomic model that he did.

Chapter 1 L ◆ 11

Atoms, Bonding, and the Periodic Table

Objectives
After this lesson, students will be able to
L.1.2.1 Explain how the reactivity of elements is related to valence electrons in atoms.
L.1.2.2 State what the periodic table tells you about atoms and the properties of elements.

Target Reading Skill

Building Vocabulary Explain that knowing the definitions of key terms helps students understand what they read.

Answers
Sample definitions: **Valence electrons:** electrons that are in the highest energy level and held most loosely; **Electron dot diagram:** diagram of an atom that includes the symbol for the element surrounded by dots that stand for valence electrons; **Chemical bond:** the force of attraction that holds two atoms together as a result of the rearrangement of electrons between them; **Noble gas:** any element in Group 18, which consists of elements with eight valence electrons; **Halogen:** any element in Group 17, which consists of elements with seven valence electrons; **Alkali metal:** any element in Group 1, which consists of elements with one valence electron

Preteach

Build Background Knowledge L2
Organizing Elements
Ask: **If you go into a music store, how do you find a particular CD?** (*Sample answer: You find the section for that type of music, search alphabetically for the artist, and then find the title among that artist's recordings.*) **Why do you think music stores organize CDs in this way?** (*The organization makes it easier to find specific types of music, artists, and recordings.*) Tell students that in this section they will learn how elements, like CDs, are organized based on certain similarities among them.

Atoms, Bonding, and the Periodic Table

Reading Preview

Key Concepts
- How is the reactivity of elements related to valence electrons in atoms?
- What does the periodic table tell you about atoms and the properties of elements?

Key Terms
- valence electrons
- electron dot diagram
- chemical bond
- symbol • atomic number
- period • group • family
- noble gas • halogen
- alkali metal

Target Reading Skill
Building Vocabulary After you read this section, reread the paragraphs that contain definitions of Key Terms. Use all the information you have learned to write a definition of each Key Term in your own words.

Lab zone Discover **Activity**

What Are the Trends in the Periodic Table?

1. Examine the periodic table of the elements that your teacher provides. Look in each square for the whole number located above the symbol of the element. As you read across a row from left to right, what trend do you see?
2. Now look at a column from top to bottom. What trend do you see in these numbers?

Think It Over
Interpreting Data Can you explain why one row ends and a new row starts? Why are certain elements in the same column?

Why isn't the world made only of elements? How do the atoms of different elements combine to form compounds? The answers to these questions are related to electrons and their energy levels. And the roadmap to understanding how electrons determine the properties of elements is the periodic table.

Valence Electrons and Bonding

In Section 1 you learned about electrons in energy levels. An atom's **valence electrons** (VAY luns) are those electrons that are in the highest energy level and held most loosely. **The number of valence electrons in an atom of an element determines many properties of that element, including the ways in which the atom can bond with other atoms.**

FIGURE 8
Valence Electrons
Skydivers in the outer ring are less securely held to the group than are members of the inner ring. Similarly, valence electrons are more loosely held by an atom than are electrons in lower energy levels.

Lab zone Discover **Activity**

Skills Focus Interpreting data L1
Materials periodic table
Time 10 minutes

Tip You may want to explain the concept of atomic number.

Expected Outcome Students will most likely recognize that the elements are arranged from left to right and from top to bottom in order of increasing atomic number.

Think It Over Students may not know that one row ends and a new row starts when the number of electrons in the highest energy level reaches 8. They also may not know that elements in the same column have the same number of electrons in the highest energy level.

Electron Dot Diagrams Each element has a specific number of valence electrons, ranging from 1 to 8. Figure 9 shows one way to depict the number of valence electrons in an element. An **electron dot diagram** includes the symbol for the element surrounded by dots. Each dot stands for one valence electron.

Chemical Bonds and Stability Most atoms are more stable—less likely to react—when they have eight valence electrons. For example, atoms of neon, argon, krypton, and xenon all have eight valence electrons and are very unreactive. These elements do not easily form compounds. Some small atoms, such as helium, are stable with just two valence electrons in their first and only energy level.

When atoms react, they usually do so in a way that makes each atom more stable. One of two things can happen: Either the number of valence electrons increases to eight (or two, in the case of hydrogen). Or, the atom gives up its most loosely held valence electrons. Atoms that react this way become chemically combined, or bonded together. A **chemical bond** is the force of attraction that holds two atoms together as a result of the rearrangement of electrons between them.

Chemical Bonds and Chemical Reactions When atoms bond, electrons may be transferred from one atom to another, or they may be shared between the atoms. In either case, the change results in a chemical reaction—that is, new substances form. Later in this chapter, you will learn which elements are likely to gain electrons, which are likely to give up electrons, and which are likely to share electrons. You will also learn how the periodic table of the elements can help you predict how atoms of different elements react.

Reading Checkpoint What information does an electron dot diagram show?

FIGURE 9
Electron Dot Diagrams
An atom's valence electrons are shown as dots around the symbol of the element. Notice that oxygen atoms have 6 valence electrons. **Predicting** *How many more electrons are needed to make an oxygen atom stable?*

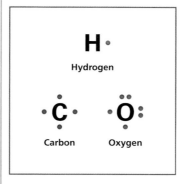

H·
Hydrogen

·C·   ·Ö:
Carbon   Oxygen

L ◆ 13

The Periodic Table

Teach Key Concepts `L2`

Using the Periodic Table

Focus Guide students in understanding how to use the periodic table.

Teach Have students look at the periodic table in Figure 10 and read the caption and labels. Read the definition of atomic number, and point out that the atomic number is the number above each element's one- or two-letter symbol. Check students' understanding by asking: **What is the atomic number of zinc (Zn)?** *(30)* **How many protons does chromium (Cr) have?** *(24)*

Apply Ask: **Which element has an atomic number of 53?** *(Iodine)* **Does any other element in the periodic table have that atomic number?** *(No, the atomic number of each element is unique.)* **learning modality: visual**

Go Online
active art

For: Periodic table activity
Visit: PHSchool.com
Web Code: cgp-1032

Students can interact with a periodic table activity online.

All in One Teaching Resources

• Transparency L4

Lab zone Build Inquiry `L3`

Inferring How Isotopes Differ

Materials periodic table (Figure 10)

Time 5 minutes

Focus Guide students in interpreting the meaning of atomic mass.

Teach Explain that the atomic mass of an element is the average mass of the element's atoms. Remind students that most of an atom's mass is in the nucleus. Ask: **Which two types of particles contribute most to an atom's mass?** *(Protons and neutrons)* Point out how the elements in period 7 have their atomic masses given in parentheses. Explain that this is because different forms of these elements, called isotopes, have different atomic masses.

The Periodic Table

The periodic table is a system used worldwide for organizing elements into categories. The way the elements are organized gives you important information about the arrangement of the electrons in their atoms. If you know the numbers of valence electrons an element has, you have a clue as to which elements combine and how.

Organizing the Elements Look at the periodic table in Figure 10. Each element is represented by a **symbol,** usually consisting of one or two letters. Above the symbol is the element's atomic number. The **atomic number** of an element is the number of protons in the nucleus of an atom. Notice that the elements are arranged in order of increasing atomic number.

FIGURE 10
The Periodic Table
Elements are organized into rows and columns based on their atomic number. **Interpreting Tables** *What other element is in the same period as hydrogen? What is the next element in the same group as oxygen?*

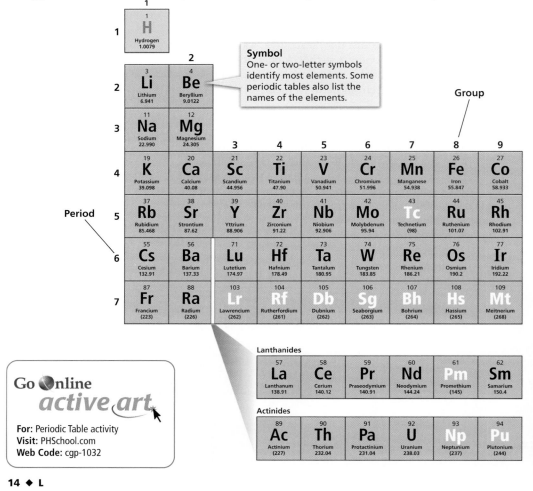

Go Online
active art

For: Periodic Table activity
Visit: PHSchool.com
Web Code: cgp-1032

14 ◆ L

Apply Ask: **If all the atoms of an element have the same atomic number, why do their isotopes have different atomic masses?** *(The isotopes have different numbers of neutrons.)* **learning modality: logical/mathematical**

Periods and Groups A row of elements across the periodic table is called a **period.** Hydrogen and helium make up the first period. The second period starts with lithium (Li) and continues across to neon (Ne). Notice that the atomic number increases one at a time across a period of elements. Because the number of protons in an atom is equal to its number of electrons, it is also true that the number of electrons increases one at a time across a period.

Elements in the same column are called a **group** or **family.** Notice the numbers across the tops of the columns of the periodic table. These numbers identify the group to which an element belongs. For example, carbon (C) is in Group 14 and oxygen (O) is in Group 16.

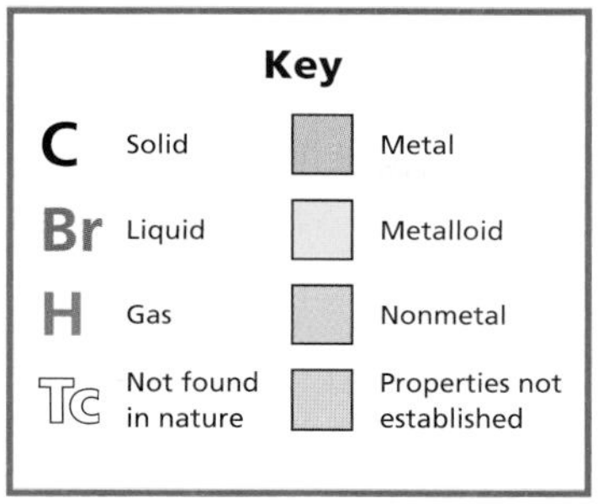

Key

C	Solid		Metal
Br	Liquid		Metalloid
H	Gas		Nonmetal
Tc	Not found in nature		Properties not established

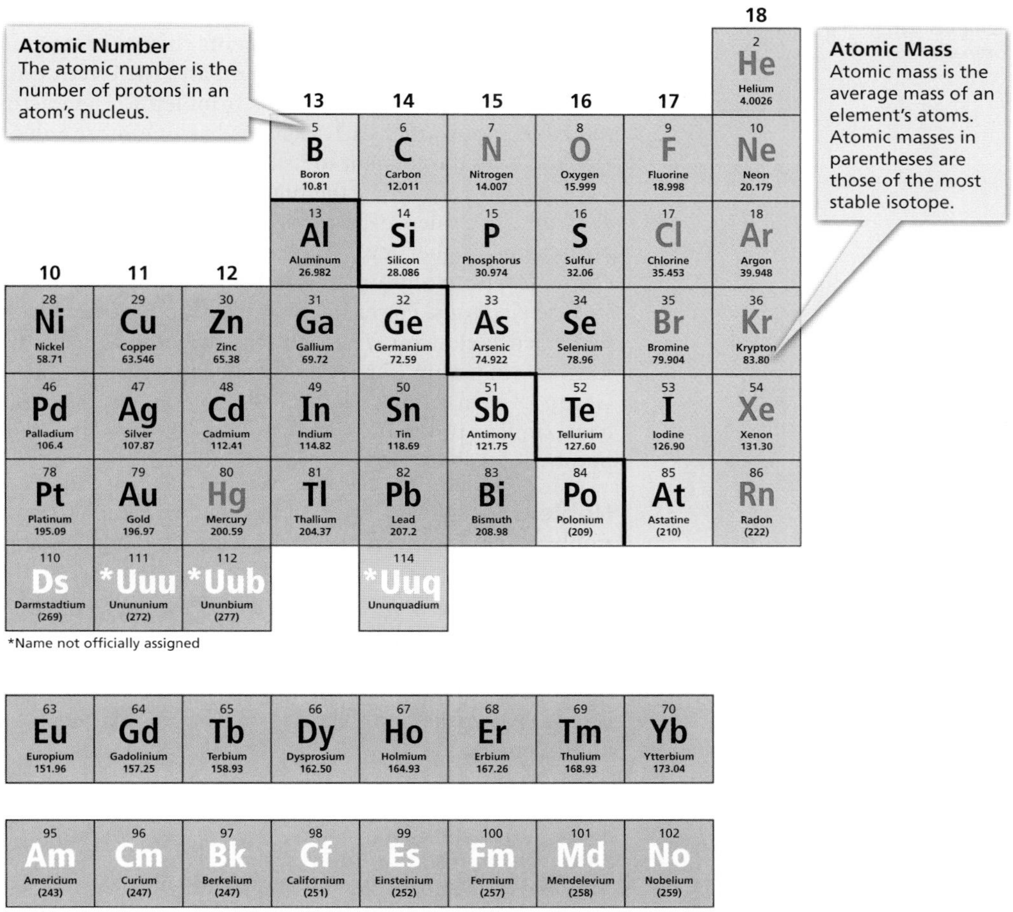

Atomic Number
The atomic number is the number of protons in an atom's nucleus.

Atomic Mass
Atomic mass is the average mass of an element's atoms. Atomic masses in parentheses are those of the most stable isotope.

18
2 **He** Helium 4.0026

13	14	15	16	17
5 **B** Boron 10.81	6 **C** Carbon 12.011	7 **N** Nitrogen 14.007	8 **O** Oxygen 15.999	9 **F** Fluorine 18.998
13 **Al** Aluminum 26.982	14 **Si** Silicon 28.086	15 **P** Phosphorus 30.974	16 **S** Sulfur 32.06	17 **Cl** Chlorine 35.453

10	11	12					
28 **Ni** Nickel 58.71	29 **Cu** Copper 63.546	30 **Zn** Zinc 65.38	31 **Ga** Gallium 69.72	32 **Ge** Germanium 72.59	33 **As** Arsenic 74.922	34 **Se** Selenium 78.96	35 **Br** Bromine 79.904
46 **Pd** Palladium 106.4	47 **Ag** Silver 107.87	48 **Cd** Cadmium 112.41	49 **In** Indium 114.82	50 **Sn** Tin 118.69	51 **Sb** Antimony 121.75	52 **Te** Tellurium 127.60	53 **I** Iodine 126.90
78 **Pt** Platinum 195.09	79 **Au** Gold 196.97	80 **Hg** Mercury 200.59	81 **Tl** Thallium 204.37	82 **Pb** Lead 207.2	83 **Bi** Bismuth 208.98	84 **Po** Polonium (209)	85 **At** Astatine (210)
110 **Ds** Darmstadtium (269)	111 ***Uuu** Unununium (272)	112 ***Uub** Ununbium (277)	114 ***Uuq** Ununquadium				

(Additional noble gas column: 18 **Ar** Argon 39.948; 36 **Kr** Krypton 83.80; 54 **Xe** Xenon 131.30; 86 **Rn** Radon (222); 10 **Ne** Neon 20.179)

*Name not officially assigned

63 **Eu** Europium 151.96	64 **Gd** Gadolinium 157.25	65 **Tb** Terbium 158.93	66 **Dy** Dysprosium 162.50	67 **Ho** Holmium 164.93	68 **Er** Erbium 167.26	69 **Tm** Thulium 168.93	70 **Yb** Ytterbium 173.04

95 **Am** Americium (243)	96 **Cm** Curium (247)	97 **Bk** Berkelium (247)	98 **Cf** Californium (251)	99 **Es** Einsteinium (252)	100 **Fm** Fermium (257)	101 **Md** Mendelevium (258)	102 **No** Nobelium (259)

Use Visuals: Figure 10 L2

Periods and Groups

Focus Guide students in identifying the basis of the organization of the periodic table in terms of periods and groups.

Teach Explain that each row of the periodic table in Figure 10 is called a period and that each column is called a group or family. Ask: **Which elements are in Period 1?** *(Hydrogen and helium).* **Which elements are in Group 1?** *(Hydrogen, lithium, sodium, potassium, rubidium, cesium, and francium)*

Apply Ask: **What is the next element in the same period as potassium?** *(Calcium)* **What is the next element in the same group as carbon?** *(Silicon)* **learning modality: visual**

Lab zone **Build Inquiry** L2

Interpreting Symbols

Materials periodic table (Figure 10)

Time 5 minutes

Focus Challenge students to interpret the color-coded symbols in the periodic table.

Teach Call students' attention to the key of the periodic table. Have them use the key to find a metal, a metalloid, and a nonmetal in the table.

Apply Ask: **Which element is not found in nature, curium or zirconium?** *(Curium)* **Which element is a solid, chlorine or iodine?** *(Iodine)* **Which two elements in the table are liquids?** *(Mercury and bromine)* **learning modality: visual**

Differentiated Instruction

English Learners/Beginning L1
Comprehension: Ask Questions Check that students understand the difference between periods and groups. Ask **Which period is sodium in?** *(Period 3)* **Which group is sodium in?** *(Group 1)* If necessary, remind students that periods are rows and groups are columns. **learning modality: visual**

English Learners/Intermediate L2
Comprehension: Ask Questions Reinforce the meanings of period and group. Then, check students' comprehension of the overall organization of the periodic table. Ask **Which element is in Period 6 and also in Group 6?** *(Tungsten)* **Is manganese (Mn) in Period 7 or Group 7?** *(Group 7)* **learning modality: visual**

Monitor Progress L2

Oral Presentation Ask students to identify the period and group of several elements in the periodic table.

Answer
Figure 10 Helium is in the same period as hydrogen. The next element in the same family as oxygen is sulfur.

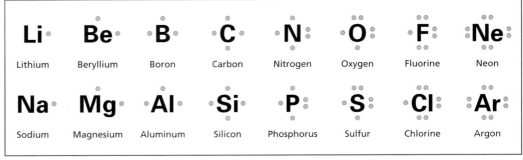

FIGURE 11

Patterns of Valence Electrons
After the number of valence electrons
reaches 8, a new period begins.
*Comparing and Contrasting How does
the number of valence electrons in
elements within the same group
compare?*

Use Visuals: Figure 11 L2
Valence Electron Patterns

Focus Guide students in recognizing that all the elements in a group have the same number of valence electrons, and help them appreciate the significance of valence electrons.

Teach Point out the pattern of valence electrons in the electron dot diagrams in Figure 11. Ask: **Which two elements are in Group 1?** *(Lithium and sodium)* **How many valence electrons does each one have?** *(One)* In a similar way, have students name the elements and numbers of valence electrons in a few more of the groups in Groups 2 through 18. Instruct students to look at Figure 10 if they are unsure to which group any of the elements belong.

Apply After students have recognized the pattern of valence electrons in groups, explain that elements with the same number of valence electrons have similar properties. For example, lithium, sodium, and the other elements in Group 1 are all alkali metals, which are very reactive. **learning modality: visual**

All in One Teaching Resources
• Transparency L5

Help Students Read L1
Vocabulary: Word Origins Explain that the noble gases were so named because they do not combine with other elements, even oxygen, which is highly reactive. Ask: **Why do the noble gases not combine with oxygen or other elements?** *(The noble gases have eight valence electrons, which make them very stable.)*

How the Periodic Table Works The periodic table is based on the structure of atoms, especially the arrangement of electrons. Think of how atoms change from left to right across a period. **As the number of protons (atomic number) increases, the number of electrons also increases. As a result, the properties of the elements change in a regular way across a period.** Figure 11 compares the electron dot diagrams of some of the elements from left to right across the table. Notice that each element has one more valence electron than the element to its left.

A period ends when the highest energy level has eight electrons. The valence electrons of atoms in the next period are in a new, higher, level. This repeating pattern means the elements within a group always have the same number of valence electrons. For example, the Group 1 elements have one valence electron. The elements in Group 2 have two. Elements in Group 17 have seven valence electrons, and the Group 18 elements have eight. The elements within a group have similar properties because they all have the same number of valence electrons in their atoms.

Noble Gases The Group 18 elements are known as the **noble gases.** Atoms of these elements have eight valence electrons, except for helium, which has two. Recall that when atoms get the maximum number of valence electrons—eight—they become stable. The noble gases already have eight valence electrons. As a result, noble gases do not react easily with other elements. Even so, chemists have been able to make noble gases form compounds with a few other elements.

Xenon
Blue-green

Neon
Orange-red

Argon
Purple

Krypton
White

FIGURE 12
"Neon" Signs
The variety of colors in a "neon" sign results
from passing an electric current through sealed
glass tubes containing different noble gases.

16 ◆ L

Reactive Nonmetals and Metals Now look at the elements in the column just to the left of the noble gases. The elements in Group 17 are called the **halogens.** Atoms in the halogen family have seven valence electrons. A gain of just one more electron gives these atoms the stable number of eight electrons, as in the noble gases. As a result, elements in the halogen family react easily with other elements whose atoms can give up or share electrons.

At the far left side of the periodic table is Group 1, called the **alkali metal** family. Atoms of the alkali metals have only one valence electron. Except for lithium, the energy level below this single electron contains a stable set of eight electrons. (Lithium atoms have a stable set of two electrons in the energy level below the valence electron.) Therefore, alkali metal atoms can become chemically more stable by losing their one valence electron. This property makes the alkali metals very reactive.

 Reading Checkpoint Where on the periodic table are the halogens found?

FIGURE 13
Reactive Elements
Elements in Group 17 (the halogens) and Group 1 (the alkali metals) are highly reactive. *Relating Cause and Effect Why are elements in these two groups so reactive?*

▼ Sodium, an alkali metal, reacts vigorously with bromine, a halogen.

▲ Steel wool burns when exposed to the halogen chlorine.

▲ When iodine, a halogen, reacts with aluminum, a purple gas is produced.

Chapter 1 L ◆ 17

Atoms and Bonding

Show the Video Field Trip so students can see how elements are arranged in the periodic table, how atoms are structured, and how bonding occurs. Discussion question: **What determines how reactive the atoms of an element are?** (*The natural tendency of atoms to either completely fill or completely empty the outer shell of electrons*)

Lab zone Teacher **Demo**   L2

Observing Reactivity of Alkaline Earth Metals

Materials small amounts of magnesium and calcium, 2 beakers of cold water, 1 beaker of hot water

Time 10 minutes

Focus Show students that metals in the same group have similar but not identical properties.

Teach Tell students that calcium and magnesium, Group 2 metals, are almost as reactive as Group 1 elements. Then, wearing goggles and a lab apron, add a small amount of magnesium to one jar of cold water and a small amount of calcium to the other jar of cold water. Ask: **Which element reacts with cold water?** (*Calcium produces bubbles and turns the water cloudy as it reacts*). Next, add a small amount of magnesium to the jar of hot water. Ask: **Does magnesium react with hot water?** (*Yes*)

Apply Ask: **Which element is more reactive, calcium or magnesium?** (*Calcium*) **learning modality: visual**

Integrating Health Science   L2

Tell students that magnesium has essential biological functions: It is an important component of chlorophyll, the plant compound needed for photosynthesis, and humans need it to activate enzymes involved in protein synthesis. Ask: **How can you get magnesium in your diet?** (*Sample answer: Whole grains and green, leafy vegetables, such as spinach.*) **learning modality: verbal**

Other Metals Look at the elements in Groups 2 through 12 of the periodic table. Like the Group 1 elements, these elements are metals. Most have one, two, or three valence electrons. They react by losing these electrons, especially when they combine with oxygen or one of the halogens.

How reactive a metal is depends on how easily its atoms lose valence electrons. Some metals, such as those in Group 2 (the alkaline earth metals), lose electrons easily and are almost as reactive as the alkali metals of Group 1. Other metals, such as platinum (Pt) in Group 10 and gold (Au) in Group 11, are unreactive. Mercury (Hg) is the only metal that is a liquid at room temperature. All the other metals are solids, although gallium (Ga) melts just above room temperature.

Science and **History**

Discovery of the Elements
In 1869, Dmitri Mendeleev published the first periodic table. At that time, 63 elements were known. Since then, scientists have discovered or created about 50 new elements.

**1875
Gallium**
The French chemist Paul-Émile Lecoq de Boisbaudran discovered an element that he called gallium. It had properties predicted by Mendeleev for an unknown element that would fit directly below aluminum in the periodic table.

**1894
Argon, Neon, Krypton, and Xenon**
British chemist William Ramsay discovered an element he named argon, after the Greek word for "lazy." The name fits because argon does not react with other elements. Ramsay looked for other nonreactive gases and discovered neon, krypton, and xenon.

**1898
Polonium and Radium**
Polish chemist Marie Curie started with three tons of uranium ore before she eventually isolated a few grams of two new elements. She named them polonium and radium.

| 1830 | 1865 | 1900 |

18 ♦ L

Background

Facts and Figures Gallium is known today to be unique in remaining in a liquid state over a greater range of temperatures than any other element. Some compounds of gallium, including gallium arsenide, are excellent semiconductors, used to make integrated circuits in computers.

For many years after the noble gases were discovered, scientists believed that they would not react with other elements.

Then, in 1962, a British chemist named Neil Bartlett proved that this was incorrect by making the first xenon compound. Later, compounds were made with radon and krypton. These three noble gases are believed to be reactive, even though they have eight valence electrons, because there is so much space and so many other electrons between their valence electrons and their nuclei.

Other Nonmetals Elements in the green section of the periodic table are the nonmetals. Carbon (C), phosphorus (P), sulfur (S), selenium (Se), and iodine (I) are the only nonmetals that are solids at room temperature. Bromine (Br) is the only liquid. All of the nonmetals have four or more valence electrons. Like the halogens, other nonmetals become stable when they gain or share enough electrons to have a set of eight valence electrons.

The nonmetals combine with metals usually by gaining electrons. But nonmetals can also combine with other nonmetals by sharing electrons. Of the nonmetals, oxygen and the halogens are highly reactive. In fact, fluorine is the most reactive element known. It even forms compounds with some of the noble gases.

Writing in Science

Research and Write Select three elements that interest you and find out more about them. Who identified or discovered the elements? How did the elements get their names? How are the elements used? To answer these questions, look up the elements in reference books.

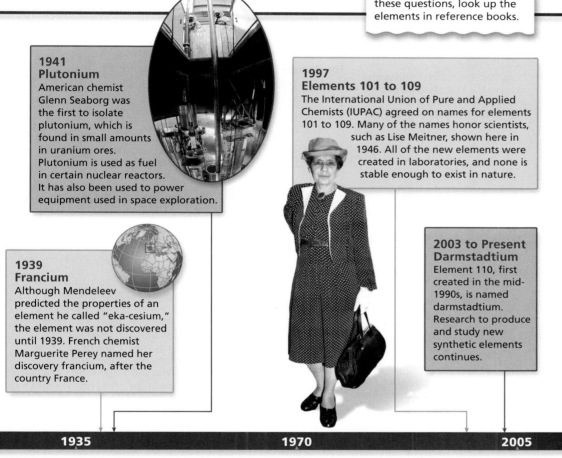

**1941
Plutonium**
American chemist Glenn Seaborg was the first to isolate plutonium, which is found in small amounts in uranium ores. Plutonium is used as fuel in certain nuclear reactors. It has also been used to power equipment used in space exploration.

**1997
Elements 101 to 109**
The International Union of Pure and Applied Chemists (IUPAC) agreed on names for elements 101 to 109. Many of the names honor scientists, such as Lise Meitner, shown here in 1946. All of the new elements were created in laboratories, and none is stable enough to exist in nature.

**1939
Francium**
Although Mendeleev predicted the properties of an element he called "eka-cesium," the element was not discovered until 1939. French chemist Marguerite Perey named her discovery francium, after the country France.

**2003 to Present
Darmstadtium**
Element 110, first created in the mid-1990s, is named darmstadtium. Research to produce and study new synthetic elements continues.

| 1935 | 1970 | 2005 |

Science and **History**

Focus Guide students in appreciating the importance of discovering new elements, and explain how synthetic elements are created.

Teach Describe what the elements in the timeline are used for. For example, say that gallium is used to make faster CPUs in computers; polonium is used to reduce electrostatic charges in printing and photography equipment; radium is used to treat cancer; and plutonium is used to produce nuclear power in nuclear reactors, to make nuclear weapons, and to power equipment on the moon. Ask: **What are noble gases, such as argon and neon, used for?** (*Light bulbs*)

Writing in Science

Writing Mode Research
Scoring Rubric
4 Exceeds criteria; includes a detailed, accurate, and well organized paper that completely answers all three questions
3 Meets criteria
2 Includes answers to only two questions and/or covers only two elements
1 Includes answers to only one question and/or covers only one element and contains errors or other inadequacies

Background

History of Science In 1997, the IUPAC named element 106 seaborgium (Sg) in honor of Glenn Seaborg, who not only helped discover plutonium but also americium, curium, berkelium, californium, and several other heavy elements during the 1940s. The IUPAC also named element 109 meitnerium (Mt) in memory of Austrian physicist Lise Meitner, who helped discover protactinium in 1918 and later was the first scientist to identify nuclear fission. More recently, element 110 was named darmstadtium in honor of physicists in Darmstadt, Germany, who first produced the element in 1994. These same scientists also produced elements 111, 112, and 114 in the mid-1990s. In 2004, Russian and American scientists reported creating elements 113 and 115. The new elements existed for less than a second.

Monitor Progress ———— L2

Skills Check Have students make a Venn diagram comparing and contrasting metals and nonmetals.

Monitor Progress

Answer

 Because it has only one valence electron like other Group 1 elements

Assess

Reviewing Key Concepts

1. a. Electrons that are in the highest energy level and held most loosely **b.** Valence electrons are most likely to be involved in chemical bonding. When elements react to form compounds, valence electrons may be transferred from one atom to another or shared between atoms. **c.** When oxygen atoms form compounds, they gain or share valence electrons to make a set of eight valence electrons. This makes them more stable.

2. a. A row of elements across the periodic table is called a period. Atomic number and number of valence electrons increase by one from left to right across a period. Elements in the same column are called a group or family. Atomic number increases from top to bottom of a group, but the number of valence electrons is the same within a group. **b.** The properties of elements change in a regular way across a period because the number of valence electrons changes regularly. **c.** The elements of Group 18 are the least reactive elements in the periodic table because they have eight valence electrons.

Reteach ▪ L1

List the following terms on the board: *noble gas, halogen, alkali metal, alkaline earth metal, nonmetal, metalloid*. Call on students to identify properties of each type of element.

Performance Assessment ▪ L2

Writing Ask student to list information about elements that is found in the periodic table.

All in One Teaching Resources

- Section Summary: *Atoms, Bonding, and the Periodic Table*
- Review and Reinforcement: *Atoms, Bonding, and the Periodic Table*
- Enrich: *Atoms, Bonding, and the Periodic Table*

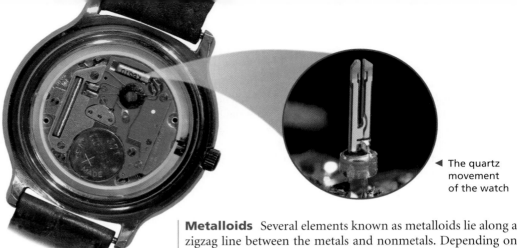

▶ The quartz movement of the watch

FIGURE 14
A Metalloid at Work
This quartz-movement watch keeps time with a small quartz crystal, a compound made of the metalloid silicon and the nonmetal oxygen. The crystal vibrates at about 32,000 vibrations per second when a voltage is applied.

Metalloids Several elements known as metalloids lie along a zigzag line between the metals and nonmetals. Depending on the conditions, these elements can behave as either metals or nonmetals. The metalloids have from three to six valence electrons and can either lose or share electrons when they combine with other elements.

Hydrogen Notice that hydrogen is considered to be a nonmetal. It is located above Group 1 in the periodic table because it has only one valence electron. However, even though hydrogen is a reactive element, its properties differ greatly from those of the alkali metals.

✓ **Reading Checkpoint** Why is hydrogen grouped above the Group 1 elements even though it is not a metal?

Section 2 Assessment

🔄 **Target Reading Skill** Building Vocabulary Use your definitions to help you answer the questions below.

Reviewing Key Concepts

1. a. Defining What are valence electrons?
   b. Reviewing What role do valence electons play in the formation of compounds from elements?
   c. Comparing and Contrasting Do oxygen atoms become more stable or less stable when oxygen forms compounds? Explain.
2. a. Summarizing Summarize how the periodic table is organized. Use the words *period* and *group*.
   b. Explaining Why do the properties of elements change in a regular way across a period?
   c. Relating Cause and Effect How reactive are the elements in Group 18? Explain this reactivity in terms of the number of valence electrons.

20 ◆ **L**

Lab zone At-Home Activity

Looking for Elements Find some examples of elements at home. Then locate the elements on the periodic table. Show your examples and the periodic table to your family. Point out the positions of the elements on the table and explain what the periodic table tells you about the elements. Include at least two nonmetals in your discussion. (*Hint:* The nonmetals may be invisible.)

Lab zone At-Home Activity

Looking for Elements ▪ L2
Students are likely to find more elements if they read through the names of the elements in the periodic table before they look for them at home. Elements students might find at home include aluminum (in soft drink cans), calcium (in dietary supplements), copper (in pots and pans), tungsten (in light bulb filaments), sodium (in table salt), gold (in jewelry), silver (in utensils), chlorine (in bleach), oxygen, (in air), and hydrogen (in water).

Comparing Atom Sizes

Problem

How is the radius of an atom related to its atomic number?

Skills Focus

making models, graphing, interpreting data

Materials

- drawing compass
- metric ruler
- calculator
- periodic table of the elements (Appendix D)

Procedure

1. Using the periodic table as a reference, predict whether the size (radius) of atoms will increase, remain the same, or decrease as you go from the top to the bottom of a group, or family, of elements.

2. The data table lists the elements in Group 2 in the periodic table. The atomic radius of each element is given in picometers (pm). Copy the data table into your notebook.

3. Calculate the relative radius of each atom compared to beryllium, the smallest atom listed. Do this by dividing each radius by the radius of beryllium. (*Hint:* The relative radius of magnesium would be 160 pm divided by 112 pm, or 1.4.) Record these values, rounded to the nearest tenth, in your data table.

4. Using a compass, draw a circle for each element with a radius that corresponds to the relative radius you calculated in Step 3. Use centimeters as your unit for the radius of each circle. **CAUTION:** *Do not push the sharp point of the compass against your skin.*

5. Label each model with the symbol of the element it represents.

Data Table			
Atomic Number	Element	Radius (pm)*	Relative Radius
4	Be	112	1
12	Mg	160	
20	Ca	197	
38	Sr	215	
56	Ba	222	

*A picometer (pm) is one billionth of a millimeter.

Analyze and Conclude

1. **Making Models** Based on your models, was your prediction in Step 1 correct? Explain.

2. **Graphing** Make a graph of the data given in the first and third columns of the data table. Label the horizontal axis *Atomic Number*. Mark the divisions from 0 to 60. Then label the vertical axis *Radius* and mark its divisions from 0 to 300 picometers.

3. **Interpreting Data** Do the points on your graph fall on a straight line or on a curve? What trend does the graph show?

4. **Predicting** Predict where you would find the largest atom in any group, or family, of elements. What evidence would you need to tell if your prediction is correct?

5. **Communicating** Write a paragraph explaining why it is useful to draw a one- to two-centimeter model of an atom that has an actual radius of 100 to 200 picometers.

More to Explore

Look up the atomic masses for the Group 2 elements. Devise a plan to model their relative atomic masses using real-world objects.

Extend Inquiry

More to Explore Relative atomic masses are approximately 1 (Be), 2.7 (Mg), 4.5 (Ca), 9.7 (Sr), and 15.3 (Ba). Sample plan: Use small fruits such as grapes to model the relative masses. Whole grapes would be used for whole numbers, and cut grapes for the decimal portions. For example, 2.7 grapes would model magnesium's relative mass.

Sample Data Table			
Atomic Number	Element	Radius (pm)	Relative Radius
4	Be	112	1
12	Mg	160	1.4
20	Ca	197	1.8
38	Sr	215	1.9
56	Ba	222	2.0

Comparing Atom Sizes

Prepare for Inquiry

Skills Objective

After this lab, students will be able to
- make models to represent the relative sizes of atoms
- graph data showing the trend in atomic size as atomic number increases in a group
- interpret data to predict the positions of elements in the periodic table

Prep Time 10 minutes
Class Time 30 minutes

Safety

Review the safety guidelines in Appendix A.

All in One Teaching Resources
- Lab Worksheet: *Comparing Atom Sizes*

Guide Inquiry

Introduce the Procedure

Have students read through the procedure. Introduce the idea of using the smallest value in a series as the basis for measuring the other values. Use a familiar example, such as pennies as a basis for other coins. Relate this to Step 3 of the Procedure.

Expected Outcome

Students' graphs should show that radius increases as atomic number increases.

Analyze and Conclude

1. Students may have predicted correctly that the radius of atoms will increase from top to bottom of a group.

2. Make sure students have correctly set up and labeled their graphs.

3. The graph should be a curved line. Higher atomic numbers have larger radii.

4. Students are likely to predict that you would find the largest atom at the bottom of the group. They would need data on the atomic radii of other families to test their predictions.

5. You can drop two zeros to convert the numbers from picometers to centimeters and maintain the correct scale.

Objectives

After this lesson, students will be able to

L.1.3.1 Describe ions, and explain how they form bonds.

L.1.3.2 Explain how the formulas and names of ionic compounds are written.

L.1.3.3 Identify the properties of ionic compounds.

Target Reading Skill ⓢ

Previewing Visuals Explain that looking at the visuals before they read helps students activate prior knowledge and predict what they are about to read.

Answers

Sample questions and answers:

Formation of an Ionic Bond

What is an ionic bond? *(An ionic bond is the attraction between two oppositely charged ions.)* **What is the overall charge on an ionic compound?** *(Overall, an ionic compound is electrically neutral.)*

All in One Teaching Resources

• Transparency L6

Preteach

Build Background Knowledge ▢L2

Electrons and Electrical Charge

Guide students in recalling what they have learned about electrons and electrical charge as a review of the knowledge needed to understand how elements become ions and form ionic bonds. Ask: **What charge does an electron have?** *(1−)* **What is the overall charge on the atom of an element?** *(Overall, an atom is neutral in charge.)* **What charges attract each other?** *(Positive and negative charges)* **Elements in which group have one valence electron?** *(Group 1)* **Elements in which group have seven valence electrons?** *(Group 17)* Tell students that these facts about electrons and electrical charge will help them understand ionic bonds, which they will read about in this section.

Reading Preview

Key Concepts

• What are ions, and how do they form bonds?
• How are the formulas and names of ionic compounds written?
• What are the properties of ionic compounds?

Key Terms

• ion • polyatomic ion
• ionic bond • ionic compound
• chemical formula • subscript
• crystal

ⓢ Target Reading Skill

Previewing Visuals Before you read, preview Figure 17. Then write two questions that you have about the diagram in a graphic organizer like the one below. As you read, answer your questions.

Formation of an Ionic Bond

Q.	What is an ionic bond?
A.	
Q.	

How Do Ions Form?

1. Place three pairs of checkers (three red and three black) on your desk. The red represent electrons and the black represent protons.
2. Place nine pairs of checkers (nine red and nine black) in a separate group on your desk.
3. Move a red checker from the smaller group to the larger group.
4. Count the number of positive charges (protons) and negative charges (electrons) in each group.
5. Now sort the checkers into a group of four pairs and a group of eight pairs. Repeat Steps 3 and 4, this time moving two red checkers from the smaller group to the larger group.

Think It Over

Inferring What was the total charge on each group before you moved the red checkers (electrons)? What was the charge on each group after you moved the checkers? Based on this activity, what do you think happens to the charge on an atom when it loses electrons? When it gains electrons?

You and a friend walk past a market that sells apples for 40 cents each and pears for 50 cents each. You have 45 cents and want an apple. Your friend also has 45 cents but wants a pear. You realize that if you give your friend a nickel, she will have 50 cents and can buy a pear. You will have 40 cents left to buy an apple. Transferring the nickel gets both of you what you want. Your actions model, in a simple way, what can happen between atoms.

If you transfer a nickel to your ▶ friend, both of you will have the money you need.

Skills Focus Inferring ▢L1

Materials 12 red checkers, 12 black checkers

Time 15 minutes

Tip Remind students that each electron (red checker) has a charge of 1− and each proton (black checker) has a charge of 1+.

Expected Outcome Students simulate the transfer of electrons between atoms.

Think It Over Before the red checkers (electrons) were moved, each group was electrically neutral. The group that gained one or two red checkers had a charge of 1− or 2−. The group that lost one or two red checkers had a charge of 1+ or 2+. An atom becomes positively charged when it loses electrons and negatively charged when it gains electrons.

FIGURE 15
How Ions Form
When an atom loses one of its electrons, it becomes a positively charged ion. The atom that gains the electron becomes a negatively charged ion.

Ions and Ionic Bonds

Atoms with five, six, or seven valence electrons usually become more stable when this number increases to eight. Likewise, most atoms with one, two, or three valence electrons can lose electrons and become more stable. When these two types of atoms combine, electrons are transferred from one type of atom to the other. The transfer makes both types of atoms more stable.

How Ions Form An **ion** (EYE ahn) is an atom or group of atoms that has an electric charge. **When an atom loses an electron, it loses a negative charge and becomes a positive ion. When an atom gains an electron, it gains a negative charge and becomes a negative ion.** Figure 16 lists some ions you will often see in this book. Use this table as a reference while you read this section and other chapters.

Polyatomic Ions Notice in Figure 16 that some ions are made of several atoms. For example, the ammonium ion is made of nitrogen and hydrogen atoms. Ions that are made of more than one atom are called **polyatomic ions** (pahl ee uh TAHM ik). The prefix *poly* means "many," so *polyatomic* means "many atoms." You can think of a polyatomic ion as a group of atoms that reacts as a unit. Like other ions, polyatomic ions have an overall positive or negative charge.

 Reading Checkpoint How does an ion with a charge of 2+ form?

Ions and Their Charges

Name	Charge	Symbol or Formula
Lithium	1+	Li^+
Sodium	1+	Na^+
Potassium	1+	K^+
Ammonium	1+	NH_4^+
Calcium	2+	Ca^{2+}
Magnesium	2+	Mg^{2+}
Aluminum	3+	Al^{3+}
Fluoride	1–	F^-
Chloride	1–	Cl^-
Iodide	1–	I^-
Bicarbonate	1–	HCO_3^-
Nitrate	1–	NO_3^-
Oxide	2–	O^{2-}
Sulfide	2–	S^{2-}
Carbonate	2–	CO_3^{2-}
Sulfate	2–	SO_4^{2-}
Phosphate	3–	PO_4^{3-}

FIGURE 16
Ions are atoms that have lost or gained electrons. Interpreting Tables *How many electrons does a sulfur atom gain when it becomes a sulfide ion?*

Chapter 1 L ◆ 23

Differentiated Instruction

Gifted and Talented L3
Modeling Polyatomic Ions Challenge students to draw electron dot diagrams for several of the more complex polyatomic ions listed in Figure 16, such as ammonium, aluminum, bicarbonate, and phosphate. Encourage students to share their completed diagrams with the class by drawing them on the board. Have them explain how they determined the correct way to represent each ion. **learning modality: logical/mathematical**

Instruct

Ions and Ionic Bonds

Teach Key Concepts L2
Formation of Ions

Focus Use the cartoon in Figure 15 to help students understand how ions form.

Teach Have students read the cartoon. Ask: **In the first frame, what do the zeroes represent?** *(Neutrality of atoms)* **Why does one atom become positive and the other atom become negative?** *(The positive atom loses an electron, and the negative atom gains an electron.)* **What do the atoms represent in the second frame?** *(Ions)*

Apply Challenge students to write an operational definition of the term *ion* based on the cartoon. *(Atoms that have an electric charge)* **learning modality: visual**

Use Visuals: Figure 16 L3
Common Ions and Their Charges

Focus Introduce common ions that students will see throughout the book.

Teach In Figure 16, point out how positively charged ions are listed first, followed by negatively charged ions, and how, within each charge group, the ions are listed by order of increasing charge.

Apply Suggest that students mark this page with a self-sticking note for easy referral, because they will use Figure 16 throughout this and later chapters. **learning modality: visual**

All in One Teaching Resources
• Transparency L7

Independent Practice L2
All in One Teaching Resources
• Guided Reading and Study Worksheet: *Ionic Bonds*

◉ **Student Edition on Audio CD**

Monitor Progress _____ L2

Skills Check Ask students to predict the charge of bromide, an ion that forms from bromine in Group 17. Remind students that Group 17 elements have seven valence electrons.

Answers
Figure 16 Two electrons

 Reading Checkpoint By losing two electrons

L ● 23

Use Visuals: Figure 17

Formation of Ionic Bonds

Focus Guide students in using the diagram to learn how ionic bonds form.

Teach Instruct students to study Figure 17. Ask: **Why do sodium and chloride ions bond together?** *(They have opposite charges, and opposite charges attract.)*

Apply Ask: **How would another Group 1 metal, such as potassium, and another Group 17 nonmetal, such as bromine, form a bond?** *(The same way as sodium and chlorine)* **learning modality: visual**

 **Teaching Resources**

• Transparency L8

Lab zone Build **Inquiry**   L2

Predicting How Ions Will Bond

Materials list of positive ions and negative ions (Figure 16)

Time 5 minutes

Focus Have students predict how positive and negative ions listed in Figure 16 might form ionic compounds together. Tell them that the correct compounds are electrically neutral, so the positive and negative charges must balance. *(Students are likely to name combinations of positive and negative ions in which the positive charge balances the negative charge to form a neutral ionic compound. Sample answer: A calcium ion, Ca^{2+}, and a carbonate ion CO_3^{2-} might form the ionic compound calcium carbonate, $CaCO_3$.)*

Apply Ask: **How many sodium ions do you predict there would be in the ionic compound sodium phosphate? Why?** *(There would be three sodium ions to balance the 3− charge of the phosphate ion.)* **learning modality: logical/mathematical**

Ionic Bonds Look at Figure 17 to see how sodium atoms and chlorine atoms combine to form sodium chloride (table salt). Notice that sodium has 1 valence electron and chlorine has 7 valence electrons. When sodium's valence electron is transferred to chlorine, both atoms become ions. The sodium atom becomes a positive ion (Na^+). The chlorine atom becomes a negative ion (Cl^-).

Because oppositely charged particles attract, the positive Na^+ ion and the negative Cl^- ion attract each other. An **ionic bond** is the attraction between two oppositely charged ions. **Ionic bonds form as a result of the attraction between positive and negative ions.** A compound that consists of positive and negative ions, such as sodium chloride, is called an **ionic compound.**

FIGURE 17
Formation of an Ionic Bond

Reactions occur easily between metals in Group 1 and nonmetals in Group 17. Follow the process below to see how an ionic bond forms between a sodium atom and a chlorine atom.
Relating Cause and Effect *Why is sodium chloride electrically neutral?*

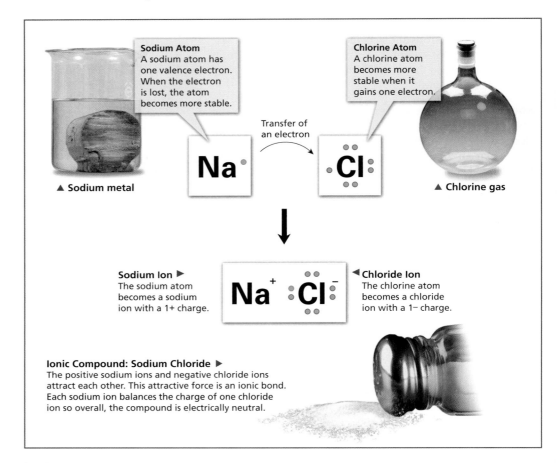

Sodium Atom
A sodium atom has one valence electron. When the electron is lost, the atom becomes more stable.

▲ Sodium metal

Transfer of an electron

Chlorine Atom
A chlorine atom becomes more stable when it gains one electron.

▲ Chlorine gas

Sodium Ion ▶
The sodium atom becomes a sodium ion with a 1+ charge.

◀ Chloride Ion
The chlorine atom becomes a chloride ion with a 1− charge.

Ionic Compound: Sodium Chloride ▶
The positive sodium ions and negative chloride ions attract each other. This attractive force is an ionic bond. Each sodium ion balances the charge of one chloride ion so overall, the compound is electrically neutral.

Chemical Formulas and Names

Compounds can be represented by chemical formulas. A **chemical formula** is a combination of symbols that shows the ratio of elements in a compound. For example, the formula for magnesium chloride is $MgCl_2$. What does the formula tell you?

Formulas of Ionic Compounds From Figure 16 you know that the charge on the magnesium ion is 2+. **When ionic compounds form, the ions come together in a way that balances out the charges on the ions. The chemical formula for the compound reflects this balance.** Two chloride ions, each with a charge of 1– will balance the charge on the magnesium ion. That's why the formula of magnesium chloride is $MgCl_2$. The number "2" is a subscript. A **subscript** tells you the ratio of elements in the compound. For $MgCl_2$, the ratio of magnesium ions to chloride ions is 1 to 2.

If no subscript is written, the number 1 is understood. For example, the formula NaCl tells you that there is a 1 to 1 ratio of sodium ions to chloride ions. Formulas for compounds of poly-atomic ions are written in a similar way. For example, calcium carbonate has the formula $CaCO_3$.

Naming Ionic Compounds Magnesium chloride, sodium bicarbonate, sodium oxide—where do these names come from? **For an ionic compound, the name of the positive ion comes first, followed by the name of the negative ion.** The name of the positive ion is usually the name of a metal. But, a few positive polyatomic ions exist, such as the ammonium ion (NH_4^+). If the negative ion is a single element, as you've already seen with sodium chloride, the end of its name changes to *-ide*. For example, MgO is named magnesium oxide. If the negative ion is polyatomic, its name usually ends in *-ate* or *-ite*, as in Figure 16. The compound NH_4NO_3, named ammonium nitrate, is a common fertilizer for gardens and crop plants.

 Reading Checkpoint What is the name of the ionic compound with the formula K_2S?

FIGURE 18
Calcium Carbonate
The white cliffs of Dover, England, are made of chalk formed from the remains of tiny sea organisms. Chalk is mostly an ionic compound, calcium carbonate.

 L ◆ 25

Lab zone Skills **Activity**

Interpreting Data
Use the periodic table and Figure 16 to identify the charges of the ions in each ionic compound listed below. Then write the formula for each compound.

- sodium bromide
- lithium oxide
- magnesium sulfide
- aluminum fluoride
- potassium nitrate
- ammonium chloride

How did you know how many of each ion to write in the formula?

Lab zone Skills **Activity**

Skills Focus Interpreting data   L2

Materials periodic table, Figure 11, and Figure 16

Time 15 minutes

Tip Remind students that bromine is in the same group as fluorine in the periodic table, and that bromine forms an ion with the same charge as fluoride.

Expected Outcome Students are expected to pair positive and negative ions in ratios that result in neutral ionic compounds: $NaBr$, Li_2O, MgS, AlF_3, KNO_3, NH_4Cl.

Extend Encourage students to find ionic compounds listed as ingredients in household products. **learning modality: visual**

Chemical Formulas and Names

Teach Key Concepts   L2
Explaining Chemical Formulas

Focus Explain how chemical formulas reflect the composition of ionic compounds.

Teach On the board, write *calcium ion* and *chloride ion*. Ask: **What is the charge of a calcium ion?** *(2+)* **What is the charge of a chloride ion?** *(1–)* Write the charges on the board next to the ions. Ask: **If calcium and chloride formed a compound, how many chloride ions would be needed to balance the charge of the calcium ion?** *(Two)* **What is the formula for calcium chloride?** *(CaCl₂)* Write the formula on the board.

Apply Have students practice writing chemical formulas by doing the Skills Activity on this page. **learning modality: verbal**

Monitor Progress _____ L2

Skills Check On the board, write Na O. Call on students to add any missing subscripts needed to make it a balanced formula for an ionic compound. Call on another student to name the compound.

Answers
Figure 17 The 1+ charge of the sodium ion is balanced by the 1– charge of the chloride ion.

Reading Checkpoint Potassium sulfide

Properties of Ionic Compounds

Teach Key Concepts $\quad$ L2
Comparing and Contrasting Ionic Compounds

Focus Have students compare and contrast ionic compounds to infer their shared properties.

Teach Name several familiar examples of ionic compounds, such as table salt (NaCl), baking soda ($NaHCO_3$), rust (Fe_2O_3). Ask: **What is different about the compounds?** (*Accept all reasonable observations. Sample answer: They have different colors.*) **What is similar about the compounds?** (*Sample answer: They are solids.*)

Apply Ask: **What do you think is a property of ionic compounds in general?** (*Sample answer: They are solids at room temperature.*) **learning modality: verbal**

Lab zone Teacher **Demo** $\quad$ L1

High Melting Point of an Ionic Compound

Materials heavy pot, stove or hot plate, wooden spoon, 100 mL salt

Time 15 minutes

Focus Demonstrate how an ionic compound fails to melt at a relatively high temperature.

Teach Before doing the demonstration, explain to students that sugar, which is not an ionic compound, can be melted in a few minutes in a pot on a stove or hot plate. Then, place the salt in the pot and heat the pot on high heat, stirring occasionally. After about 5 minutes, invite students to observe whether the salt has melted. Explain that salt must be heated to more than 800°C before it will melt, which is several times hotter than the temperature of a stove or hot plate.

Apply Ask: **Why do you think salt has such a high melting point?** (*Sample answer: Its ionic bonds require a lot of energy to break for melting to occur.*) **learning modality: visual**

Lab zone Try This **Activity**

Crystal Clear
Can you grow a salt crystal?

1. Add salt to a jar containing about 200 mL of hot tap water and stir. Keep adding salt until no more dissolves and it settles out when you stop stirring.
2. Tie a large crystal of coarse salt into the middle of a piece of thread.
3. Tie one end of the thread to the middle of a pencil.
4. Suspend the other end of the thread in the solution by laying the pencil across the mouth of the jar. Do not allow the crystal to touch the solution.
5. Place the jar in a quiet, undisturbed area. Check the size of the crystal over the next few days.

Observing Does the salt crystal change size over time? What is its shape? What do you think is happening to the ions in the solution?

Properties of Ionic Compounds

Table salt, baking soda, and iron rust are different compounds with different properties. You wouldn't want to season your food with either iron rust or baking soda. However, these compounds are alike in some ways because they are all ionic compounds. **In general, ionic compounds are hard, brittle crystals that have high melting points. When dissolved in water or melted, they conduct electricity.**

Ionic Crystals Figure 19 shows a chunk of halite, or table salt, NaCl. Pieces of halite have sharp edges, corners, flat surfaces, and a cubic shape. Equal numbers of Na^+ and Cl^- ions in solid sodium chloride are attracted in an alternating pattern, as shown in the diagram. The ions form an orderly, three-dimensional arrangement called a **crystal.**

In an ionic compound, every ion is attracted to ions of opposite charge that surround it. It is attracted to ions above, below, and to all sides. The pattern formed by the ions remains the same no matter what the size of the crystal. In a single grain of salt, the crystal pattern extends for millions of ions in every direction. Many crystals of ionic compounds are hard and brittle, due to the strength of their ionic bonds and the attractions among all the ions.

High Melting Points What happens when you heat an ionic compound such as table salt? When you heat a substance, its energy increases. When ions have enough energy to overcome the attractive forces between them, they break away from each other. In other words, the crystal melts to a liquid. Because ionic bonds are strong, a lot of energy is needed to break them. As a result, ionic compounds have high melting points. They are all solids at room temperature. Table salt must be heated to 801°C before the crystal melts.

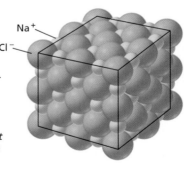

FIGURE 19
Ionic Crystals
The ions in ionic compounds are arranged in specific three-dimensional shapes called crystals. Some crystals have a cube shape like these crystals of halite, or sodium chloride.
Making Generalizations *What holds the ions together in the crystal?*

26 ◆ L

Lab zone Try This **Activity**

Skills Focus Observing $\quad$ L2

Materials 15 cm thread, coarse salt such as kosher salt or sea salt, jar or cup, pencil, hot tap water, stirring rod or spoon

Time 15 minutes for setup, 3 minutes a day for 3 days for observation

Tip The hotter the water, the more salt that will dissolve.

Expected Outcome The crystal will increase in size as sodium and chloride ions in the solution wick up the thread and join the crystal.

Extend Allow students to examine salt crystals under a microscope and compare the shape of the crystals to the large crystal produced in this activity. **learning modality: visual**

FIGURE 20
Ions in Solution
A solution of sodium chloride conducts electricity across the gap between the two black rods of a conductivity tester. As a result, the bulb lights up.

Electrical Conductivity When ionic compounds dissolve in water, the solution conducts electricity. The flow of electricity is the flow of charged particles, and ions are charged particles. However, crystals of ionic compounds do not conduct electricity well. The ions in the crystal are tightly bound to each other. If charged particles cannot move, no electricity can flow. When ionic crystals dissolve in water, however, the bonds between ions are broken. So, the ions are free to move, and the solution conducts electricity. Likewise, after an ionic compound melts, the ions are able to move freely, and the liquid conducts electricity.

 Reading Checkpoint What is a crystal?

Go Online
SciLINKS NSTA

For: Links on ionic compounds
Visit: www.SciLinks.com
Web Code: scn-1213

Section 3 Assessment

Target Reading Skill Previewing Visuals Compare your questions and answers about Figure 17 with those of a partner.

Reviewing Key Concepts

1. a. Reviewing What are the two basic ways in which ions form from atoms?
   b. Comparing and Contrasting Contrast sodium and chloride ions, including how they form. Write the symbol for each ion.
   c. Relating Cause and Effect What holds the ions together in sodium chloride? Indicate the specific charges that are involved.

2. a. Identifying What information is given by the formula of an ionic compound?
   b. Explaining The formula for sodium sulfide is Na_2S. Explain what this formula means.
   c. Applying Concepts Write the formula for calcium chloride. Explain how you determined this formula.

3. a. Listing List three properties of ionic compounds.
   b. Making Generalizations Relate each property that you listed to the characteristics of ionic bonds.

Writing in Science

Firsthand Account Pretend that you are the size of an atom, observing a reaction between a potassium atom and a fluorine atom. Write an account of the formation of an ionic bond as the atoms react. Tell what happens to the valence electrons on each atom and how each atom is changed by losing or gaining electrons.

Chapter 1 L ◆ 27

For: Links on ionic compounds
Visit: www.SciLinks.org
Web Code: scn-1213

Download a worksheet that will guide students' review of Internet sources on ionic compounds.

Monitor Progress _____ L2

Answers
Figure 19 Ionic bonds

Reading Checkpoint An orderly, three-dimensional arrangement of ions

Assess

Reviewing Key Concepts

1. a. Atoms can lose or gain electrons. **b.** A sodium ion (Na^+) forms when a sodium atom loses one electron and becomes positively charged. A chloride ion (Cl^-) forms when a chlorine atom gains one electron and becomes negatively charged. **c.** An ionic bond holds the ions together. The sodium ion has a charge of 1+, and the chloride ion has a charge of 1−.
2. a. The ratio of positive ions to negative ions **b.** Sodium sulfide consists of two sodium ions and one sulfide ion. **c.** The formula is $CaCl_2$, because two chloride ions (Cl^{1-}) are needed to balance one calcium ion (Ca^{2+}).
3. a. Ionic compounds are hard, brittle crystals that have high melting points and can conduct electricity when melted or in solution. **b.** Ionic bonds are strong due to the attraction between oppositely charged ions. This makes crystals of ionic compounds hard and brittle and causes the compounds to have high melting points. Because the ions are charged, they can conduct electricity when the compound is melted or dissolved.

Reteach L1
Call on students to describe the properties of ionic compounds.

Performance Assessment L2
Drawing Have students draw an electron dot diagram of potassium iodide.

All in One Teaching Resources
• Section Summary: *Ionic Bonds*
• Review and Reinforcement: *Ionic Bonds*
• Enrich: *Ionic Bonds*

Lab zone Chapter Project

Keep Students on Track At this point, students can use their model atoms to make models of ionic crystals.

Writing in Science

Writing Mode Firsthand account
Scoring Rubric
4 Exceeds criteria; includes a detailed eyewitness account that correctly describes the reaction of potassium and fluorine
3 Meets criteria
2 Includes a firsthand description but is too brief and/or contains some errors
1 Includes only a general description and/or contains serious errors

Shedding Light on Ions

Prepare for Inquiry

Key Concept
Solutions containing ions can conduct electricity. Students will determine whether solutions conduct electricity and decide on the nature of their bonds.

Skills Objective
After this lab, students will be able to
- control variables to test which solutions conduct electricity
- interpret data from the tests to determine which solutions conduct electricity
- infer the nature of the bonds in each solution tested

 Prep Time 30 minutes
Class Time 40 minutes

Advance Planning
- Gather additional materials students can test, such as vegetable oil, hydrogen peroxide, orange juice, vinegar, sugar, baking soda, Epsom salts, and/or powdered skim milk.
- Obtain 16- or 18-gauge wire. The resistance of wire with a higher gauge is too great. Cut the wire into lengths of about 25–30 cm. With wire strippers, remove about 2 cm of insulation from the ends of the wires.
- Use fresh batteries and 2.2-V bulbs.
- If necessary, you can use 6-V dry cells instead of 1.5-V dry cells. However, some eletrolysis may occur using the higher voltage.

Alternative Materials
Instead of having students make their own conductivity testers, as described in the procedure, you may provide students with conductivity probes.

Safety
 Caution students to handle the light bulbs carefully. Tell them ends of the wires are sharp. Review the safety guidelines in Appendix A.

All in One Teaching Resources
- Lab Worksheet: *Shedding Light on Ions*

Shedding Light on Ions

Problem
What kinds of compounds produce ions in solution?

Skills Focus
controlling variables, interpreting data, inferring

Materials
- 2 dry cells, 1.5 V
- small light bulb and socket   } or conductivity probe
- 4 lengths of wire with alligator clips on both ends
- 2 copper strips
- distilled water
- small beaker
- small plastic spoon
- sodium chloride
- graduated cylinder, 100-mL
- sucrose
- additional materials supplied by your teacher

Procedure
1. Make a conductivity tester as described below or, if you are using a conductivity probe, see your teacher for instructions. Then make a data table in your notebook similar to the one above.

Data Table	
Sample	Observations
Tap water	
Distilled water	
Sodium chloride	
Sodium chloride in water	

2. Pour about 50 mL of tap water into a small beaker. Place the copper strips in the beaker. Be sure the strips are not touching each other. Attach the alligator clip of the free end of one wire to a copper strip. Do the same with the other wire and the other copper strip. Record your observations.

3. Disconnect the wires from the copper strips. Take the strips out of the beaker, and pour out the tap water. Dry the inside of the beaker and the copper strips with a paper towel.

4. Pour 50 mL of distilled water into the beaker. Reconnect the conductivity tester and test the water as in Step 2. Keep the copper strips about the same distance apart as in Step 2. Record your observations.

5. Use 3 spoonfuls of sodium chloride to make a small pile on a clean piece of paper. Dry off the copper strips of the conductivity tester and use it to test the conductivity of the sodium chloride. Record your observations.

Making a Conductivity Tester

A. Use wire with alligator clips to connect the positive terminal of a dry cell to a lamp socket. **CAUTION:** *The bulb is fragile and can break.*

B. Similarly connect another wire between the negative terminal of the cell and the positive terminal of the second cell.

C. Connect one end of a third wire to the negative terminal of the second dry cell.

D. Connect one end of a fourth wire to the other terminal of the lamp socket.

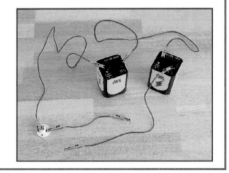

---

28 ◆ L

Guide Inquiry

Invitation
Place the leads of a conductivity tester into a beaker of distilled water to show students that the bulb does not light up. Then, add salt to the distilled water until the light starts to glow. Ask: **Why did the salt allow the distilled water to carry electricity?** (*Ions of the dissolved salt carried the charge.*)

Introduce the Procedure
Tell students that they will construct and/or use a conductivity tester to determine whether different solutions conduct electricity. From the data, they will decide whether or not the solutions are ionic.

6. Add 1 spoonful of sodium chloride to the distilled water in the beaker. Stir with the spoon until the salt dissolves. Repeat the conductivity test and record your observations.

7. Disconnect the conductivity tester and rinse the beaker, spoon, and copper strips with distilled water. Dry the beaker as in Step 3.

8. Test sucrose (table sugar) in the same ways that you tested sodium chloride in Steps 4 through 7. Test additional materials supplied by your teacher.
   • If the material is a solid, mix 1 spoonful of it with about 50 mL of distilled water and stir until the material dissolves. Test the resulting mixture.
   • If the substance is a liquid, simply pour about 50 mL into the beaker. Test it as you did the other mixtures.

Analyze and Conclude

1. **Controlling Variables** Why did you test both tap water and distilled water before testing the sodium chloride solution?

2. **Interpreting Data** Could you have used tap water in your tests instead of distilled water? Explain.

3. **Drawing Conclusions** Based on your observations, add a column to your data table indicating whether each substance produced ions in solution.

4. **Inferring** Sodium chloride is an ionic compound. How can you account for any observed differences in conductivity between dry and dissolved sodium chloride?

5. **Communicating** Based on your observations, decide whether or not you think sucrose (table sugar) is made up of ions. Explain how you reached your answer, using evidence from the experiment.

Design an Experiment

Design an experiment to test the effects of varying the spacing between the copper strips of the conductivity tester. *Obtain your teacher's permission before carrying out your investigation.*

L ◆ 29

Troubleshooting the Experiment
• Before students assemble their conductivity testers, have them test the bulbs using wires and a battery.
• Students should use solutions of the same concentration to make valid comparisons among substances.

Data Table	
Sample	**Observations**
Tap water	Conducts current
Distilled water	Does not conduct current
Sodium chloride	Does not conduct current
Sodium chloride in water	Conducts current

Expected Outcome
Most substances containing ionic bonds will be good conductors when dissolved in water. Molecular compounds will not conduct electricity as well. (*Note:* Students will not yet be able to use the term *molecular compounds*, which they will learn about in the following chapter.).

Analyze and Conclude
1. Both tap water and distilled water were used as controls. Testing tap water showed that the circuit was functioning, because tap water contains ions and conducts electricity. Testing distilled water showed that water without dissolved ions does not conduct electricity.

2. No; tap water is a conductor and would not allow you to determine whether the dissolved substances were also conductors.

3. Substances that students identify as conductors or nonconductors will depend on the substances tested. Tap water, salt water, and any other solutions of ionic compounds are likely to be good conductors, whereas vegetable oil, sucrose solution, and other solutions of molecular compounds are unlikely to be good conductors.

4. The ions in dry sodium chloride are bound together in a rigid crystal structure. When sodium chloride dissolves, the ionic bonds break, allowing the ions to move freely through the solution and carry a charge.

5. Students are expected to observe that a sucrose solution does not carry a charge and to decide that it is not made up of ions.

Extend Inquiry

Design an Experiment Students can test the same ionic solution twice, changing only the spacing of the copper strips from one test to the next. When the strips are farther apart, a weaker conductor may not be able to carry the charge far enough. The opposite may be true when the strips are closer together.

Objectives

After this lesson, students will be able to

L.1.4.1 State what holds covalently bonded atoms together.

L.1.4.2 Identify the properties of molecular compounds.

L.1.4.3 Explain how unequal sharing of electrons occurs and how it affects molecules.

Target Reading Skill

Asking Questions Explain that changing a head into a question helps students anticipate the ideas, facts, and events they are about to read.

Answers

Possible questions and answers:
How do covalent bonds form? *(Covalent bonds form when two atoms share electrons.)* **What are molecular compounds?** *(Molecular compounds are compounds that contain molecules bonded with covalent bonds.)* **How does unequal sharing of electrons affect the atoms in molecular compounds?** *(Unequal sharing of electrons causes the bonded atoms to have slight electrical charges.)*

All in One Teaching Resources

• Transparency L9

Preteach

Build Background Knowledge   L2

How Atoms Form Bonds

Remind students that atoms form bonds in more than one way. Ask: **In addition to ionic bonding, in which atoms give up or gain electrons, what is another way atoms can form bonds?** *(By sharing electrons)* Tell students that in this section they will learn about bonds that form when atoms share electrons.

Reading Preview

Key Concepts

• What holds covalently bonded atoms together?
• What are the properties of molecular compounds?
• How does unequal sharing of electrons occur, and how does it affect molecules?

Key Terms

• covalent bond   • molecule
• double bond   • triple bond
• molecular compound
• polar bond   • nonpolar bond

Target Reading Skill

Asking Questions Before you read, preview the red headings. In a graphic organizer like the one below, ask a *what* or *how* question for each heading. As you read, answer your questions.

Covalent Bonds

Question	Answer
How do covalent bonds form?	Covalent bonds form when...

Lab zone Discover **Activity**

Can Water and Oil Mix?

1. Pour water into a small jar that has a tight-fitting lid until the jar is about a third full.
2. Add an equal amount of vegetable oil to the jar. Cover the jar tightly.
3. Shake the jar vigorously for 20 seconds. Observe the contents.
4. Allow the jar to sit undisturbed for 1 minute. Observe again.
5. Remove the top and add 3 drops of liquid detergent. Cover the jar and repeat Steps 3 and 4.

Think It Over
Forming Operational Definitions Based on your observations, write an operational definition of *detergent.* How might your observations relate to chemical bonds in the detergent, oil, and water molecules?

Uh oh, you have a big project due in English class next week! You need to write a story and illustrate it with colorful posters. Art has always been your best subject, but writing takes more effort. Luckily, you're working with a partner who writes well but doesn't feel confident in art. If you each contribute your skills, together you can produce a high-quality finished project.

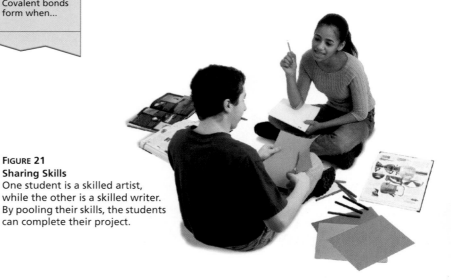

FIGURE 21
Sharing Skills
One student is a skilled artist, while the other is a skilled writer. By pooling their skills, the students can complete their project.

Lab zone Discover **Activity**

Skills Focus Forming operational definitions

Materials small jar with tight-fitting top, water, vegetable oil, liquid detergent

Time 10 minutes

Tip Baby food jobs are good choices for this activity.

Expected Outcome Water and vegetable oil will not mix until liquid detergent is added.

Think It Over Sample definition: Detergent is a substance that allows oil and water to mix. Students might explain that bonds between oil molecules and bonds between water molecules do not break and allow the two substances to mix unless liquid detergent is added.

How Covalent Bonds Form

Just as you and your friend can work together by sharing your talents, atoms can become more stable by sharing electrons. The chemical bond formed when two atoms share electrons is called a **covalent bond.** Covalent bonds usually form between atoms of nonmetals. In contrast, ionic bonds usually form when a metal combines with a nonmetal.

Electron Sharing Recall that the noble gases are not very reactive. In contrast, all other nonmetals, including hydrogen, can bond to other nonmetals by sharing electrons. Most non-metals can even bond with another atom of the same element, as is the case with fluorine in Figure 22. When you count the electrons on each atom, count the shared pair each time. By sharing electrons, each atom has a stable set of eight. **The force that holds atoms together in a covalent bond is the attraction of each atom's nucleus for the shared pair of electrons.** The two bonded fluorine atoms form a molecule. A **molecule** is a neutral group of atoms joined by covalent bonds.

How Many Bonds? Look at the electron dot diagrams in Figure 23. Count the valence electrons around each atom. The number of covalent bonds these atoms can form equals the number of electrons needed to make a total of eight (or in the case of hydrogen, two).

For example, oxygen has six valence electrons, so it can form two covalent bonds. In a water molecule, oxygen forms one covalent bond with each of two hydrogen atoms. As a result, the oxygen atom has a stable set of eight valence electrons. Each hydrogen atom can form one bond because it needs only a total of two electrons to be stable. Do you see why water's formula is H_2O, instead of H_3O, H_4O, or just HO?

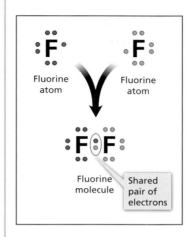

FIGURE 22
Sharing Electrons
By sharing electrons in a covalent bond, each fluorine atom has a stable set of eight valence electrons.

FIGURE 23
Covalent Bonds
The oxygen atom in water and the nitrogen atom in ammonia are each surrounded by eight electrons as a result of sharing electrons with hydrogen atoms.
Interpreting Diagrams *How many electrons does each hydrogen atom have as a result of sharing?*

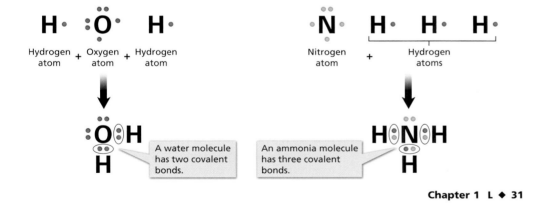

Chapter 1   L ◆ 31

Differentiated Instruction

Less Proficient Readers   L1
Interpreting Diagrams   Guide students in a closer comparison of covalent bonds with the now-familiar ionic bonds. Have students look for differences between Figures 17 and 22. Ask them to describe what happens to the valence electrons in each type of bond. **learning modality: visual**

Gifted and Talented   L3
Explaining Differences in Bonding
Challenge students to use their knowledge of valence electrons to explain why covalent bonds usually form between atoms of nonmetals, whereas ionic bonds usually form between atoms of metals and nonmetals. **learning modality: logical/ mathematical**

Instruct

How Covalent Bonds Form

Teach Key Concepts   L2
Comparing and Contrasting Covalent and Ionic Bonds

Focus Introduce covalent bonds by comparing and contrasting them with ionic bonds.

Teach Remind students that ionic bonds form between oppositely charged ions that have gained or lost electrons. Then, tell them that covalent bonds form between uncharged atoms that share electrons.

Apply Ask: **In a fluorine molecule, how many valence electrons does each fluorine atom have?** (*Eight*) **learning modality: verbal**

Use Visuals: Figure 23   L2
Number of Covalent Bonds

Focus Say that the number of covalent bonds atoms form equals the number of electrons needed for eight (two for hydrogen) valence electrons.

Teach Have students study the figure and read the caption. Ask: **How many valence electrons does oxygen have before and after bonding with hydrogen?** (*Six before; eight after*) **How many valence electrons does nitrogen have before and after bonding with hydrogen?** (*Five before; eight after*)

Apply Ask: **How many hydrogen atoms would you expect to bind to an atom with four valence electrons?** (*Four*) **learning modality: visual**

All in One Teaching Resources

• Transparency L10

Independent Practice   L2

All in One Teaching Resources

• Guided Reading and Study Worksheet: *Covalent Bonds*

 Student Edition on Audio CD

Monitor Progress _____   L2

Drawing Have students draw electron dot diagrams to show how two chlorine atoms bond together to form a chlorine molecule.

Answer
Figure 23 Two electrons

L ● 31

32 • L

Use Visuals: Figure 24 L2
Formation of Double and Triple Bonds

Focus Help students understand why some molecules contain double or triple bonds.

Teach Have students look at the figure and read the caption and labels. Ask: **If two oxygen molecules were to share just two electrons instead of four, how many valence electrons would each oxygen atom have?** *(Six)* **Why must two oxygen atoms share four electrons?** *(So that each atom has eight)*

Apply Have students answer the caption question. **learning modality: visual**

 **Teaching Resources**

• Transparency L11

Molecular Compounds

Teach Key Concepts L2
Summarizing Molecular Compounds

Focus Use a graphic organizer to summarize the important points about molecular compounds and their properties.

Teach On the board, make a concept map to show that molecular compounds consist of covalently bonded atoms, have low melting and boiling points, and do not conduct electricity well. Have students copy the concept map in their science notebooks and use it for review.

Apply Challenge students to explain the properties of molecular compounds. For example, Ask: **Why do you think molecular compounds do not conduct electricity well?** *(Sample answer: Molecular compounds consist of electrically neutral atoms, not ions, so they do not have charged particles to carry a current.)* **learning modality: visual**

For: Links on molecular compounds
Visit: www.SciLinks.org
Web Code: scn-1214

Download a worksheet that will guide students' review of Internet sources on molecular compounds.

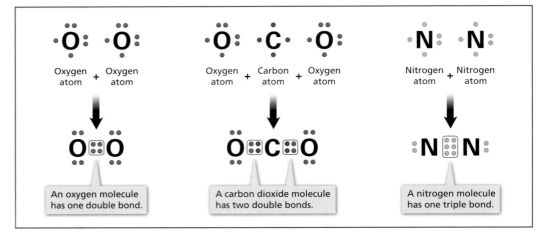

FIGURE 24
Double and Triple Bonds
An oxygen molecule contains one double bond, while a carbon dioxide molecule has two double bonds. A nitrogen molecule contains one triple bond. *Interpreting Diagrams In a nitrogen molecule, how many electrons does each nitrogen atom share with the other?*

For: Links on molecular compounds
Visit: www.SciLinks.org
Web Code: scn-1214

Double Bonds and Triple Bonds Look at the diagram of the oxygen molecule (O_2) in Figure 24. What do you see that's different? This time the two atoms share two pairs of electrons, forming a **double bond.** In a carbon dioxide molecule (CO_2), carbon forms a double bond with each of two oxygen atoms. Elements such as nitrogen and carbon can form **triple bonds** in which their atoms share three pairs of electrons.

 What is the difference between a double bond and a triple bond?

Molecular Compounds

A **molecular compound** is a compound that is composed of molecules. The molecules of a molecular compound contain atoms that are covalently bonded. Molecular compounds have very different properties than ionic compounds. **Compared to ionic compounds, molecular compounds generally have lower melting points and boiling points, and they do not conduct electricity when dissolved in water.**

Low Melting Points and Boiling Points Study the table in the Analyzing Data box on the next page. It lists the melting points and boiling points for a few molecular compounds and ionic compounds. In molecular solids, forces hold the molecules close to one another. But, the forces between molecules are much weaker than the forces between ions in an ionic solid. Compared with ionic solids, less heat must be added to molecular solids to separate the molecules and change the solid to a liquid. That is why most familiar compounds that are liquids or gases at room temperature are molecular compounds.

Comparing Molecular and Ionic Compounds

The table compares the melting points and boiling points of a few molecular compounds and ionic compounds. Use the table to answer the following questions.

1. **Graphing** Create a bar graph of just the melting points of these compounds. Put the molecular compounds on the left and the ionic compounds on the right. Arrange the bars in order of increasing melting point. The *y*-axis should start at –200°C and go to 900°C.

2. **Interpreting Data** Describe what your graph reveals about the melting points of molecular compounds compared to those of ionic compounds.

3. **Inferring** How can you account for the differences in melting points between molecular compounds and ionic compounds?

4. **Interpreting Data** How do the boiling points of the molecular and ionic compounds compare?

Melting Points and Boiling Points of Molecular and Ionic Compounds

Substance	Formula	Melting Point (°C)	Boiling Point (°C)
Methane	CH_4	–182.4	–161.5
Rubbing alcohol	C_3H_8O	–89.5	82.4
Water	H_2O	0	100
Zinc chloride	$ZnCl_2$	290	732
Magnesium chloride	$MgCl_2$	714	1,412
Sodium chloride	$NaCl$	800.7	1,465

Molecular compound Ionic compound

5. **Predicting** Ammonia's melting point is –78°C and its boiling point is –34°C. Is ammonia a molecular compound or an ionic compound? Explain.

Poor Conductivity Most molecular compounds do not conduct electricity. No charged particles are available to move, so electricity cannot flow. Materials such as plastic and rubber are used to insulate wires because these materials are composed of molecular substances. Even as liquids, molecular compounds are poor conductors. Pure water, for example, does not conduct electricity. Neither does table sugar or alcohol when they are dissolved in pure water.

Unequal Sharing of Electrons

Have you ever played tug of war? If you have, you know that if both teams pull with equal force, the contest is a tie. But what if the teams pull on the rope with unequal force? Then the rope moves toward the side of the stronger team. The same is true of electrons in a covalent bond. **Atoms of some elements pull more strongly on shared electrons than do atoms of other elements. As a result, the electrons are pulled more toward one atom, causing the bonded atoms to have slight electrical charges.** These charges are not as strong as the charges on ions.

Chapter 1 L ◆ 33

Differentiated Instruction

Special Needs L1
Organizing Information Help students make a table comparing and contrasting molecular and ionic compounds. Tell them to use the table for review and as a reference guide when they are doing activities and labs for this chapter.
learning modality: visual

Gifted and Talented L3
Using Analogies Call students' attention to the position of water in the table in the Analyzing Data feature. Challenge students to use an analogy to explain why water's melting point and boiling point fall in between those of ionic compounds and those of the other molecular compounds in the table. **learning modality: verbal**

Math Skill Making and interpreting graphs

Focus Direct students in analyzing melting and boiling points of compounds.

Teach Remind students that compounds need energy to break bonds when they change state (in this case, melt or boil).

Answers

1. Check that graphs are correctly set up and labeled before students plot the data.

2. Melting points of molecular compounds are lower than those of ionic compounds.

3. Molecular compounds have lower melting points; they have relatively weak covalent bonds that require less energy to break.

4. Boiling points of molecular compounds are lower than those of ionic compounds.

5. Students may predict that ammonia is a molecular compound because it has relatively low melting and boiling points.

Unequal Sharing of Electrons

Teach Key Concepts L2
Unequal Electron Sharing

Focus Use the familiar example of water to explain why some molecules are polar.

Teach Draw an electron dot diagram of a water molecule. Explain that oxygen's more massive nucleus exerts a greater pull on the shared electrons. Add arrows to indicate this pull. Ask: **What happens to the charge of oxygen if it pulls electrons more strongly?** (*It becomes negative.*) **What happens to the charge of hydrogen if it pulls electrons less strongly?** (*It becomes positive.*) Add plus and minus signs to indicate polarity.

Apply Ask: **Which do you think has a stronger positive charge, hydrogen atoms in water or sodium ions in sodium chloride?** (*Sodium ions; the hydrogen atoms do not actually gain or lose electrons as ions do.*) **learning modality: visual**

Monitor Progress L2

Writing Have students describe how molecular compounds form.

Answers
Figure 24 Six electrons

✓ Reading Checkpoint In a double bond, four electrons are shared. In a triple bond, six electrons are shared.

L ● 33

Use Visuals: Figure 26 L2
Nonpolar and Polar Molecules

Focus Guide students in identifying why water is polar whereas carbon dioxide is not.

Teach Ask: **How do the shapes of the two molecules modeled in Figure 26 differ?** *(Carbon dioxide has a straight-line shape. Water has a bent shape.)* **How do the differences in shape affect the charges of the molecules?** *(Sample answer: In carbon dioxide, oxygen atoms pull on the electrons more strongly than carbon does, but they pull in opposite directions and cancel each other out. In water, the oxygen end of the molecule has a slight negative charge and the hydrogen end has a slight positive charge because oxygen pulls the electrons more strongly.)*

Apply Ask: **How do you think the slight positive and negative charges affect the properties of molecules like water?** *(Students might predict that the molecules would resemble ionic compounds. For example, they might have higher melting and boiling points than other covalent molecules or be better conductors of electricity.)* **learning modality: visual**

 **Teaching Resources**

• Transparency L12

Lab zone Teacher **Demo** L2

Attraction Between Polar Molecules

Materials glass, water, clear plastic drinking straw

Time 5 minutes

Focus Demonstrate how polar molecules attract each other.

Teach Place a clear drinking straw in a glass of water. Have students observe how the water appears to "climb up" the side of the straw. (The same effect occurs at the sides of the glass, but may be less apparent there.) Explain that water molecules behave this way because they are attracted to the sides of the straw and even more so to each other.

Apply Ask: **Would a nonpolar liquid behave this way? Why or why not?** *(No, because molecules of a nonpolar substance are not charged and therefore are not attracted to each other)* **learning modality: visual**

FIGURE 25
Nonpolar and Polar Bonds
Fluorine forms a nonpolar bond with another fluorine atom. In hydrogen fluoride, fluorine attracts electrons more strongly than hydrogen does, so the bond formed is polar.

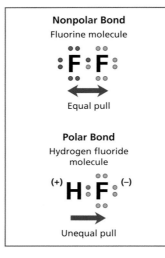

Nonpolar Bond
Fluorine molecule

Equal pull

Polar Bond
Hydrogen fluoride molecule

$(+)$ **H : F** $(-)$

Unequal pull

FIGURE 26
Nonpolar and Polar Molecules
A carbon dioxide molecule is a nonpolar molecule because of its straight-line shape. In contrast, a water molecule is a polar molecule because of its bent shape.
Interpreting Diagrams *What do the arrows in the diagram show?*

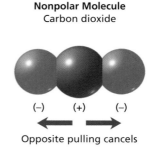

Nonpolar Molecule
Carbon dioxide

$(-)$ $(+)$ $(-)$

Opposite pulling cancels

Polar Molecule
Water

$(+)$

$(-)$

$(+)$

Electrons pulled toward oxygen

Polar Bonds and Nonpolar Bonds The unequal sharing of electrons is enough to make the atom with the stronger pull slightly negative and the atom with the weaker pull slightly positive. A covalent bond in which electrons are shared unequally is called a **polar bond.** Of course, if two atoms pull equally on the electrons, neither atom becomes charged. A covalent bond in which electrons are shared equally is a **nonpolar bond.** Compare the bond in fluorine (F_2) with the bond in hydrogen fluoride (HF) in Figure 25.

Polar Bonds in Molecules It makes sense that a molecule with nonpolar bonds will itself be nonpolar. But a molecule may contain polar bonds and still be nonpolar overall. In carbon dioxide, the oxygen atoms attract electrons much more strongly than carbon does. So, the bonds between the oxygen and carbon atoms are polar. But, as you can see in Figure 26, a carbon dioxide molecule has a shape like a straight line. So, the two oxygen atoms pull with equal strength in opposite directions. In a sense, the attractions cancel out, and the molecule is nonpolar.

In contrast, other molecules that have polar covalent bonds are themselves polar. In a water molecule, the two hydrogen atoms are at one end of the molecule, while the oxygen atom is at the other end. The oxygen atom attracts electrons more strongly than do the hydrogen atoms. As a result, the oxygen end has a slight negative charge and the hydrogen end has a slight positive charge.

Attractions Between Molecules If you could shrink small enough to move among a bunch of water molecules, what would you find? The negatively charged oxygen ends of the polar water molecules attract the positively charged hydrogen ends of nearby water molecules. These attractions pull water molecules toward each other. In contrast, there is little attraction between nonpolar molecules, such as carbon dioxide molecules.

The properties of polar and nonpolar compounds differ because of differences in attractions between their molecules. For example, water and vegetable oil don't mix. The molecules in vegetable oil are nonpolar, and nonpolar molecules have little attraction for polar water molecules. On the other hand, the water molecules are attracted more strongly to one another than to the molecules of oil. Thus, water stays with water, and oil stays with oil.

If you did the Discover activity, you found that adding detergent helped oil and water to mix. This is because one end of a detergent molecule has nonpolar covalent bonds. The other end includes an ionic bond. The detergent's nonpolar end mixes easily with the oil. Meanwhile, the charged ionic end is attracted to polar water molecules, so the detergent dissolves in water.

 Reading Checkpoint Why is water (H_2O) a polar molecule but a fluorine molecule (F_2) is not?

FIGURE 27
Getting Out the Dirt
Most laundry dirt is oily or greasy. Detergents can mix with both oil and water, so when the wash water goes down the drain, the soap and dirt go with it.

Section 4 Assessment

Target Reading Skill Asking Questions Use the answers to the questions you wrote about the headings to help you answer the questions below.

Reviewing Key Concepts

1. **a.** Identifying What is the attraction that holds two covalently bonded atoms together?
   b. Inferring A carbon atom can form four covalent bonds. How many valence electrons does it have?
   c. Interpreting Diagrams What is a double bond? Use Figure 24 to explain how carbon dioxide achieves a stable set of eight electrons for each atom.

2. **a.** Reviewing How are the properties of molecular compounds different from those of ionic compounds?
   b. Relating Cause and Effect Why are most molecular compounds poor conductors of electricity?

3. **a.** Reviewing How do some atoms in covalent bonds become slightly negative or slightly positive? What type of covalent bonds do these atoms form?

   b. Comparing and Contrasting Both carbon dioxide molecules and water molecules have polar bonds. Why then is carbon dioxide a nonpolar molecule while water is a polar molecule?
   c. Predicting Predict whether carbon dioxide or water would have a higher boiling point. Explain your prediction in terms of the attractions between molecules.

Lab zone At-Home Activity

Laundry Chemistry Demonstrate the action of soaps and detergents to your family. Pour some vegetable oil on a clean cloth and show how a detergent solution can wash the oil away better than water alone can. Explain to your family the features of soap and detergent molecules in terms of their chemical bonds.

Chapter 1 L ◆ 35

Lab zone At-Home Activity

Laundry Chemistry L2 Advise students to explain first why oil and water do not mix. Then they can explain how soap or detergent molecules form bonds on one end with a water molecule and on the other end with an oil molecule, causing the oil to break up and wash away.

Lab zone Chapter Project

Keep Students on Track
Students can use some of their model atoms to represent covalent molecules. Encourage them to create models of molecules with single, double, and triple bonds. Remind them that all of the atoms (except hydrogen) in their molecules should have eight valence electrons.

L ● 35

Bonding in Metals

Objectives

After this lesson, students will be able to

L.1.5.1 Describe how metal atoms are bonded in solid metal.

L.1.5.2 Explain how metallic bonding results in useful properties of metals.

Target Reading Skill

Relating Cause and Effect Explain that cause is the reason for what happens. The effect is what happens because of the cause. Relating cause and effect helps students relate the reason for what happens to what happens as a result.

Answers

Graphic organizers should show that metallic bonding causes the properties of metals, which include electrical conductivity, heat conductivity, ductility, malleability, and luster.

All in One Teaching Resources

• Transparency L13

Preteach

Build Background Knowledge

L2

Inferring Properties of Metals

Have students name common objects containing metal and infer properties of metals based on the objects. Ask: **What common objects are made wholly or mostly of metal?** *(Sample answers: Jewelry, aluminum foil, wires, pots and pans)* **Based on the uses of metals in these objects, what do you think are some properties of metals?** *(Sample answers: Flexibility, ability to conduct heat and electricity)*

Bonding in Metals

Reading Preview

Key Concepts

• How are metal atoms bonded in solid metal?

• How does metallic bonding result in useful properties of metals?

Key Terms

• metallic bond • alloy
• ductile • malleable

Target Reading Skill

Relating Cause and Effect As you read, identify the properties of metals that result from metallic bonding. Write the information in a graphic organizer like the one below.

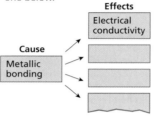

```
                    Effects
                ┌──────────────┐
                │ Electrical   │
                │ conductivity │
                └──────────────┘
     Cause          ┌──────────┐
  ┌──────────┐  →   │          │
  │ Metallic │      └──────────┘
  │ bonding  │  →   ┌──────────┐
  └──────────┘      │          │
                →   └──────────┘
                    ┌──────────┐
                →   │          │
                    └──────────┘
```

FIGURE 28
Metal in Architecture
The Guggenheim Museum in Bilbao, Spain, provides a dramatic example of some properties of metals. The museum's shiny outer "skin" is made of the lightweight metal titanium, which can be pressed into large, thin, flexible sheets.

Lab zone Discover Activity

What Do Metals Do?

1. Your teacher will give you pieces of different metals. Examine each metal and try changing its shape by bending, stretching, folding, or any other action you can think of. **CAUTION:** *Handle metal pieces with sharp edges carefully.*

2. What properties are common to these metals? What properties are different?

3. What properties make each metal suitable for its use?

Think It Over

Inferring Paper clips (made mostly of iron), aluminum foil, and copper wire are made from large chunks of metals. What properties must these metals have to be made into these products?

Why would you choose metal to cover the complex shape of the building in Figure 28? You couldn't cover the building with brittle, crumbly nonmetals such as sulfur or silicon. What physical properties make metal an ideal material for making furniture, musical instruments, electrical wire, pots and pans, eating utensils, and strong beams for buildings? Why do metals have these physical properties?

Lab zone Discover Activity

Skills Focus Inferring **L1**

Materials small pieces of three different metals

Time 10 minutes

Tip Make sure the pieces of metal do not have sharp edges.

Expected Outcome Students are expected to be able to bend and fold the materials and reshape them in other ways.

Think It Over The metals must be able to be bent, flattened into thin sheets, or pulled into strands.

Metallic Bonding

The properties of solid metals can be explained by the structure of metal atoms and the bonding between those atoms. Recall that most metals have 1, 2, or 3 valence electrons. When metal atoms combine chemically with atoms of other elements, they usually lose valence electrons, becoming positively charged metal ions. Metals lose electrons easily because their valence electrons are not strongly held.

The loosely held electrons in metal atoms result in a type of bonding that is characteristic of metals. Like many solids, metals exist as crystals. The metal atoms are very close together and in specific arrangements. These atoms are actually positively charged ions. Their valence electrons are free to drift among the ions. Each metal ion is held in the crystal by a **metallic bond**—an attraction between a positive metal ion and the electrons surrounding it. Look at Figure 29. **A metal crystal consists of positively charged metal ions embedded in a "sea" of valence electrons.** The more valence electrons an atom can add to the "sea," the stronger the metallic bonds within the crystal will be.

 Reading Checkpoint What is a metallic bond?

FIGURE 29
Metallic Bonding
Solid metals consist of positively charged ions surrounded by a loose "sea" of valence electrons.
Problem Solving Why would nonmetals be unlikely to have the type of bonding shown here?

Metallic Properties

Metallic bonding explains many of the common physical properties of metals and their alloys. An **alloy** is a material made of two or more elements that has the properties of a metal.

Suppose that you placed one hand on an unheated aluminum pan and the other hand on a wooden tabletop. The aluminum pan would feel cooler than the tabletop even though both are at the same temperature. You feel the difference because aluminum conducts heat away from your hand much faster than wood does. **The "sea of electrons" model of solid metals explains their ability to conduct heat and electricity, the ease with which they can be made to change shape, and their luster.**

Heat Conductivity Heat travels through materials as the increased motion of the particles in the hotter parts of the material are passed along to the particles in the cooler parts. The freedom of motion of electrons in metals makes it easy for thermal energy to be transferred along the crystal.

Go Online
SciLINKS NSTA

For: Links on metallic bonding
Visit: www.SciLinks.org
Web Code: scn-1215

Making Judgments About the Uses and Properties of Metals

Time 10 minutes

Focus Guide students in judging how the properties of metals suit their uses.

Teach Lead the class in brainstorming a list of metal objects, using Figure 30 as a starting point. On the board, list the objects that students name. Then, for each object, have students identify which metallic properties make metal well suited for use in that object. For example, electrical conductivity and ductility make metal well suited for use in electric wire, and malleability and luster make metal well suited for use in jewelry.

Apply Ask: **What other materials might be used in these objects?** (*Students might identify other materials, such as wood or plastic, that could be used in some of the objects.*) **How well suited would these other materials be? Why?** (*Generally, other materials would not be as well suited as metals because they lack metals' properties.*)
learning modality: verbal

Teacher **Demo**   L2

How Objects Demonstrate Properties of Metals

Materials aluminum objects such as a beverage can, baking pan, foil wrap, ornament

Time 10 minutes

Focus Have students identify how aluminum objects demonstrate the properties of metals.

Teach Show students the objects, and explain that they are made from aluminum, a metal. Review the properties of metals, and challenge students to describe uses of the aluminum objects that demonstrate each property. Accept all reasonable responses. (*Sample answer: A beverage can that is chilling in a cooler demonstrates heat conductivity.*)

Apply Ask: **What other properties of aluminum make it useful for these purposes?** (*Students might say that aluminum is also useful because it is also lightweight, strong, recyclable, and rustproof.*) Make sure students understand that these

other properties of aluminum do not necessarily characterize all metals. For example, iron is much heavier than aluminum and rusts easily. **learning modality: visual**

FIGURE 30
Properties of Metals

The unique properties of metals result from the ability of their electrons to move about freely.
Interpreting Diagrams *What happens to metal ions when a metal is struck by a hammer? Why does this happen?*

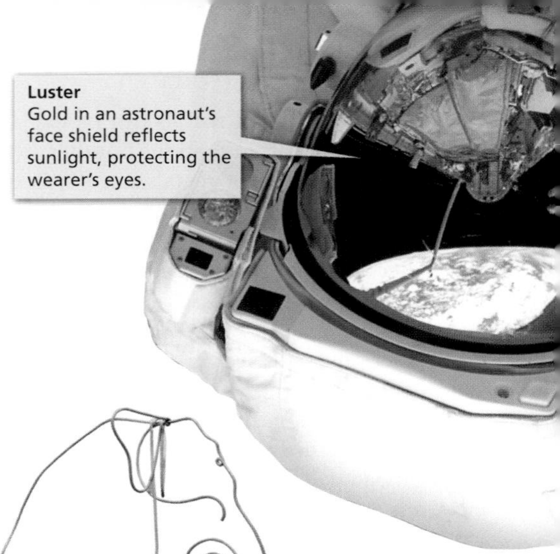

Luster
Gold in an astronaut's face shield reflects sunlight, protecting the wearer's eyes.

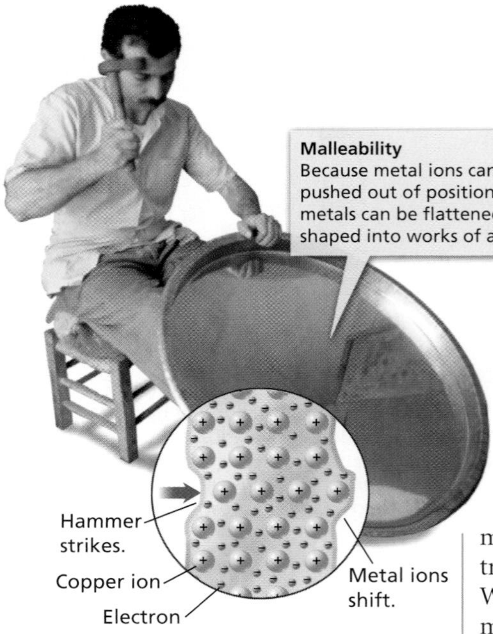

Malleability
Because metal ions can be pushed out of position, metals can be flattened and shaped into works of art.

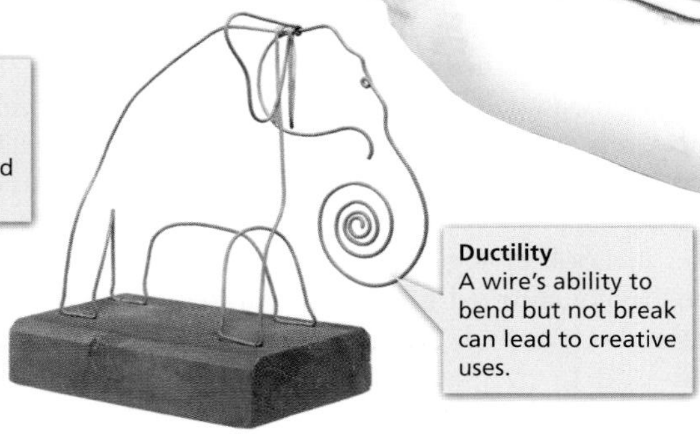

Ductility
A wire's ability to bend but not break can lead to creative uses.

Hammer strikes.
Copper ion
Electron
Metal ions shift.

Electrical Conductivity Recall from Section 3 that electricity can flow when charged particles are free to move. Metals conduct electricity easily because the electrons in a metal crystal can move freely among the atoms. When connected to a device such as a battery, electrons move into the metal at one point and out at another point.

Changes in Shape A metal's ability to conduct electricity would not be very useful if the metal couldn't be made into thin wires that could bend. Most metals are flexible and can be reshaped easily. They can be stretched, pushed, or compressed into different shapes without breaking. Metals act this way because the ions in metal crystals are not attracted to other ions as in ionic crystals. Instead, they are attracted to the loose electrons all around them. As a result, the ions can be pushed out of position, as shown in Figure 30.

Because the metal ions in a crystal move easily, metals are **ductile,** which means that they can be bent easily and pulled into thin strands or wires. Metals are also **malleable**—able to be rolled into thin sheets, as in aluminum foil, or beaten into complex shapes.

38 ◆ **L**

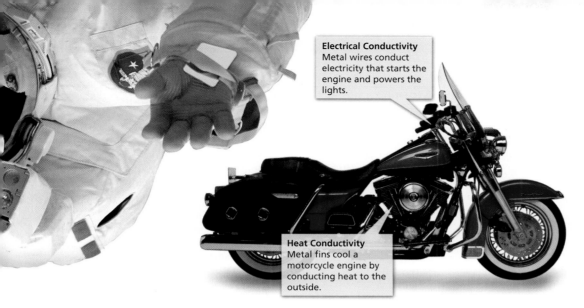

Electrical Conductivity Metal wires conduct electricity that starts the engine and powers the lights.

Heat Conductivity Metal fins cool a motorcycle engine by conducting heat to the outside.

Luster Polished metals exhibit luster, that is, they are shiny and reflective. A metal's luster is due to its valence electrons. When light strikes these electrons, they absorb the light and then give it off again. This property makes metals useful for making products as varied as mirrors, buildings, jewelry, and astronaut helmets.

 Reading Checkpoint Why do metals exhibit luster?

Section 5 Assessment

🎯 **Target Reading Skill** Relating Cause and Effect Refer to your graphic organizer about metallic properties to help you answer Question 2 below.

Reviewing Key Concepts

1. **a.** Describing Describe the structure of a metal crystal.
   b. Relating Cause and Effect Explain how metal atoms form metallic bonds in crystals. What role do the valence electrons play?
   c. Comparing and Contrasting Review what you learned about ionic bonds in Section 3. How does a metallic bond differ from an ionic bond?
2. **a.** Listing Name five properties of metals. What accounts for these properties?
   b. Explaining Explain how heat travels through metals.
   c. Applying Concepts Why is it safer to use a nonmetal mixing spoon when cooking something on a stove?

Writing in Science

Product Label Choose a familiar metal object and create a "product label" for it. Your label should describe at least two of the metal's properties and explain why it exhibits those properties. You can include illustrations on your label as well.

Chapter 1 L ◆ 39

Monitor Progress ____ L2

Answers
Figure 30 Metal ions are pushed out of position, because the ions are not attracted to other ions, only to the loose electrons surrounding them.

✓ **Reading Checkpoint** Because their valence electrons absorb light and then give it off again

Assess

Reviewing Key Concepts

1. **a.** A metal crystal consists of positively charged metal ions embedded in a "sea" of valence electrons. **b.** Each metal atom contributes a positive ion and one or more loosely held valence electrons. Attractions between valence electrons and positive ions hold metal atoms together. **c.** A metallic bond is the attraction between a positive metal ion and the electrons around it. An ionic bond is the attraction between positive and negative ions.
2. **a.** Five properties are: heat conductivity, electrical conductivity, ductility, malleability, and luster. The loosely held valence electrons, which allow ions and valence electrons in metals to move, account for these properties. **b.** Heat travels through metals as increased motion of particles in hotter parts of the metal is passed along to particles in cooler parts. **c.** A metal spoon would conduct heat to your hand, possibly causing a burn.

Reteach L1

Call on students to name properties of metals. Call on other students to describe an example of each property.

Performance Assessment L2

Drawing Have students draw a diagram to illustrate metallic bonding.
Students can keep their diagrams in their portfolios. **Portfolio**

L ● 39

interactive **Textbook**

- Complete student edition
- Section and chapter self-assessment
- Assessment reports for teachers

Help Students Read   L1
Building Vocabulary

Word Origins On the board, write the term *valence*. Explain that the term comes from the Latin word meaning "power." Ask: **What vocabulary term includes the word *valence*?** (*Valence electrons*) **What do valence electrons have to do with power?** (*They are the electrons with the highest energy.*)

Latin Plural Form Tell students that the plural of the word *nucleus* is *nuclei*. Write both singular and plural forms on the board. Call on students to use each form in a sentence.

Connecting Concepts
Concept Maps Help students develop one way to show how the information in this chapter is related. Elements, which are the building blocks of matter, are made of atoms. The properties of atoms and their bonds depend largely on their valence electrons. Have students brainstorm to identify key concepts, key terms, details, and examples. Then, write each one on a self-sticking note, and attach it at random to chart paper or the board.

Tell students that the concept map will be organized in hierarchical order, beginning at the top with the key concepts. Ask students these questions to guide them in organizing the information on the self-sticking notes: **How are atoms related to elements? How do elements change across the periodic table? How do ionic, covalent, and metallic bonds differ? What are the properties of compounds with these types of bonds?** Prompt students by using connecting words, such as "are made of," "which have," "can be," and "have properties of," to indicate the basis for the organization of the concept map. The phrases should form a sentence between or among concepts.

① Elements and Atoms
Key Concepts
- Elements are the building blocks of matter because all matter is composed of one element or a combination of two or more elements.
- Atomic theory grew as a series of models that developed from experimental evidence. As more evidence was collected, the theory and models were revised.

Key Terms

matter	model
element	electrons
compound	nucleus
mixture	protons
atom	energy level
scientific theory	neutrons

② Atoms, Bonding, and the Periodic Table
Key Concepts
- The number of valence electrons in an atom of an element determines many properties of that element, including the ways in which the atom can bond with other atoms.
- The properties of elements change in a regular way across a period in the periodic table.

Key Terms

valence electrons	group
electron dot diagram	family
chemical bond	noble gas
symbol	halogen
atomic number	alkali metal
period	

40 ◆ L

③ Ionic Bonds
Key Concepts
- When an atom loses an electron, it becomes a positive ion. When an atom gains an electron, it becomes a negative ion.
- Ionic bonds form as a result of the attraction between positive and negative ions.
- When ionic compounds form, the charges on the ions balance out.
- Ionic compounds are hard, brittle crystals that have high melting points and conduct electricity when dissolved in water.

Key Terms

ion	chemical formula
polyatomic ion	subscript
ionic bond	crystal
ionic compound	

④ Covalent Bonds
Key Concepts
- The force that holds atoms together in a covalent bond is the attraction of each atom's nucleus for the shared pair of electrons.
- Molecular compounds have low melting and boiling points and do not conduct electricity.
- In polar covalent bonds, the bonded atoms have slight electrical charges.

Key Terms

covalent bond	molecular compound
molecule	polar bond
double bond	nonpolar bond
triple bond	

⑤ Bonding in Metals
Key Concepts
- A metal crystal consists of positively charged metal ions in a "sea" of valence electrons.
- Solid metals conduct heat and electricity, can change shape easily, and have luster.

Key Terms

metallic bond	ductile
alloy	malleable

Answer
Accept logical presentations by students.

All in One Teaching Resources
- Key Terms Review: *Atoms and Bonding*
- Connecting Concepts: *Atoms and Bonding*

Review and Assessment

For: Self-Assessment
Visit: PHSchool.com
Web Code: cga-2010

Organizing Information

Comparing and Contrasting
Copy the graphic organizer about chemical bonds onto a separate sheet of paper. Then complete it. (For more on Comparing and Contrasting, see the Skills Handbook.)

Types of Chemical Bonds

Feature	Ionic Bond	Polar Covalent Bond	Nonpolar Covalent Bond	Metallic Bond
How Bond Forms	a. ___?___	Unequal sharing of electrons	b. ___?___	c. ___?___
Charge on Bonded Atoms?	Yes; positive or negative	d. ___?___	e. ___?___	Yes; positive
Example	f. ___?___	g. ___?___	O₂ molecule	h. ___?___

Reviewing Key Terms

Choose the letter of the best answer.

1. All compounds are made up of two or more
   a. elements.　　b. electrons.
   c. nuclei.　　d. mixtures.

2. The nucleus of an atom has a positive charge because the nucleus contains
   a. electrons.　　b. protons.
   c. mass.　　d. neutrons.

3. On the periodic table, elements with the same number of valence electrons are in the same
   a. square.　　b. period.
   c. block.　　d. group.

4. When an atom loses or gains electrons, it becomes a(n)
   a. ion.　　b. formula.
   c. crystal.　　d. subscript.

5. A covalent bond in which electrons are shared unequally is a
   a. double bond.
   b. triple bond.
   c. polar bond.
   d. nonpolar bond.

6. Because it can be pounded into thin sheets, copper is said to be
   a. an alloy.
   b. conductive.
   c. ductile.
   d. malleable.

If the statement is true, write *true***. If it is false, change the underlined word or words to make the statement true.**

7. In the modern atomic model, most of the volume of an atom is occupied by its <u>nucleus</u>.

8. The <u>atomic number</u> of an element is the number of protons in the nucleus of an atom.

9. A <u>polyatomic ion</u> is made up of more than one ion.

10. An <u>alloy</u> is a mixture of elements that has the properties of a metal.

 **Writing** in Science

Travel Brochure Pretend you have just visited a city modeled on the periodic table. Write a travelogue about how the "city" is organized. Be sure to describe some of the elements you visited and how they are related to their neighbors.

DISCOVERY CHANNEL
SCHOOL

Atoms and Bonding
Video Preview
Video Field Trip
▶ Video Assessment

Chapter 1 L ◆ 41

Review and Assessment

Organizing Information

a. Attraction between oppositely charged ions
b. Equal sharing of electrons
c. Attraction between positively charged ions and surrounding electrons
d. Yes; slightly positive or slightly negative
e. No
f. NaCl crystal (or other ionic compound)
g. H₂O molecule (or other polar covalent molecule)
h. Calcium (or other metal)

Reviewing Key Terms

1. a　2. b　3. d　4. a　5. c　6. d
7. electrons
8. true
9. true
10. true

Writing in Science

Writing Mode Persuasion

Scoring Rubric
4 Exceeds criteria; includes an interesting and detailed description showing in-depth understanding of the periodic table
3 Meets criteria
2 Includes a description but lacks details and/or reveals some misconceptions about the periodic table
1 Includes a general description only and/or reveals little knowledge of the periodic table

DISCOVERY CHANNEL
SCHOOL
Video Assessment

Atoms and Bonding

Show the Video Assessment to review chapter content and as a prompt for the writing assignment. Discussion questions: **What do the elements in a single group on the periodic table have in common?** (*They have the same number of electrons in their outer shell.*) **Where are the most reactive elements located on the periodic table?** (*In Groups 1 and 17*)

Go Online
PHSchool.com
For: Self-Assessment
Visit: PHSchool.com
Web Code: cga-2010

Students can take a practice test online that is automatically scored.

All in One Teaching Resources
- Transparency L15
- Chapter Test
- Performance Assessment Teacher Notes
- Performance Assessment Student Worksheet
- Performance Assessment Scoring Rubric

◎ **Exam View® Computer Test Bank CD-ROM**

Checking Concepts

11. Rutherford discovered that an atom is mostly empty space, with electrons moving around a small, positively charged nucleus in the center of the atom.

12. An element whose atoms have eight valence electrons is less reactive, because it does not require any additional electrons to become stable.

13. Because a lot of energy is required to break their strong ionic bonds

14. Two atoms of hydrogen, one atom of sulfur, and four atoms of oxygen

15. Because each atom exerts the same pull on the shared electrons but in opposite directions

16. The electrons in metals are only loosely held by the positively charged ions, allowing them to move freely among the ions and conduct electricity.

Thinking Critically

17. A scientific theory is a well-tested idea that explains and connects many observations and established concepts. The friend's theory is just untested speculation.

18. Sample answer: Elements within the same group have the same number of valence electrons. The number of valence electrons determines the kinds of bonds they form.

19. Both molecules are nonpolar. The two oxygen atoms in each molecule pull equally but in opposite directions on the shared electrons, so they cancel each other out.

20. Because water is polar, water molecules have positive and negative ends. This causes water molecules to be attracted to each other and remain in a liquid state at room temperature. Nonpolar molecules, lacking this type of attraction, can move farther apart and remain as a gas at room temperature.

Review and Assessment

Checking Concepts

11. What discoveries about the atom did Rutherford make in his experiments?

12. Which element is less reactive, an element whose atoms have seven valence electrons or an element whose atoms have eight valence electrons? Explain.

13. Why do ionic compounds generally have high melting points?

14. The formula of sulfuric acid is H_2SO_4. How many atoms of hydrogen, sulfur, and oxygen are in one molecule of sulfuric acid?

15. Why is the covalent bond between two atoms of the same element a nonpolar bond?

16. Explain how metallic bonding causes metals to conduct electricity.

Thinking Critically

17. **Applying Concepts** Your friend tells you that she has a theory that eating cabbage will make hair grow faster. How does your friend's use of the word theory differ from a scientist's use of the word?

18. **Making Generalizations** What information does the organization of the periodic table tell you about atoms and the bonds they form?

19. **Classifying** Classify each molecule below as either a polar molecule or a nonpolar molecule. Explain your reasoning.

Oxygen

Carbon dioxide

20. **Relating Cause and Effect** Many molecular compounds with small molecules are gases at room temperature. Water, however, is a liquid. Use what you know about polar and nonpolar molecules to explain this difference. (*Hint:* Molecules of a gas are much farther apart than molecules of a liquid.)

Applying Skills

Use the electron dot diagrams below to answer Questions 21–25.

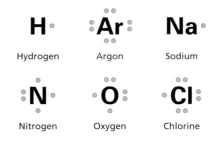

H·	·Ar·	Na·
Hydrogen	Argon	Sodium
·N·	·O·	·Cl·
Nitrogen	Oxygen	Chlorine

21. **Predicting** When nitrogen and hydrogen combine, what will be the ratio of hydrogen atoms to nitrogen atoms in a molecule of the resulting compound? Explain.

22. **Inferring** Which of these elements can become stable by losing one electron? Explain.

23. **Drawing Conclusions** Which of these elements is least likely to react with other elements? Explain.

24. **Interpreting Diagrams** Which of these elements would react with two atoms of sodium to form an ionic compound? Explain.

25. **Classifying** What type of bond forms when two atoms of nitrogen join to form a nitrogen molecule? When two atoms of oxygen join to form an oxygen molecule?

Lab zone Chapter **Project**

Performance Assessment Present your models to the class, telling what the parts of each model represent. Explain why you chose particular items to model the atoms and chemical bonds. Which kind of bonds were easier to show? Why? What more would you like to know about bonding that could help improve your models?

Lab zone Chapter **Project**

Performance Assessment In their presentations, students should describe how their models represent atoms, bonds, and compounds. They also should explain why they chose the materials they did and describe any problems they had building their models. After the presentations, suggest that students compare their models with other students' models of the same compounds. They should note any differences and consider how the differences affect the quality and usefulness of the models. To help improve their models, students might say they would like to know more about relative sizes of atoms of different elements or more about the modern atomic model.

Standardized Test Prep

Choose the letter of the best answer.

Use the electron dot diagrams above to answer Questions 1–3.

1. Oxygen has 6 valence electrons, as indicated by the 6 dots around the letter symbol "O." Based on this information, how many covalent bonds could an oxygen atom form?
 A six
 B three
 C two
 D none

2. If a reaction occurs between potassium (K) and oxygen (O), what will be the ratio of potassium ions to oxide ions in the resulting compound, potassium oxide?
 F 1 : 1   G 1 : 2
 H 2 : 1   J 2 : 2

3. The element boron (B) is directly above aluminum (Al) on the periodic table. Which statement about boron is true?
 A Boron is the same period as aluminum and has two valence electrons.
 B Boron is in the same group as aluminum and has two valence electrons.
 C Boron is in the same period as aluminum and has three valence electrons.
 D Boron is in the same group as aluminum and has three valence electrons.

4. The chemical formula for a glucose molecule is $C_6H_{12}O_6$. The subscripts represent the
 F mass of each element.
 G number of atoms of each element in a glucose molecule.
 H total number of bonds made by each atom.
 J number of valence electrons.

5. An ice cube (solid H_2O) and a scoop of table salt (NaCl) are left outside on a warm, sunny day. Which best explains why the ice cube melts and the salt does not?
 A The attractive forces between molecules of H_2O are much weaker than those between ions in NaCl.
 B NaCl can dissolve in H_2O.
 C The mass of the H_2O was less than the mass of the NaCl.
 D NaCl is white and H_2O is colorless.

Constructed Response

6. In a working light bulb, electricity passes through a thin tungsten wire filament that is wound in a coil. Describe two properties that make the metal tungsten a good material for the filament of a light bulb. Indicate how the type of bonding in tungsten contributes to these properties.

Applying Skills

21. There will be three hydrogen atoms to one nitrogen atom, because that combination gives the nitrogen atom eight valence electrons and each hydrogen atom two valence electrons.

22. Sodium can become stable by losing one electron, because then it will have eight valence electrons.

23. Argon is least likely to react, because it has a stable set of eight valence electrons.

24. Oxygen would react with two atoms of sodium to form an ionic compound. An oxide ion has a charge of 2− and needs two sodium ions, each with a 1+ charge, to balance it.

25. A triple bond forms when two atoms of nitrogen join, and a double bond forms when two atoms of oxygen form.

Standardized Test Prep

1. C   **2.** H   **3.** D   **4.** G   **5.** A
6. As a metal, tungsten is ductile and conducts electricity, making it a good material for the filament of a light bulb. Metallic bonds in tungsten allow electrons and ions to move. As a result, the metal can be shaped into wires and conduct electricity.

Chapter **2** **Chemical Reactions**

Chapter at a Glance

PRENTICE HALL
Teacher**EXPRESS**
Plan • Teach • Assess

 Chapter **Project** *Design and Build a Closed Reaction Chamber*

Technology

Local Standards

All in One **Teaching Resources**
- Chapter Project Teacher Notes, pp. 110–111
- Chapter Project Students Overview, pp. 112–113
- Chapter Project Student Worksheets, pp. 114–115
- Chapter Project Scoring Rubric, p. 116

Discovery
CHANNEL
SCHOOL
Video Preview

Section 1
3–4 periods
1 1/2–2 blocks

Observing Chemical Change
L.2.1.1 State how matter and changes in matter can be described.
L.2.1.2 Explain how you can tell when a chemical reaction occurs.

Go **Online**
*SCi*LINKS. NSTA

Section 2
2–3 periods
1–1 1/2 blocks

Describing Chemical Reactions
L.2.2.1 Identify what information a chemical equation contains.
L.2.2.2 State the principle of conservation of mass.
L.2.2.3 Explain what a balanced chemical equation must show.
L.2.2.4 Name three categories of chemical reactions.

Go **Online**
active art

Go **Online**
PHSchool.com

Section 3
3–4 periods
1 1/2–2 blocks

Controlling Chemical Reactions
L.2.3.1 Explain how activation energy is related to chemical reactions.
L.2.3.2 Identify factors that affect the rate of a chemical reaction.

Discovery
CHANNEL
SCHOOL
Video Field Trip

Go **Online**
PHSchool.com

Section 4
3–4 periods
1/2–1 block

Fire and Fire Safety
L.2.4.1 List the three things necessary to maintain a fire.
L.2.4.2 Explain why you should know about the causes of fire and how to prevent a fire.

Go **Online**
*SCi*LINKS. NSTA

Review and Assessment

Test Preparation

All in One **Teaching Resources**
- Key Terms Review, p. 154
- Transparency L29
- Performance Assessment Teacher Notes, p. 162
- Performance Assessment Scoring Rubric, p. 163
- Performance Assessment Student Worksheet, p. 164
- Chapter Test, pp. 165–168

Discovery
CHANNEL
SCHOOL
Video Assessment

Go **Online**
PHSchool.com

**Test Preparation
Blackline Masters**

Lab zone Chapter Activities Planner

Student Edition	Inquiry	Time	Materials	Skills	Resources
Chapter Project	Open-ended	Ongoing (3 weeks)	**All in One** Teaching Resources See p. 110	Designing a solution, building a prototype, evaluating the design, interpreting data, communicating	**Lab zone Easy Planner** **All in One** Teaching Resources Support pp. 110–111
Section 1					
Discover Activity, p. 46	Guided	10 minutes	Safety goggles, spoon, baking soda, clear plastic cup, white vinegar, large bowl or sink	Observing	**Lab zone Easy Planner**
Skills Activity, p. 48	Directed	10 minutes	Large crystal of rock salt, small hammer, newspapers, safety goggles, cup of water, stirring rod	Classifying	**Lab zone Easy Planner**
Try This Activity, p. 51	Directed	10 minutes	Safety goggles, lab apron, limewater, 2 plastic cups, tap water, carbonated water	Drawing conclusions	**Lab zone Easy Planner**
Skills Lab, pp. 54–55	Guided	40 minutes	4 small plastic cups; birthday candles; 2 plastic spoons; sugar; tongs; clay; matches; sodium carbonate (powdered solid); graduated cylinder, 10 mL; aluminum foil, about 10-cm square; dilute hydrochloric acid in a dropper bottle; copper sulfate solution; sodium carbonate solution	Observing, predicting, drawing conclusions	**Lab zone Easy Planner** **Lab Activity Video** **All in One** Teaching Resources Skills Lab: *Where's the Evidence?*, pp. 124–127
Section 2					
Discover Activity, p. 56	Guided	10 minutes	24 coins including pennies, nickels, dimes, and quarters	Making models	**Lab zone Easy Planner**
Try This Activity, p. 58	Directed	15 minutes	Several nuts and bolts, balance	Making models	**Lab zone Easy Planner**
Section 3					
Discover Activity, p. 66	Guided	10 minutes	Safety goggles, lab apron, 125 mL vitamin C solution at three temperatures, iodine, 3 clear plastic cups, spoon	Inferring	**Lab zone Easy Planner**
Skills Activity, p. 69	Directed	15 minutes	Gelatin cube, plastic knife, ruler	Interpreting data	**Lab zone Easy Planner**
At-Home Activity, p. 71	Guided	Home		Applying concepts	**Lab zone Easy Planner**
Skills Lab, pp. 72–73	Guided	40 minutes	Forceps, stopwatch, test tube with a one-hole stopper, 0.1% hydrogen peroxide solution, filter paper disks soaked in liver preparation (catalase enzyme) and kept at four different temperatures (room temperature, 0–4°C, 37°C, and 100°C), container to hold water (beaker or bowl)	Calculating, interpreting data, drawing conclusions	**Lab zone Easy Planner** **Lab Activity Video** **All in One** Teaching Resources Skills Lab: *Temperature and Enzyme Activity*, pp. 145–147
Section 4					
Discover Activity, p. 74	Guided	15 minutes	Safety goggles, small candle, clay or candle holder, match, beaker, large spoon, baking soda, water, vinegar	Developing hypotheses	**Lab zone Easy Planner**
At-Home Activity, p. 77	Open-ended	Home		Designing a solution	**Lab zone Easy Planner**

Section 1 Observing Chemical Change

 3–4 periods 1 1/2–2 blocks

ABILITY LEVELS
L1 Basic to Average
L2 For All Students
L3 Average to Advanced

Objectives

L.2.1.1 State how matter and changes in matter can be described.
L.2.1.2 Explain how you can tell when a chemical reaction occurs.

Key Terms

- matter • chemistry • physical property • chemical property • physical change
- chemical reaction • precipitate • endothermic reaction • exothermic reaction

Local Standards

Preteach

Build Background Knowledge

Students name familiar changes in matter as an introduction to the physical and chemical changes they will read about in the section.

 Discover Activity *What Happens When Chemicals React?* **L1**

Targeted Print and Technology Resources

All in One Teaching Resources

L2 Reading Strategy Transparency L16: Asking Questions

 Presentation-Pro CD-ROM

Instruct

Properties and Changes of Matter Introduce physical and chemical properties of matter by discussing several examples.

Evidence for Chemical Reactions Describe the two main types of observable chemical change, and have students identify them in the reaction between magnesium and oxygen.

 **Skills Lab** *Where's the Evidence?* **L2**

Targeted Print and Technology Resources

All in One Teaching Resources

L2 Guided Reading, pp. 119–121
L2 Transparencies L17, L18
L2 Skills Lab: *Where's the Evidence?*, pp. 124–127

 Lab Activity Video/DVD
Skills Lab: Where's the Evidence?

www.SciLinks.org Web Code: scn-1221

Student Edition on Audio CD

Assess

Section Assessment Questions

Have students use their completed graphic organizers of questions and answers to answer the questions.

Reteach

Students answer questions based on the boldface sentences in the section.

Targeted Print and Technology Resources

All in One Teaching Resources

- Section Summary, p. 118
L1 Review and Reinforce, p. 122
L3 Enrich, p. 123

Section 2 **Describing Chemical Reactions**

ABILITY LEVELS
L1 Basic to Average
L2 For All Students
L3 Average to Advanced

2–3 periods 1–1 1/2 blocks

Objectives

L.2.2.1 Identify what information a chemical equation contains.
L.2.2.2 State the principle of the conservation of mass.
L.2.2.3 Explain what a balanced chemical equation must show.
L.2.2.4 Name three categories of chemical reactions.

Local Standards

Key Terms

• chemical equation • reactant • product • conservation
of mass • open system • closed system • coefficient • synthesis • decomposition
• replacement

Preteach

Build Background Knowledge

Students brainstorm familiar symbols and explain how symbols
are helpful, as an introduction to the use of symbols to
describe chemical reactions.

 **Discover Activity** *Do You Lose Anything?* **L1**

Targeted Print and Technology Resources

 **Teaching Resources**
L2 Reading Strategy: Building Vocabulary

⊙ **Presentation-Pro CD-ROM**

Instruct

What Are Chemical Equations? Show students the
general plan of all chemical equations.

Conservation of Mass Ask questions about Figure 9 to
guide students in understanding the principle of conservation
of mass.

Balancing Chemical Equations Explain why chemical
equations must be balanced, and show students how to
balance a sample equation.

Classifying Chemical Reactions Have students read
about categories of chemical reactions and then apply the
concepts by classifying several sample chemical reactions.

Targeted Print and Technology Resources

 **Teaching Resources**
L2 Guided Reading, pp. 130–134
L2 Transparencies L19, L20, L21

PHSchool.com Web Code: cgp-2022
PHSchool.com Web Code: cgh-2020

⊙ **Student Edition on Audio CD**

Assess

Section Assessment Questions

🔄 Have students use their completed sentences using key
terms to answer the questions.

Reteach

Students help make a table comparing and contrasting
synthesis, degradation, and replacement reactions.

Targeted Print and Technology Resources

 **Teaching Resources**
• Section Summary, p. 129
L1 Review and Reinforce, p. 135
L3 Enrich, p. 136

44D

Section 3 **Controlling Chemical Reactions**

ABILITY LEVELS
L1 Basic to Average
L2 For All Students
L3 Average to Advanced

 3–4 periods 1 1/2–2 blocks

Objectives

L.2.3.1 Explain how activation energy is related to chemical reactions.
L.2.3.2 Identify factors that affect the rate of a chemical reaction.

• **Key Terms**

• activation energy • concentration •
catalyst • enzyme • inhibitor

Preteach

Local Standards

Build Background Knowledge
Students infer from a familiar example how temperature affects the rate of chemical reactions.

Targeted Print and Technology Resources

 **Discover Activity** *Can You Speed Up or Slow Down a Reaction?* **L2**

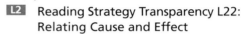 **Teaching Resources**
L2 Reading Strategy Transparency L22: Relating Cause and Effect

---

Instruct

Presentation-Pro CD-ROM

Energy and Reactions Use a questioning strategy to define and explain activation energy.

Rates of Chemical Reactions List and discuss four factors that affect rates of chemical reactions. **L3**

 Skills Lab *Temperature and Enzyme Activity*

Targeted Print and Technology Resources

 Teaching Resources
L2 Guided Reading, pp. 139–142
L2 Transparencies L23, L24, L25
L3 Skills Lab: *Temperature and Enzyme Activity,* pp. 145–147

📼 **Lab Activity Video/DVD**
Skills Lab: *Temperature and Enzyme Activity*

PHSchool.com Web Code: cgd-2023

Student Edition on Audio CD

Assess

Section Assessment Questions

 Have students use their completed graphic organizers of cause and effect to answer the questions.

Reteach
Students define the key terms.

Targeted Print and Technology Resources

Teaching Resources
• Section Summary, p. 138
L1 Review and Reinforce, p. 143
L3 Enrich, p. 144

Section 4 Fire and Fire Safety

 1–2 periods 1/2–1 block

Objectives

L.2.4.1 List the three things necessary to maintain a fire.

L.2.4.2 Explain why you should know about the causes of fire and how to prevent a fire.

Key Terms

- combustion • fuel

Local Standards

Preteach

Build Background Knowledge

Students share experiences they have had with fire and recall fire safety rules they have learned.

 **Discover Activity** *How Does Baking Soda Affect a Fire?* **L1**

Targeted Print and Technology Resources

 **Teaching Resources**

L2 Reading Strategy Transparency L26: Using Prior Knowledge

○ **Presentation-Pro CD-ROM**

Instruct

Understanding Fire Use the fire triangle to show students what every fire needs to burn.

Home Fire Safety Review methods for fighting fires and how to prevent injuries and deaths from fires.

Targeted Print and Technology Resources

 Teaching Resources

L2 Guided Reading, pp. 150–151
L2 Transparencies L27, L28

www.SciLinks.org
Web Code: scn-1224

○ **Student Edition on Audio CD**

Assess

Section Assessment Questions

 Have students use their completed graphic organizers of what they know and what they learned to answer the questions.

Reteach

Students name fire-prevention and fire safety features of a fire-safe house.

Targeted Print and Technology Resources

Teaching Resources

- Section Summary, p. 149
L1 Review and Reinforce, p. 152
L3 Enrich, p. 153

Chapter 2 **Content Refresher**

Section 1 **Observing Chemical Change**

Physical and Chemical Changes Matter can undergo changes that are physical or chemical. Physical changes in matter do not result in the formation of new substances. An example of physical change is a change of state, such as solid to liquid or liquid to gas. Chemical changes in matter, on the other hand, do result in the formation of new substances. The same atoms are found in the products as in the reactants of a chemical change, but they are combined differently. Because new substances are produced when chemical changes occur, the products have different properties than the reactants. For example, when hydrogen and oxygen combine in a certain proportion, they form water. Liquid water does not burn or support combustion, whereas hydrogen burns and oxygen supports combustion.

Address Misconceptions

Students may think that certain physical changes of state are chemical changes because the changes appear to be so significant. For a strategy for overcoming this misconception, see **Address Misconceptions** in Section 1, *Observing Chemical Change.*

Energy is conserved in chemical reactions. This means that the energy of the reactants must equal the energy of the products, plus or minus some amount of energy that is released or absorbed. Chemical reactions release energy when the reactants have more stored chemical energy than the products. Such reactions are called *exothermic*. The excess stored chemical energy in the reactants is converted to heat energy as the reaction proceeds. Exothermic reactions can occur spontaneously. Chemical reactions absorb energy when reactants have less stored chemical energy than the products. Such reactions are called *endothermic*. Endothermic reactions usually occur only when energy is added to a system.

Section 2 **Describing Chemical Reactions**

Chemical Equations Chemical equations are used to describe chemical reactions. There are three basic steps in writing a chemical equation: first, determine the names of the reactants and products; second, write the formulas for the reactants and products in equation form, using + signs and a yield arrow →; third, balance the equation. For example, hydrogen and oxygen combine to form water, or $H_2 + O_2 \rightarrow H_2O$. To be balanced, the equation must have the same number of atoms of each element on both sides, or $2 H_2 + O_2 \rightarrow 2 H_2O$.

In addition to + and →, there are other symbols sometimes used in chemical equations. The Greek letter delta, Δ, placed above the arrow indicates that heat must be added for the reaction to occur. When the symbol for a product is followed by an upward-pointing arrow, it indicates that the product is a gas. When a product is followed by a downward-pointing arrow, it indicates that the product is a precipitate. A double arrow ($\rightleftharpoons$) indicates that the reaction is in equilibrium, so that changes in one direction are balanced by changes in the opposite direction.

Address Misconceptions

Students may think that chemical formulas and chemical equations are the same thing, because the terms formula *and* equation *are sometimes used interchangeably in other subjects.* For a strategy for overcoming this misconception, see **Address Misconceptions** in Section 2, *Describing Chemical Reactions.*

Help Students Read

Predicting

Types of Chemical Reactions

Strategy Review the common meanings of terms that students will be reading about in the text, such as *synthesis*, *decomposition*, and *replacement*, which are three different types of chemical reactions. Knowing the common meanings of the terms may help students predict their scientific meanings and improve their reading comprehension.

Example

1. Before students read about classifying chemical reactions, use questions to elicit common meanings of the terms *synthesis*, *decomposition*, and *replacement*.

2. Ask students to predict what occurs in synthesis, decomposition, and replacement reactions, based on their knowledge of the common meanings of the terms.

3. Have students read about the three types of reactions in the text and confirm whether their predictions were correct.

See Section 2, *Describing Chemical Reactions*, for a script using the Predicting strategy with students.

Section 3 Controlling Chemical Reactions

Rates of Chemical Reactions In order for a chemical reaction to occur, the reactant particles must collide and have enough energy to reach the transition state and change into the products. When these conditions are easily met, reactions occur rapidly. However, if even one of the conditions is not easily met, reactions are much slower. Several factors influence these conditions and affect the rates of chemical reactions. They include concentration and temperature. Generally, reactions occur more quickly at higher concentrations because this increases the rate at which particles collide. Reactions also usually occur more quickly at higher temperatures because this increases the energy of the reactants.

Reaction rates also can be increased by catalysts. A catalyst is a substance that speeds up a chemical reaction without being chemically changed in the process. A catalyst provides a different reaction mechanism that requires less activation energy, which is the minimum energy needed for the reaction to occur. A lower activation energy results in a reaction that occurs more quickly. The graph shows the difference in activation energy (the peaks of the curves) required for a reaction to occur with and without the presence of a catalyst. When the catalyst is present, the activation energy is much lower.

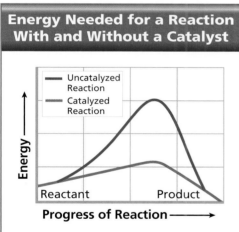

Enzymes, such as the digestive enzymes that help break down food in the digestive system, are among the most powerful catalysts. Tiny amounts of enzymes speed up reactions that would take far longer to occur or would not occur at all at normal body temperature without enzymes. Some enzymes can make reactions occur as much as a billion times faster than they would occur in the absence of the enzymes.

More than 1,500 enzymes have been identified. They are classified based on the type of reactions they control. For example, enzymes that speed up oxidation reactions are called *oxidases*, and those that speed up reduction reactions are called *reducing enzymes*. Most specific enzymes are named by adding the suffix -ase to the name of the substrate with which they

react. For example, the enzyme that catalyzes the decomposition of urea is called *urease*, and the enzymes that catalyze protein hydrolysis are called *proteinases*. Most enzymes catalyze just one reaction, although a few, including pepsin, control several different reactions.

Section 4 Fire and Fire Safety

Fire Facts and Fire Fighting Fire is due to combustion, which is a rapid chemical reaction between a fuel and oxygen. Most common fuels, including wood and gasoline, consist primarily of carbon and hydrogen. Any fuel must be in a gaseous state in order to burn, and it must be heated to its ignition point, or kindling temperature, before it will burn. A source of ignition, such as a spark or flame, provides the initial heat that decomposes a solid or liquid fuel to a flammable gas so it can burn. Later, the heat from the fire itself decomposes the fuel, leading to a chain reaction that perpetuates the combustion reaction as long as fuel and oxygen are available.

The rate at which a fire burns depends on several factors, including the type of fuel, the surface area of the fuel, and the amount of oxygen present. For example, most plastics burn faster than wood. Increasing the surface area of a fuel gives the fuel's gases more area from which to escape and come into contact with oxygen. Therefore, the greater the surface area, the faster the fire burns. A fire that lacks sufficient oxygen will burn slowly and may soon die out.

For the purpose of fire fighting, fires are generally classified into four categories, as shown in the table. The table also lists a substance that can be used to extinguish each class of fire. Class A fires are the most common, and they usually are extinguished with water. Wetting agents, called detergents, can be used to help the water penetrate the burning material. Water cannot be use to fight class B and C fires. Because flammable liquids float on water and water conducts electricity, using water against Class B and C fires usually just makes them worse.

Classes of Fires and Extinguishing Substances

Class	Type of Material (Examples)	Possible Extinguishing Substance
A	Solids (wood, paper)	Water
B	Flammable liquids (gasoline, oil)	Foam
C	Electrical apparatus (appliances, wiring)	Carbon dioxide
D	Flammable metals (magnesium, sodium)	Inert gas such as argon

interactive Textbook
- Complete student edition
- Video and audio
- Simulations and activities
- Section and chapter activities

Chapter 2

Chemical Reactions

interactive Textbook

Sparks fly as sodium metal reacts with water. ▶

44 ◆ L

Chapter Project L3

Objectives
In this Chapter Project, students will design and build a closed reaction chamber and use it to confirm that matter is not created or destroyed in a chemical reaction. After completing this Chapter Project, students will be able to
- design a solution for the problem of containing reactants and products in chemical reactions
- build a prototype of their design
- evaluate their design and revise it as needed
- interpret data from a reaction in the chamber to determine whether the results support the principle of conservation of mass
- communicate their design process, the final design solution, and their interpretation of the chemical reaction data

Skills Focus
Designing a solution, building a prototype, evaluating the design, interpreting data, communicating

Project Time Line 3 weeks

All in One Teaching Resources
- Chapter Project Teacher Notes
- Chapter Project Worksheet 1
- Chapter Project Worksheet 2
- Chapter Project Scoring Rubric

Developing a Plan
Spend one class launching the project, showing students the materials available, and leading students in brainstorming ideas for closed reaction chambers. Give students a week to design their chambers and build prototypes. Allow them another week to evaluate and revise their designs, and use the finished chambers to test the reaction. In the third week, students can prepare and give their presentations.

Possible Materials
- To build their prototypes, students may need rulers, scissors, utility knives, hot glue guns, and duct tape.
- For reaction vessels, they will need tin cans, plastic bottles, balloons, and elastic bands.
- Provide a heat source, such as a candle, hot plate, or Bunsen burner.
- To hold the reaction vessel steady, students can use a ring stand or metal tongs.

Video Preview

Chemical Reactions

Show the Video Preview to introduce chemical reactions and launch the Chapter Project. Discussion question: **What chain of events leads to the explosion of fireworks?** *(The fuse ignites a mixture of potassium nitrate, sulfur, and charcoal inside a cardboard tube. The reaction produces hot gases that blow the cardboard tube apart.)*

Lab zone™ Chapter **Project**

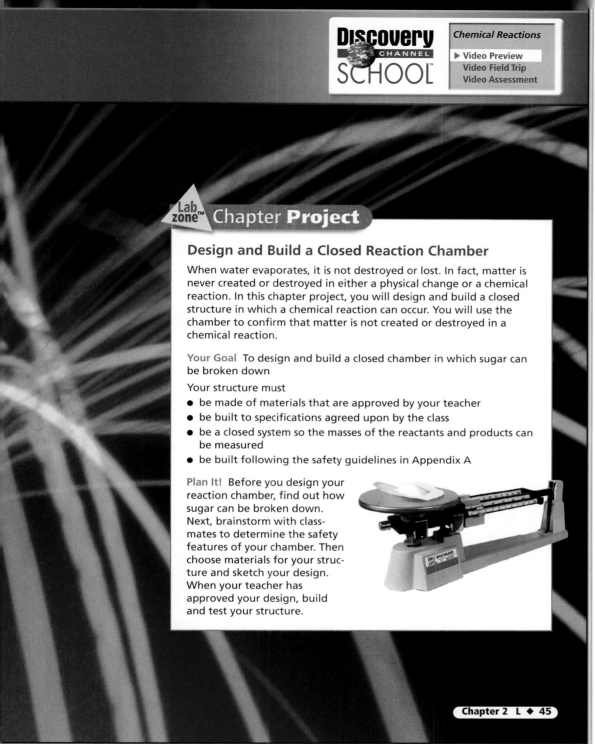

Design and Build a Closed Reaction Chamber

When water evaporates, it is not destroyed or lost. In fact, matter is never created or destroyed in either a physical change or a chemical reaction. In this chapter project, you will design and build a closed structure in which a chemical reaction can occur. You will use the chamber to confirm that matter is not created or destroyed in a chemical reaction.

Your Goal To design and build a closed chamber in which sugar can be broken down

Your structure must
● be made of materials that are approved by your teacher
● be built to specifications agreed upon by the class
● be a closed system so the masses of the reactants and products can be measured
● be built following the safety guidelines in Appendix A

Plan It! Before you design your reaction chamber, find out how sugar can be broken down. Next, brainstorm with classmates to determine the safety features of your chamber. Then choose materials for your structure and sketch your design. When your teacher has approved your design, build and test your structure.

Chapter 2 **L ◆ 45**

Launching the Project

Identify the problem by having students name reactants and products in a familiar open chemical reaction, such as logs burning in a campfire. Explain how you can measure the mass of the logs and ashes but not the mass of the oxygen that combined with the logs nor the carbon dioxide and water vapor that were released in the reaction. Tell students that in this project, they will design a closed reaction chamber to contain the reactants and products of burning sugar.

Performance Assessment

The Chapter Project Scoring Rubric will help you evaluate how well students complete the Chapter Project. You may want to share the scoring rubric with your students so they will know what is expected. Students will be assessed on
● the effectiveness of their reaction chambers in containing chemical reactions
● the accuracy with which they performed the chemical reactions and interpreted the data
● the thoroughness and organization of their presentations

Students can keep their design plans and revisions as well as their presentation notes in their portfolios.

Portfolio

Objectives

After this lesson, students will be able to
L.2.1.1 State how matter and changes in matter can be described.
L.2.1.2 Explain how you can tell when a chemical reaction occurs.

Target Reading Skill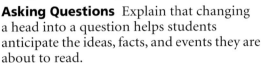

Asking Questions Explain that changing a head into a question helps students anticipate the ideas, facts, and events they are about to read.

Answers

Sample questions and answers: **What are physical properties of matter?** (*Physical properties are characteristics that can be observed without changing one substance into another.*) **What is the evidence for chemical reactions?** (*The evidence for chemical reactions is the formation of new substances and changes in energy.*)

All in One Teaching Resources
• Transparency L16

Preteach

Build Background Knowledge   L2

Changes in Matter

Invite volunteers to name some changes in matter with which they are familiar. Prompt students by suggesting rusting bicycle chains, growing plants, burning candles, melting ice, or other familiar changes. Record students' responses on the board. You may want to leave the responses on the board and refer to them as students work through the section. Tell students that in this section they will read more about changes in matter like the changes listed on the board.

Reading Preview

Key Concepts

• How can matter and changes in matter be described?
• How can you tell when a chemical reaction occurs?

Key Terms

• matter • chemistry
• physical property
• chemical property
• physical change
• chemical reaction • precipitate
• endothermic reaction
• exothermic reaction

Target Reading Skill

Asking Questions Before you read, preview the red headings. In a graphic organizer like the one below, ask a *what* or *how* question for each heading. As you read, write the answers to your questions.

Properties and Changes of Matter

Question	Answer
What are physical properties of matter?	Physical properties are . . .

Lab zone Discover Activity

What Happens When Chemicals React?

1. Put on your safety goggles. Place 2 small spoonfuls of baking soda into a clear plastic cup.
2. Holding the cup over a large bowl or sink, add about 125 mL of vinegar. Swirl the cup gently.
3. Look at the material in the cup. What changes do you see? Feel the outside of the cup. What do you notice about the temperature?
4. Carefully fan the air above the liquid toward you. What do you smell?

Think It Over
Observing What changes did you detect using your senses of smell and touch?

Picture yourself toasting marshmallows over a campfire. You see the burning logs change from a hard solid to a soft pile of ash. You hear popping and hissing sounds from the fire as the wood burns. You smell smoke. You feel the heat on your skin. Finally, you taste the results. The crisp brown surface of the toasted marshmallow tastes quite different from the soft white surface of a marshmallow just out of its bag. Firewood, skin, and marshmallows are all examples of matter. **Matter** is anything that has mass and takes up space. The study of matter and how matter changes is called **chemistry.**

Chemical change can ▶ lead to a treat.

Lab zone Discover Activity

Skills Focus Observing   L1

Materials safety goggles, spoon, baking soda, clear plastic cup, white vinegar, large bowl or sink

Time 10 minutes

Tips Demonstrate how to fan the air above the liquid in order to smell it. Tell students not to taste the mixture.

Expected Outcome The mixture will fizz, the contents of the cup will become cooler, and the vinegar smell will disappear.

Think It Over Students may say that they could hear the mixture fizzing, feel the cup become cooler, and no longer smell vinegar.

Properties and Changes of Matter

Part of studying matter is describing it. When you describe matter, you explain its characteristics, or properties, and how it changes. **Matter can be described in terms of two kinds of properties—physical properties and chemical properties. Changes in matter can be described in terms of physical changes and chemical changes.**

Properties of Matter A **physical property** is a characteristic of a substance that can be observed without changing the substance into another substance. The temperature at which a solid melts is a physical property. For example, ice melts at a temperature of zero degrees Celsius. Color, hardness, texture, shine, and flexibility are some other physical properties of matter. The ability of a substance to dissolve in water and how well it conducts heat and electricity are examples of still more physical properties of matter.

A **chemical property** is a characteristic of a substance that describes its ability to change into other substances. To observe the chemical properties of a substance, you must change it to another substance. For example, when magnesium burns, it combines with oxygen in the air, forming a new substance called magnesium oxide. People who make objects out of magnesium must be careful because the metal can catch fire. Burning is only one type of chemical property. Other examples of chemical properties are tarnishing and rusting.

FIGURE 1
Properties of Water
This geyser gives off hot water and water vapor, which condenses into a visible cloud in the cold air. The temperatures at which water boils and freezes are physical properties of water.
Predicting *How will the snow change when spring arrives?*

Chemical Properties of Water
• Made of hydrogen atoms and oxygen atoms in a 2 to 1 ratio
• Does not burn
• Reacts with some metals

Physical Properties of Water
• Clear, colorless liquid at room temperature
• Boils at 100°C
• Freezes at 0°C

L ◆ 47

Differentiated Instruction

English Learners/Beginning Comprehension: Prior Knowledge L1
Describe examples of physical and chemical changes with which students are likely to be familiar. For example, say that breaking a raw egg yolk with a fork is a physical change, whereas cooking the egg yolk until it is hard is a chemical change. **learning modality: verbal**

English Learners/Intermediate Vocabulary: Writing L2 Have students write the section's key terms in sentences. Tell them to base their sentences on the information in the boldface sentences and sentences in which boldface terms appear. Show them how by doing the first key term with them. **learning modality: verbal**

Instruct

Properties and Changes of Matter

Teach Key Concepts L2
Physical and Chemical Properties

Focus Introduce physical and chemical properties of matter.

Teach Have students read the boldface sentences and the sentences defining physical property and chemical property. Then, on the board list some physical properties, such as color and heat conductivity, and some chemical properties, such as chemical make-up and reactivity. Point out the examples of physical and chemical properties of water in Figure 1. Ask: **Is the freezing point of water a physical or chemical property?** (*Physical property*) **Is the ability of water to rust some metals a physical or chemical property?** (*Chemical property*)

Extend Explain that physical properties of matter depend on chemical properties. For example, the boiling point of water depends on the chemical make-up of water molecules and the attraction of water molecules for each other. **learning modality: verbal**

Independent Practice L2

All in One Teaching Resources
• Guided Reading and Study Worksheet: *Observing Chemical Change*

◉ **Student Edition on Audio CD**

Monitor Progress L2

Oral Presentation Name some properties of matter, and call on students to state whether they are physical or chemical properties.

Answer
Figure 1 When spring arrives, the snow will melt and become liquid water.

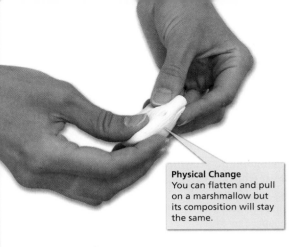

48 ◆ L

Address Misconceptions   L1

Changes of State

Focus Students may think that certain physical changes of state are chemical changes, not physical changes, because the changes appear to be so significant.

Teach Identify some physical changes involving a change of state, such as solid iron changing to molten iron and liquid water changing to water vapor. Explain that the physical changes can be reversed to return the substances to their original state.

Apply Ask: **How can molten iron be returned to a solid state?** *(It can be cooled.)* **learning modality: verbal**

Lab zone Teacher **Demo**

Demonstrating Differences in Compounds   L1

Materials 2 small pieces of dark fabric, hydrogen peroxide, water, plastic dropper

Time 10 minutes

Focus State that some chemical changes result in the same elements combining in different ways to make new compounds with dissimilar properties.

Teach Explain that both water and hydrogen peroxide are made of oxygen and hydrogen, but the elements are combined in different ratios: H_2O for water and H_2O_2 for hydrogen peroxide. Show students the two pieces of fabric. On one, place a few drops of water. On the other, place a few drops of hydrogen peroxide. After 30 minutes, ask students to observe each piece of fabric. Ask: **What evidence is there that hydrogen peroxide and water are different compounds?** *(They have different properties: hydrogen peroxide bleaches fabric, water does not.)*

Apply Challenge students to identify differences between other compounds with the same elements in different proportions, such as carbon monoxide (CO) and carbon dioxide (CO_2). **learning modality: visual**

Physical Change
You can flatten and pull on a marshmallow but its composition will stay the same.

FIGURE 2
Changes in Matter
Matter can undergo both physical change and chemical change.

Chemical Change
If you toast a marshmallow, the sugars and other substances will cook or burn, producing a crust made of new substances.

Lab zone Skills **Activity**

Classifying

Classify each of the following changes as either a chemical change or a physical change. Explain your reasoning for each case.

- A piece of metal is heated to a high temperature and changes to a liquid.
- When two solutions are poured into the same container, a powdery solid forms and settles to the bottom.
- Water left in a dish overnight has disappeared by the next day.
- A blacksmith hammers a piece of red-hot iron into the shape of a knife blade.

Changes of Matter You probably have seen solid water (ice) change to liquid water. Water is the same substance, whether it is frozen or liquid. Therefore, changing from a solid to a liquid is a physical change. A **physical change** is any change that alters the form or appearance of a substance but that does not make the substance into another substance. You cause a physical change when you squash a marshmallow. The shape of the marshmallow changes but not the taste! It's still made of the same compounds that have the same properties. Other examples of physical changes are bending, crushing, breaking, cutting, and anything else that changes only the shape or form of matter. Braiding your hair is another example of a physical change.

Sometimes when a change occurs in a substance, the substance itself is changed. For example, the brown crust on a toasted marshmallow is the result of sugar changing to different substances in a mixture called caramel. A change in matter that produces one or more new substances is a chemical change, or **chemical reaction.** The burning of gasoline in a car's engine is a chemical change. The new substances formed end up as the car's exhaust.

 Reading Checkpoint **What kind of change occurs when you toast the outside of a marshmallow?**

Lab zone Skills **Activity**

Skills Focus Classifying   L2

Time 10 minutes

Tip Have students read the definitions of physical change and chemical reaction on this page before they begin the activity.

Expected Outcome Students are expected to classify all but the second change as physical, because the changes involve altering only the form of a substance. The second change produces a new substance (the powdery solid), so it should be classified as a chemical change.

Extend Ask students to explain how or if the physical changes could be reversed to return the substances to their original form. **learning modality: verbal**

Bonding and Chemical Change Chemical changes occur when bonds break and new bonds form. As a result, new substances are produced. In Chapter 1, you read that atoms form bonds when they share or transfer electrons. The reaction pictured in Figure 3 involves both the breaking of shared bonds and a transfer of electrons.

Oxygen gas (O_2) in the air consists of molecules made of two oxygen atoms that share electrons. These bonds are broken when oxygen reacts with magnesium metal (Mg). Each magnesium atom transfers two of its electrons to an oxygen atom. The oxygen atom becomes a negative ion, and the magnesium atom becomes a positive ion.

You can probably guess what happens next. From Chapter 1, you may recall that oppositely charged ions attract. An ionic bond forms between the Mg^{2+} ions and the O^{2-} ions. The ionic compound magnesium oxide (MgO) is produced, and energy is released. Magnesium oxide—a white, crumbly powder—has properties that differ from those of either shiny magnesium or oxygen gas. For example, while magnesium melts at about 650°C, it takes temperatures of more than 2,800°C to melt magnesium oxide!

For: Links on chemical changes
Visit: www.SciLinks.org
Web Code: scn-1221

FIGURE 3
Bonding and Chemical Change
As magnesium burns, bonds between atoms break and new bonds form. The reaction gives off energy. **Interpreting Diagrams** *Why does the oxygen ion have a 2– charge?*

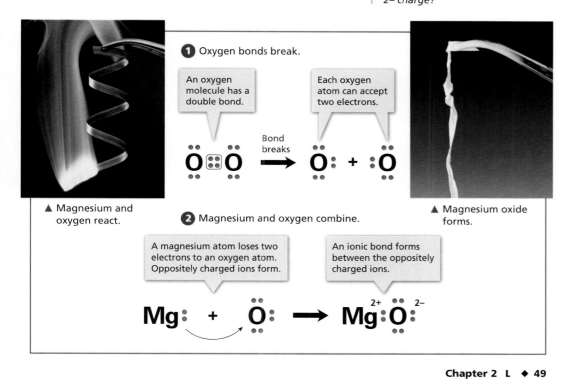

① Oxygen bonds break.

An oxygen molecule has a double bond.

Each oxygen atom can accept two electrons.

Bond breaks

▲ Magnesium and oxygen react.

② Magnesium and oxygen combine.

A magnesium atom loses two electrons to an oxygen atom. Oppositely charged ions form.

An ionic bond forms between the oppositely charged ions.

▲ Magnesium oxide forms.

Chapter 2 L ◆ 49

Differentiated Instruction

Less Proficient Readers L1
Relating Text and Figures Have students use Figure 3 to help them understand how oxygen and magnesium bond. As they read this page, tell them to find diagrams or pictures in the figure that illustrate what they are reading. **learning modality: visual**

Gifted and Talented L3
Inferring Point out that the formation of magnesium oxide in Figure 3 releases energy. Challenge students to use what they know about covalent and ionic bonds to explain why energy is released in this chemical reaction. **learning modality: logical/mathematical**

For: Links on chemical changes
Visit: www.SciLinks.org
Web Code: scn-1221

Download a worksheet that will guide students' review of Internet sources on chemical changes.

Use Visuals: Figure 3 L2
Bonding and Chemical Change

Focus Use Figure 3 to illustrate how bonds break and new bonds form in a chemical change.

Teach Point out that a chemical change occurs when bonds form between atoms or when bonds break and new bonds form. Call students' attention to Figure 3. Ask: **What chemical change is shown in the figure?** *(Burning of magnesium)* **What bonds break in this chemical change?** *(Covalent bonds between oxygen atoms in oxygen molecules)* **What new bonds form?** *(Ionic bonds between magnesium ions and oxygen ions)*

Apply Explain that iron combines with oxygen in a similar way as magnesium, except the reaction with iron is much slower. Ask: **What new substance do you think is produced when iron and oxygen combine?** *(Iron oxide, or rust)* **learning modality: visual**

All in One Teaching Resources
• Transparency L17

Monitor Progress L2

Writing Have students explain how physical and chemical changes differ.

Answers
Figure 3 The oxygen ion has a 2– charge because it gains two electrons from magnesium.

Reading Checkpoint When you toast the outside of a marshmallow, a chemical change occurs.

L ● 49

Evidence for Chemical Reactions

Teach Key Concepts   L2
Observable Chemical Changes

Focus Introduce the two main types of observable chemical change, and have students apply the concepts to the reaction between magnesium and oxygen.

Teach Read the boldface sentence on this page. On the board, list the two main types of observable chemical change: Formation of New Substances, Changes in Energy. State that these two types of change provide evidence that chemical reactions have occurred.

Apply Remind students of the chemical reaction between magnesium and oxygen, shown in Figure 3. Ask: **What new substance was formed in that reaction?** *(Magnesium oxide)* **What change in energy could be observed?** *(The flame produced when magnesium burned provides evidence that energy was released.)* **learning modality: verbal**

Use Visuals: Figure 4   L2
Evidence for Chemical Reactions

Focus Guide students in identifying evidence for chemical change in Figure 4.

Teach Have students look at the figure and read the caption and labels. Ask: **What evidence is there in a green leaf that chemical reactions in the leaf produce chlorophyll?** *(The leaf turns a darker shade of green.)* **Besides changes in color, what are some other clues, based on the figure, that a chemical change has occurred?** *(Sample answer: Formation of a precipitate, changes in texture, production of gas bubbles)*

Apply Challenge students to think of other examples of observable chemical change. *(Sample answer: A colored fabric fading in the sunlight, leaves turning red in the fall, a hard raw potato becoming soft and fluffy when it is baked)* **learning modality: visual**

Evidence for Chemical Reactions

Look at the photograph on pages 44–45. Even without reading the caption, you probably could guess it shows a chemical reaction. But how do you know? How can you tell when a chemical reaction occurs? **Chemical reactions involve two main kinds of changes that you can observe—formation of new substances and changes in energy.**

Changes in Properties One way to detect chemical reactions is to observe changes in the properties of the materials involved. Changes in properties result when new substances form. What kinds of changes should you look for? Look at Figure 4. First, a color change may signal that a new substance has formed. Second, a solid may appear when two solutions are mixed. A solid that forms from solution during a chemical reaction is called a **precipitate** (pree SIP uh tayt).

FIGURE 4
Evidence for Chemical Reactions

Many kinds of change provide evidence that a chemical reaction has occurred. **Applying Concepts** *What other evidence might tell you a chemical reaction has occurred?*

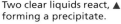

Two clear liquids react, ▲ forming a precipitate.

◄ The light green leaves of early spring slowly turn darker as chemical reactions in the leaves produce more of the green compound chlorophyll.

Third, a gas might be produced from solids or liquids. If the reaction occurs in a liquid, you may see the gas as bubbles. Finally, other kinds of observable changes in properties can also signal a chemical reaction. For example, moist bread dough forms a dry, porous solid after baking.

Although you may observe a property change in matter, the change does not always indicate that a chemical reaction has taken place. Sometimes physical changes give similar results. For example, when water boils, the gas bubbles you see are made of molecules of water, just as the original liquid was. The sign of a chemical reaction is that one or more new substances are produced. For example, when an electric current is passed through water during electrolysis, two gases are produced, hydrogen gas (H_2) and oxygen gas (O_2).

 Reading Checkpoint How is a precipitate evidence for a chemical reaction?

Lab zone **Try This Activity**

Mostly Cloudy

1. Put on your safety goggles and apron.
2. Pour about 5 mL of limewater into a plastic cup.
3. Pour an equal amount of plain water into another plastic cup.
4. Add about 5 mL of carbonated water to each of the cups.

Drawing Conclusions In which cup do you think a chemical reaction occurred? What evidence supports your conclusion?

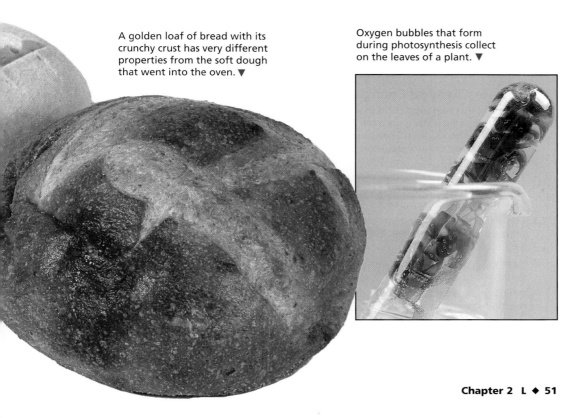

A golden loaf of bread with its crunchy crust has very different properties from the soft dough that went into the oven. ▼

Oxygen bubbles that form during photosynthesis collect on the leaves of a plant. ▼

Chapter 2 L ◆ **51**

Lab zone **Teacher Demo**

Observing Chemical Changes

Materials photochromatic eyeglasses

Time 5 minutes

Focus Demonstrate how photochromatic eyeglasses darken due to chemical changes that occur when they are exposed to sunlight.

Teach Show students the glasses before they have been exposed to sunlight. Then, place the glasses in bright natural light and have students observe as the lenses darken. Explain that tiny crystals of silver chloride and copper chloride are embedded in the glass. The silver chloride bonds break when bright light strikes them, and the chlorine and silver ions become chlorine and silver atoms. The presence of ordinary silver in the glass causes it to darken. When the light is no longer bright, copper ions convert the chlorine back to chloride ions and silver chloride ionic compounds form again. Demonstrate by removing the glasses from bright light and letting them lighten again.

Apply Ask: **When the glasses darken, what new substances are formed?** *(Chlorine and silver atoms)* **How do you know the new substances have formed?** *(The presence of silver atoms causes the glass to darken.)* **learning modality: visual**

Lab zone **Try This Activity**

Skills Focus Drawing conclusions

Materials safety goggles, lab apron, limewater, 2 plastic cups, tap water, carbonated water

Time 10 minutes

Tips To make limewater, dissolve solid lime (calcium hydroxide, available at garden centers) in water until no more solid will dissolve. Filter the solution.

CAUTION: *Wear safety goggles and lab apron.*

Expected Outcome A chemical reaction occurs in the limewater cup. The evidence is a white precipitate (calcium carbonate).

Extend Ask: **How do you know that a reaction did not occur in the cup of tap water?** *(There is no evidence of a reaction in the tap water.)* **learning modality: logical/mathematical**

Monitor Progress

Oral Presentation Call on students to state types of evidence for chemical reactions. Call on other students to describe examples of each type.

Answers

Figure 4 Other evidence might include changes in properties such as heat conductivity or reactivity.

Reading Checkpoint A precipitate is evidence for a chemical reaction because it shows that a new substance has formed.

Help Students Read
Build Vocabulary: Word/Part Analysis

Write the terms *endothermic* and *exothermic* on the board. Draw vertical lines to divide each word into its prefix and root. Explain that *endo-* means "in" and that *exo-* means "out." State that *-thermic* refers to heat. Ask: **Based on the meanings of the word parts, what does endothermic mean?** *(Sample answer: Heat in)* **What does exothermic mean?** *(Sample answer: Heat out)* Explain that an endothermic reaction is a reaction in which heat or other energy is absorbed, and an exothermic reaction is a reaction in which heat or other energy is released.

Math — Analyzing Data

Math Skill Interpreting graphs

Focus Guide students in analyzing temperature data to determine whether a reaction is endothermic or exothermic.

Teach Have students read the problem and study the graph. Remind them of the meanings of *endothermic* and *exothermic*. Check that students understand how the graph relates to the experiment by asking: **What does time zero on the graph represent?** *(The time at which the two substances were placed together in the flask and began to react)*

Answers
1. At 4 minutes, the temperature in the flask was about 23°C. The first time the temperature was 6°C was at about 7 minutes.

2. 20°C

3. The reaction was endothermic, because it absorbed thermal energy from the reaction mixture, causing the temperature to drop.

4. The reaction stopped at about 2°C. You can tell because that is the lowest temperature reached.

5. If the temperature increased instead, the reaction would be exothermic, because an exothermic reaction is one in which energy is released.

All in One Teaching Resources
• Transparency L18

FIGURE 5
An Endothermic Reaction
Energy must be added continuously to fry an egg. *Making Generalizations In terms of energy, what kind of reaction usually occurs when food is cooked?*

Energy can change egg whites from a clear liquid into a white solid.

Math — Analyzing Data

Energy in Chemical Changes
A student places two substances in a flask and measures the temperature once per minute while the substances react. The student plots the time and temperature data and creates the graph at right.

1. **Reading Graphs** What was the temperature in the flask at 4 minutes? When was the first time the temperature was 6°C?

2. **Calculating** How many degrees did the temperature drop between 2 minutes and 5 minutes?

3. **Interpreting Data** Is the reaction endothermic or exothermic? Explain.

4. **Inferring** At what temperature did the reaction stop? How can you tell?

5. **Drawing Conclusions** Suppose the temperature in the flask increased instead of decreased as the reaction occurred. In terms of energy, what kind of reaction would it be? Explain.

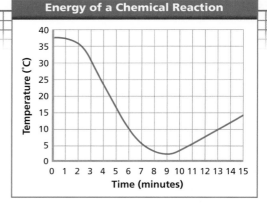

Energy of a Chemical Reaction

(Graph: Temperature (°C) on y-axis from 0 to 40, Time (minutes) on x-axis from 0 to 15)

Changes in Energy From your everyday experience, you know about various types of energy, such as heat, light, and electricity. As matter changes, it can either absorb or release energy. A change in energy occurs during a chemical reaction. Some reactions absorb energy, while others release energy. One common indication that energy has been absorbed or released is a change in temperature.

If you did the Discover activity, you observed that the mixture became colder. When baking soda (sodium bicarbonate) reacts with vinegar, the reaction takes heat from the solution, making it feel cooler. This kind of reaction is an example of an endothermic reaction. An **endothermic reaction** (en doh THUR mik) is a reaction in which energy is absorbed. However, endothermic reactions do not always result in a decrease in temperature. Many endothermic reactions occur only when heat is constantly added. For example, the reactions that occur when you fry an egg are endothermic.

FIGURE 6
An Exothermic Reaction
Enough energy is released by the burning of airplane fuel to keep a plane moving fast enough to fly.

In contrast, the reaction between fuel and oxygen in an airplane engine releases energy, mostly in the form of heat. The heat causes gases in the engine to expand. The expansion and movement of the gases out of the plane exerts a force that moves the plane forward. A reaction that releases energy in the form of heat is called an **exothermic reaction** (ek soh THUR mik). You will learn more about energy and chemical changes in Section 3.

 Reading Checkpoint What is an endothermic reaction?

Section 1 Assessment

Target Reading Skill Asking Questions Use the answers to questions you wrote about the headings to help you answer the questions below.

Reviewing Key Concepts

1. a. Explaining What is the difference between the physical properties and the chemical properties of a substance?
   b. Posing Questions When silver coins are found in ancient shipwrecks, they are coated with a black crust. What question could you ask to help you decide whether the silver underwent a chemical change or a physical change? Explain.
   c. Making Generalizations In terms of chemical bonds and electrons, what kinds of changes occur between atoms when substances undergo chemical reactions?

2. a. Listing What are five kinds of evidence you can use to determine if a chemical reaction has occurred?
   b. Interpreting Photographs How do the properties of the cooked egg shown in Figure 5 differ from the properties of a raw egg?
   c. Comparing and Contrasting How are endothermic and exothermic reactions the same? How are they different?

Writing in Science

Persuasive Letter Imagine you have a pen pal who is studying chemistry just like you are. Your pen pal claims the change from liquid water to water vapor is a chemical change. Write a brief letter that might convince your pen pal otherwise.

Chapter 2 L ◆ 53

 Lab zone Chapter **Project**

Keep Students on Track Guide students in developing a design in which a tin can is capped with the top half of a plastic bottle that has the same circumference as the can. Remind students to make an airtight seal between the can and bottle. They can check by blowing into the top of the bottle and listening for escaping air.

Writing in Science

Writing Mode Persuasion
Scoring Rubric
4 Exceeds criteria; letter is detailed and convincing
3 Meets criteria
2 Letter is too brief and/or contains some errors
1 Letter includes a very brief description and/or contains serious errors

---

Where's the Evidence?

Prepare for Inquiry

Key Concept
There is often visible evidence that a chemical reaction has taken place. Students will observe different types of evidence of chemical reactions.

Skills Objective
After this lab, students will be able to
- observe evidence of chemical reactions
- predict how substances will react when they are mixed
- draw conclusions about whether chemical reactions have occurred

Prep Time 60 minutes

Class Time 40 minutes

Advance Planning
- Prepare copper sulfate solution by dissolving 25 g of $CuSO_4 \cdot 5H_2O$ in 1 L of water.
- Prepare sodium carbonate solution by dissolving 13 g of $Na_2CO_3 \cdot H_2O$ in 1 L of water.
- Prepare 1.0 *M* HCl solution by carefully adding 83 mL of concentrated HCl into enough water to make 1,000 mL of solution. **CAUTION:** *Always add acid to water, never the other way around.* Pour the dilute HCl into individual dropper bottles for student use.

Safety

Caution students not to mix or burn any materials except as directed in the procedure. Fire safety should be reviewed before students perform Part 2. Instruct students how to safely light the candle. Review the safety guidelines in Appendix A.

All in One Teaching Resources
- Lab Worksheet: *Where's the Evidence?*

Guide Inquiry

Invitation
Review the difference between a physical change and a chemical change. Ask students to list observations they might make that a chemical change has occurred.

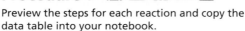

Where's the Evidence?

Problem
What are some signs that a chemical reaction has taken place?

Skills Focus
observing, predicting, drawing conclusions

Materials
- 4 small plastic cups
- birthday candles
- 2 plastic spoons
- sugar
- tongs
- clay
- matches
- sodium carbonate (powdered solid)
- graduated cylinder, 10 mL
- aluminum foil, about 10-cm square
- dilute hydrochloric acid in a dropper bottle
- copper sulfate solution
- sodium carbonate solution

Procedure
Preview the steps for each reaction and copy the data table into your notebook.

PART 1
1. Put a pea-sized pile of sodium carbonate into a clean plastic cup. Record in the data table the appearance of the sodium carbonate.
2. Observe a dropper containing hydrochloric acid. Record the appearance of the acid. **CAUTION:** *Hydrochloric acid can burn you or anything else it touches. Wash spills immediately with water.*
3. Make a prediction about how you think the acid and the sodium carbonate will react when mixed. Record your prediction.
4. Add about 10 drops of hydrochloric acid to the sodium carbonate. Swirl to mix the contents of the cup. Record your observations.

PART 2
5. Fold up the sides of the aluminum foil square to make a small tray.
6. Use a plastic spoon to place a pea-sized pile of sugar into the tray.
7. Carefully describe the appearance of the sugar in your data table.

Data Table				
Reaction	Observations Before Reaction	Predictions	Observations During Reaction	Observations After Reaction
1. Sodium carbonate (powder) + hydrochloric acid				
2. Sugar + heat				
3. Copper sulfate + sodium carbonate solutions				

Introduce the Procedure
Have students read through the procedure, and answer any questions. Tell them they will be observing three different reactions and concluding from their observations whether or not the reactions are chemical changes. Stress the importance of carefully making and recording observations.

Expected Outcome
In Part 1, sodium carbonate and hydrochloric acid react to produce carbon dioxide gas. In Part 2, sugar melts and then decomposes into pure carbon and water vapor. In Part 3, the solutions of copper sulfate and sodium carbonate react to produce copper carbonate (a green precipitate).

8. Secure a small candle on your desktop in a lump of clay. Carefully light the candle with a match only after being instructed to do so by your teacher. **CAUTION:** *Tie back long hair and loose clothing.*

9. Predict what you think will happen if you heat the sugar. Record your prediction.

10. Use tongs to hold the aluminum tray. Heat the sugar slowly by moving the tray gently back and forth over the flame. Make observations while the sugar is heating.

11. When you think there is no longer a chemical reaction occurring, blow out the candle.

12. Allow the tray to cool for a few seconds and set it down on your desk. Record your observations of the material left in the tray.

PART 3

13. Put about 2 mL of copper sulfate solution in one cup. **CAUTION:** *Copper sulfate is poisonous and can stain your skin and clothes. Do not touch it or get it in your mouth.* Put an equal amount of sodium carbonate solution in another cup. Record the appearance of both liquids.

14. Write a prediction of what you think will happen when the two solutions are mixed.

15. Combine the two solutions and record your observations. **CAUTION:** *Dispose of the solutions as directed by your teacher.*

16. Wash your hands when you have finished working.

Analyze and Conclude

1. **Predicting** How do the results of each reaction compare with your predictions?

2. **Observing** How did you know when the reaction in Part 1 was over?

3. **Interpreting Data** What was the evidence of a chemical reaction in Part 1? In Part 2?

4. **Drawing Conclusions** Was the reaction in Part 2 endothermic or exothermic? Explain.

5. **Observing** Was the product of the reaction in Part 3 a solid, a liquid, or a gas? How do you know?

6. **Drawing Conclusions** How do you know if new substances were formed in each reaction?

7. **Communicating** Make a table or chart briefly describing each chemical change in this lab, followed by the evidence for the chemical change.

More to Explore

Use your observation skills to find evidence of chemical reactions involving foods in your kitchen. Look for production of gases, color changes, and formation of precipitates. Share your findings with your classmates.

Analyze and Conclude

1. Accept all well-explained, logical answers relating predictions to observations.

2. Students may suggest that there was no more bubbling or vapor.

3. The evidence in Part 1 was the production of gas bubbles. The evidence in Part 2 was the production of a black, crusty solid.

4. The reaction was endothermic, because heat energy from the candle was needed to make it occur.

5. The product of the reaction in Part 3 was a solid. You know because a visible, green precipitate was produced.

6. You know that new substances were formed because properties such as color and solubility changed in the reactions.

7. Students' charts or tables should describe their observations for the three reactions and interpret the observations to determine evidence of chemical change.

Extend Inquiry

More to Explore Sample answers: An egg white changes color and texture as the egg is fried. Meat changes color as it is cooked. A cake rises as gas is released inside during baking.

Troubleshooting the Experiment

- In Part 1, students will probably refer to the bubbles as air bubbles. Remind them that not all gases are air and bubbles may be caused by other gases.

- In Part 2, students must pay close attention so they do not miss the melting of the sugar before the chemical reaction begins. They will probably say that "smoke" is produced. It is actually water vapor produced by the decomposition of the sugar. The solid product is pure carbon.

- In Part 3, the green color of the copper carbonate precipitate may be difficult to see in the blue copper sulfate solution. Point it out to students if they do not see it.

Objectives
After this lesson, students will be able to
L.2.2.1 Identify what information a chemical equation contains.
L.2.2.2 State the principle of conservation of mass.
L.2.2.3 Explain what a balanced chemical equation must show.
L.2.2.4 Name three categories of chemical reactions.

Target Reading Skill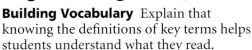
Building Vocabulary Explain that knowing the definitions of key terms helps students understand what they read.

Answers
Sample sentences: A **chemical equation** is a short, easy way to show a chemical reaction. A substance you have at the beginning of a reaction is a **reactant.** A new substance produced in a reaction is a **product.** **Conservation of mass** means that during a chemical reaction, matter is not created or destroyed. In an **open system,** matter can enter from or escape to the surroundings. In a **closed system,** matter is not allowed to enter or leave. A **coefficient** is a number in a chemical equation telling you how many atoms or molecules of a reactant or product take part in the reaction. **Synthesis** means combining two or more elements or compounds to make a more complex substance. **Decomposition** means breaking down compounds into simpler products. **Replacement** is the process in which one element replaces another in a compound or two elements in different compounds trade places.

Preteach

Build Background Knowledge L2
Identifying and Using Symbols
Ask: **What symbols did you observe on your way to school today?** *(Sample answer: Stop sign, green light, house number)* Tell students they will learn in this section how symbols are used to describe chemical reactions.

Reading Preview
Key Concepts
- What information does a chemical equation contain?
- What does the principle of conservation of mass state?
- What must a balanced chemical equation show?
- What are three categories of chemical reactions?

Key Terms
- chemical equation
- reactant • product
- conservation of mass
- open system • closed system
- coefficient • synthesis
- decomposition • replacement

 Target Reading Skill
Building Vocabulary Using a word in a sentence helps you think about how best to explain the word. After you read the section, reread the paragraphs that contain definitions of Key Terms. Use all of the information you have learned to write a meaningful sentence using each Key Term.

Lab zone Discover **Activity**

Do You Lose Anything?
1. Place about two dozen coins on a table. Sort them into stacks of pennies, nickels, dimes, and quarters.
2. Count and record the number of coins in each stack. Calculate and record the value of each stack and the total of all stacks combined.
3. Mix all the coins together and then divide them randomly into four unsorted stacks.
4. Again calculate the value of each stack and the total amount of money. Count the total number of each type of coin.
5. Repeat Steps 3 and 4.

Think It Over
Making Models What happened to the total value and types of coins when you rearranged them? Did rearranging the coins change the properties of any coin? If you think of the coins as each representing a different type of atom, what does this model tell you about chemical reactions?

You look at your cellular phone display and read the message "U wan2 gt pza 2nite?" You reply "No. MaB TPM. CUL8R." These messages are short for saying "Do you want to get some pizza tonight?" and "No. Maybe tomorrow afternoon (PM). See you later."

Cellular phone messages use symbols and abbreviations to express ideas in shorter form. A type of shorthand is used in chemistry too. "Hydrogen molecules react with oxygen molecules to form water molecules" is a lengthy way to describe the reaction between hydrogen and oxygen. And writing it is slow. Instead, chemists often use chemical equations in place of words.

◄ **A message on a cellular display**

Lab zone Discover **Activity**

Skills Focus Making models L1
Materials 24 coins including pennies, nickels, dimes, and quarters
Time 10 minutes
Tip Suggest that students use data tables to record their counts for each trial.
Expected Outcome The total value and types of coins do not change. Rearranging

the coins does not change the properties of any coin.

Think It Over Students may infer that, like the total number and types of coins in the activity, the total numbers and types of atoms do not change during chemical reactions.

What Are Chemical Equations?

A **chemical equation** is a short, easy way to show a chemical reaction, using symbols instead of words. Although chemical equations are shorter than sentences, they contain more information. **Chemical equations use chemical formulas and other symbols instead of words to summarize a reaction.**

Formulas in an Equation All chemical equations use formulas to represent the substances involved in a reaction. Recall from Chapter 1 that a chemical formula is a combination of symbols that represents the elements in a compound. For example, CO_2 is the formula for carbon dioxide. The formula tells you that this compound is made up of the elements carbon and oxygen and each molecule has 1 carbon atom and 2 oxygen atoms. Figure 7 lists formulas of other compounds that may be familiar to you.

Structure of an Equation All chemical equations have a common structure. A chemical equation tells you the substances you start with in a reaction and the substances you get at the end. The substances you have at the beginning are called the **reactants.** When the reaction is complete, you have new substances called the **products**.

The formulas for the reactants are written on the left, followed by an arrow. You read the arrow as "yields." The formulas for the products are written on the right. When there are two or more reactants, they are separated by plus signs. In a similar way, plus signs are used to separate two or more products. Below is the general plan for a chemical equation.

Reactant + Reactant ⟶ Product + Product

The number of reactants and products can vary. Some reactions have only one reactant or product. Other reactions have two, three, or more reactants or products. In Figure 8, you can see the equation for a reaction that occurs when limestone ($CaCO_3$) is heated. Count the number of reactants and products, and familiarize yourself with the parts of the equation.

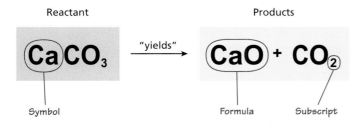

Reactant   Products

Symbol   Formula   Subscript

FIGURE 7
The formula of a compound identifies the elements in the compound and the ratios in which their atoms are present.

Formulas of Familiar Compounds	
Compound	**Formula**
Water	H_2O
Carbon dioxide	CO_2
Propane	C_3H_8
Sugar (sucrose)	$C_{12}H_{22}O_{11}$
Rubbing alcohol	C_3H_8O
Ammonia	NH_3
Sodium chloride	$NaCl$
Baking soda	$NaHCO_3$

FIGURE 8
A Chemical Equation
Like a building, a chemical equation has a basic structure.
Interpreting Diagrams *What does the subscript 3 in the formula for calcium carbonate tell you?*

Chapter 2 L ◆ 57

Differentiated Instruction

English Learners/Beginning Comprehension: Modified Cloze [L1]
Make a simple paragraph summarizing this page. Leave important words blank, and make a list of omitted terms. Show students how to fill in the first blank, and then have them fill in the rest of the blanks. **learning modality: verbal**

English Learners/Intermediate Comprehension: Modified Cloze [L2] Give students the same paragraph, but include some incorrect choices in the list of omitted terms. Demonstrate how to fill in a blank before instructing students to fill in the remaining blanks. **learning modality: verbal**

Instruct

What Are Chemical Equations?

Teach Key Concepts [L2]
Chemical Equations

Focus Read the definition of chemical equation.

Teach On the board, write the general plan for all chemical equations:
Reactant + Reactant → Product + Product
Tell students that reactants and products are written as chemical formulas and the arrow is read as "yields." Say that the number of reactants and products can vary.

Apply Ask students to read the chemical equation in Figure 8. *(Heating calcium carbonate yields calcium oxide and carbon dioxide.)* **learning modality: verbal**

All in One Teaching Resources
• Transparency L19

Address Misconceptions
Formulas and Equations

Focus Students may think that chemical formulas and chemical equations are the same, because *formula* and *equation* are sometimes used interchangeably in other subjects.

Teach Explain the terms as they are used in chemistry: A chemical formula describes a compound, and a chemical equation describes a reaction.

Apply On the board, write: $ZnSO_4$. Also write $Zn + H_2SO_4 \rightarrow ZnSO_4 + H_2$. Ask: **Which one is a formula?** *($ZnSO_4$)* **What does the equation say?** *(Zinc and sulfuric acid react to yield zinc sulfate and hydrogen.)* **learning modality: verbal**

Independent Practice [L2]
All in One Teaching Resources
• Guided Reading and Study Worksheet: *Describing Chemical Reactions*

Student Edition on Audio CD

Monitor Progress [L2]

Writing Have students write the general plan for a chemical equation.

Answer
Figure 8 That each molecule of calcium carbonate contains three oxygen atoms

L ● 57

Conservation of Mass

Teach Key Concepts
Conservation of Mass

Focus Use Figure 9 to illustrate the principle of conservation of mass.

Teach Read the sentence that states the principle of conservation of mass. Have students look at Figure 9 and read the caption. Point out the chemical formula at the top of the figure and the numbers on the three scales. Tell students to assume that scale units are grams. Ask: **What are the reactants in the reaction, and what are their masses?** *(Iron, 14.0 g, and sulfur, 8.0 g)* **What is the product of the reaction, and what is its mass?** *(Iron sulfide, 22.0 g)*

Apply Ask: **How does the reaction in the figure illustrate the conservation of mass?** *(The total mass of the reactants equals the mass of the product. Therefore, mass is conserved.)* **learning modality: visual**

Build Inquiry

Measuring Reactants and Products

Materials self-sealing plastic bag, baking soda, 10 mL vinegar, small spoon, plastic cup, balance, safety goggles

Time 10 minutes

Focus Tell students they will measure reactants and products in a chemical reaction to determine whether mass is conserved.

Teach Have students put on safety goggles, place a spoonful of baking soda in the bag, and use the balance to find the mass of the baking soda and bag. Then, have students find the mass of the empty cup, add 10 mL of vinegar to the cup, find the mass of the cup and vinegar together, and subtract the cup's mass to find the mass of the vinegar. Ask: **If you add vinegar to the soda in the bag, what should the mass of the product equal?** *(The sum of the masses of the bag, soda, and vinegar)* Tell students to pour the vinegar into the bag and quickly zip the bag closed. After the contents of the bag mix, have students find the total mass and compare it with their predictions.

Apply Ask: **If the measured mass is less than the predicted mass, what might explain the differences?** *(Some of the gas produced in the reaction may have escaped from the bag before it was closed.)* **learning modality: kinesthetic**

$$Fe + S \xrightarrow{\;\;} FeS$$

Iron Sulfur Iron Sulfide

FIGURE 9
Conservation of Mass
Mass is conserved in chemical reactions.

Lab zone Try This **Activity**

Still There

1. Measure the mass of a collection of bolts, each with a nut attached to it.
2. Remove all the nuts from the bolts. Measure the total mass of the nuts. Then do the same with the bolts. Add these values.
3. Rearrange your collection, putting two or three nuts on one bolt, one nut on another bolt, and so on. You can even leave a few pieces unattached.
4. Measure the total mass again. Compare this figure with the totals from Steps 1 and 2.

Making Models How does your activity model the idea of conservation of mass?

Conservation of Mass

Look closely at the values for mass in Figure 9. Iron and sulfur can react to form iron sulfide. The photograph represents a principle first demonstrated by the French chemist Antoine Lavoisier in 1774. This principle is called **conservation of mass,** and it states that during a chemical reaction, matter is not created or destroyed. All the atoms present at the start of the reaction are present at the end.

Modeling Conservation of Mass Think about what happens when classes change at your school during the day. A class is made of a group of students and a teacher together in a room. When the bell rings, people from each class move from room to room, ending up in different classes. The number of people in the school has not changed. But their arrangement has.

Now imagine that all the students and teachers are atoms, each class is a molecule, and the changing of classes is a chemical reaction. At the end of the reaction, the same atoms are present, but they are grouped together differently. The amount of matter does not change. **The principle of conservation of mass states that in a chemical reaction, the total mass of the reactants must equal the total mass of the products.**

Open and Closed Systems At first glance, some reactions may seem to violate the principle of conservation of mass. It's not always easy to measure all the matter involved in a reaction. For example, if you burn a match, oxygen comes from the surrounding air. But how much? Likewise, the products escape into the air. Again, how much?

Lab zone Try This **Activity**

Skills Focus Making models

Materials several nuts and bolts, balance

Time 15 minutes

Tips Remind students of the principle of conservation of mass. Tell them they will model the principle in this activity.

Expected Outcome The total mass of nuts and bolts is the same, regardless of arrangement. This is how the activity models conservation of mass.

Extend Have students use nuts and bolts to model the reaction Fe + S → FeS. Students can use bolts for iron atoms, nuts for sulfur atoms, and combined nuts and bolts for iron sulfide. **learning modality: kinesthetic**

A burning match is an example of an open system. In an **open system**, matter can enter from or escape to the surroundings. The burned out fire in Figure 10 is another example of an open system. If you want to measure all the matter before and after a reaction, you have to be able to contain it. In a **closed system**, matter is not allowed to enter or leave. The pear decaying under glass in Figure 10 is a closed system. So is a chemical reaction inside a sealed plastic bag.

 Reading Checkpoint What is a closed system?

FIGURE 10
Open and Closed System
A wood fire is an open system because gases escape into the air. A pear in a glass dome is a closed system because the reactants and products are contained inside the dome.
Problem Solving *What masses would you need to measure before and after a wood fire to show conservation of mass?*

Open System
Except for the ash, products of the wood fire have escaped up the chimney or into the room.

Closed System
The total mass of the pear and the substances produced during its decay are contained by the glass dome.

Fresh pear   Decayed pear

Chapter 2 L ◆ 59

Use Visuals: Figure 10   L2
Open and Closed Systems

Focus Use the illustrations in Figure 10 to help students visualize differences between open and closed systems.

Teach Have students read the caption and labels in Figure 10. Ask: **What reaction takes place in the closed system in the figure?** *(Decay of a pear)* **What prevents matter from entering or leaving the closed system?** *(The dome over the plate)* **How would you expect the mass of the closed system at the end of the reaction to compare with the mass of the same system at the start of the reaction? Why?** *(You would expect the mass of the closed system to be the same after the reaction as it was at the start, because no matter can enter or leave the system.)* **What reaction takes place in the open system in the figure?** *(Burning of wood)* **What are the reactants in this reaction?** *(Wood and oxygen)* **Where does the oxygen come from?** *(The air in the room)* **What are the products in this reaction?** *(Ashes and gases such as carbon dioxide)* **Where do the gaseous products go?** *(Up the chimney and into the air in the room)*

Apply Ask: **Can you measure all the reactants and products in the open system?** *(No; you can measure the wood and ashes, but not the oxygen, carbon dioxide, and other gases.)* **learning modality: visual**

Monitor Progress _____ L2

Skills Check Have students compare and contrast open and closed systems in terms of their characteristics and how they affect the measurement of reactants and products.

Answers
Figure 10 Before the fire, you would need to measure the masses of the reactants, wood and oxygen. After the fire, you would need to measure the masses of the products, ashes, carbon dioxide, and other gases.

Reading Checkpoint A closed system is one in which matter is not allowed to enter or leave.

Balancing Chemical Equations

Teach Key Concepts L2
Conservation of Mass and Balanced Equations

Focus Explain why chemical equations must be balanced, and show students how to balance a sample equation.

Teach Have students read the boldface sentence on this page. Explain that the principle of conservation of mass requires that chemical equations balance. Write the following equation on the board: $H_2 + O_2 \rightarrow H_2O$. Ask: **How many hydrogen atoms are there on each side of this equation?** *(Two)* **How many oxygen atoms are there on each side of the equation?** *(Two on the reactant side, one on the product side)* **Is the equation balanced? Why or why not?** *(No, because there are unequal numbers of oxygen atoms on the two sides)* Show students how to balance the equation by writing the coefficient 2 in front of H_2 on the reactant side and the coefficient 2 in front of H_2O on the product side. Read the definition of the term *coefficient*. Explain that the coefficients in this equation indicate that two hydrogen molecules are involved in the reaction for each molecule of oxygen and that two molecules of water are produced. Have students again count the number of oxygen atoms on both sides of the equation. Ask: **Is the equation balanced now?** *(Yes)*

Apply Write the following equation on the board, and challenge students to balance it: $Ca + O_2 \rightarrow CaO_2$ *(2 Ca + O$_2$ → 2 CaO$_2$)* **learning modality: logical/mathematical**

All in One Teaching Resources
• Transparency L20

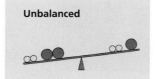

Unbalanced

Balancing Chemical Equations

The principle of conservation of mass means that the same number of atoms exists in the products as in the reactants. **To describe a reaction accurately, a chemical equation must show the same number of each type of atom on both sides of the equation.** Chemists say an equation is balanced when it accurately represents conservation of mass. How can you write a balanced chemical equation?

❶ **Write the Equation** Suppose you want to write a balanced chemical equation for the reaction between hydrogen and oxygen that forms water. To begin, write the correct formulas for both reactants and product.

$$H_2 \quad + \quad O_2 \quad \longrightarrow \quad H_2O$$
Reactants   Products

Place the reactants, H_2 and O_2, on the left side of the arrow, separated by a plus sign. Then write the product, H_2O, on the right side of the arrow.

❷ **Count the Atoms** Count the number of atoms of each element on each side of the equation. You find two atoms of oxygen in the reactants but only one atom of oxygen in the products.

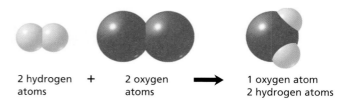

2 hydrogen atoms + 2 oxygen atoms ⟶ 1 oxygen atom / 2 hydrogen atoms

How can you get the number of oxygen atoms on both sides to be the same? You cannot change the formula for water to H_2O_2 because H_2O_2 is the formula for hydrogen peroxide, a completely different compound. So, how can you show that mass is conserved?

❸ **Use Coefficients to Balance Atoms** To balance the equation, use coefficients. A **coefficient** (koh uh FISH unt) is a number placed in front of a chemical formula in an equation. It tells you how many atoms or molecules of a reactant or a product take part in the reaction. If the coefficient is 1, you don't need to write it.

Balance the number of oxygen atoms by writing the coefficient 2 for water. That's like saying "2 × H_2O." Now there are two oxygen atoms—one in each molecule of water.

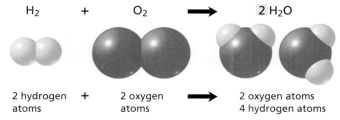

H_2	+	O_2	→	2 H_2O
2 hydrogen atoms	+	2 oxygen atoms	→	2 oxygen atoms 4 hydrogen atoms

Unbalanced

Balancing the oxygen atoms throws off the hydrogen atoms. There are now two hydrogen atoms in the reactants and four in the product. How can you balance the hydrogen? Try doubling the number of hydrogen atoms on the left side of the equation by writing the coefficient 2 for hydrogen.

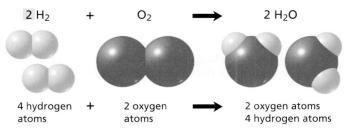

2 H_2	+	O_2	→	2 H_2O
4 hydrogen atoms	+	2 oxygen atoms	→	2 oxygen atoms 4 hydrogen atoms

Balanced

❹ **Look Back and Check** The equation is balanced. It tells you that two molecules of hydrogen react with one molecule of oxygen to yield two molecules of water. Count the atoms in the balanced equation again to see that the equation is correct.

Math Analyzing Data

Balancing Chemical Equations

Magnesium metal (Mg) reacts with oxygen gas (O_2) forming magnesium oxide (MgO). To write a balanced equation for this reaction, first write the equation using the formulas of the reactants and products. Then, count the number of atoms of each element.

1. **Balancing Chemical Equations** Balance the equation for the reaction of sodium metal (Na) with oxygen gas (O_2), forming sodium oxide (Na_2O).
2. **Balancing Chemical Equations** Balance the equation for the reaction of tin (Sn) with chlorine gas (Cl_2), forming tin chloride ($SnCl_2$).

Balancing Equations

❶ Write the Equation
$$Mg + O_2 \longrightarrow MgO$$

❷ Count the Atoms
$$Mg + O_2 \longrightarrow MgO$$
$$1 \quad\quad 2 \quad\quad 1 \ 1$$

❸ Use Coefficients to Balance the Atoms
$$Mg + O_2 \longrightarrow 2\,MgO$$
$$\quad\quad\quad 2 \quad\quad\quad 2$$

$$2\,Mg + O_2 \longrightarrow 2\,MgO$$
$$2 \quad\quad 2 \quad\quad 2\ 2$$

❹ Look Back and Check

Math Skills

Math Skill Formulas and equations

Focus Give students a chance to balance a chemical equation.

Teach Have students read the activity, except for the Practice Problem. Address any questions students may have. Point out that the first step in balancing a chemical equation is counting the numbers of atoms on both sides of the equation to see if they are equal. Tell students to count the atoms first when they do the Practice Problem.

Answers
1. $4\,Na + O_2 \rightarrow 2\,Na_2O$
2. $Sn + Cl_2 \rightarrow SnCl_2$

Use Visuals: *Balancing Atoms* L1

Focus Use the diagrams to help students understand how chemical equations are balanced.

Teach Have students look at the diagram on page 60. Ask: **What does each blue circle represent?** *(One hydrogen atom)* **What does each red circle represent?** *(One oxygen atom).* Have students look at the top diagram on page 61. Ask: **How is the balanced side different from the unbalanced side?** *(The balanced side has two more hydrogen atoms than the unbalanced side, making both sides of the scale the same.)*

Apply Have students draw similar diagrams to illustrate balancing the two equations in the Math Skills activity. **learning modality: visual**

Differentiated Instruction

Special Needs L1
Drawing Formulas and Equations

Suggest to students who have not had algebra or who have difficulty with math that they use drawings to represent chemical formulas and equations. Have students draw atoms and molecules, similar to those on these pages, when they are working with formulas and equations. With drawings, students can actually count atoms and molecules. This will help them understand conservation of mass and also help them balance chemical equations. **learning modality: visual**

Monitor Progress _____ L2

Skills Check Have students balance the equation: $C + F_2 \rightarrow CF_4$ $(C + 2\,F_2 \rightarrow CF_4)$

L ● 61

Help Students Read L1

Predicting Refer to the Content Refresher in this chapter, which provides guidelines for using the predicting strategy.

Before students read this page, review the common meanings of *synthesis, decomposition,* and *replacement.* Then, have students predict what these three types of chemical reactions involve before they read about them in the text. Making predictions about the reactions before they read may improve their reading comprehension. Ask: **What does synthesis mean?** (*Sample answer: Joining together, building up*) **What does decomposition mean?** (*Sample answer: Breaking down, decaying*) **What does replacement mean?** (*Sample answer: Substituting one thing for another*) Point out that some chemical reactions are synthesis reactions, some are decomposition reactions, and others are replacement reactions. Ask: **What do you think a synthesis reaction involves?** (*Atoms of elements joining together to form compounds*) **What do you think a decomposition reaction involves?** (*Compounds breaking down into atoms or simple compounds*) **What do you think a replacement reaction involves?** (*Atoms of one element replacing atoms of another element in a compound*)

Classifying Chemical Reactions

Teach Key Concepts L2
Categories of Chemical Reactions

Focus Read the boldface sentence to introduce the three categories of chemical reactions.

Teach Have students read the definition of each category in the text. Then, write the following chemical equations on the board:
1. $2 H_2O_2 \rightarrow 2 H_2O + O_2$
2. $2 H_2 + O_2 \rightarrow 2 H_2O$
3. $FeS + 2 HCl \rightarrow FeCl_2 + H_2S$
Ask: **Which category of reaction does each equation represent?** (*1. decomposition, 2. synthesis, 3. replacement*)

Apply Challenge students to identify the category of the reactions listed in the Math Practice in the Section Assessment. (*4. replacement, 5. synthesis*) **learning modality: visual**

All in One Teaching Resources
• Transparency L21

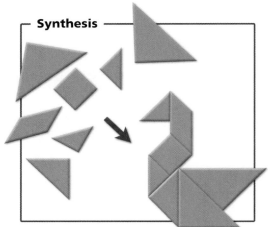
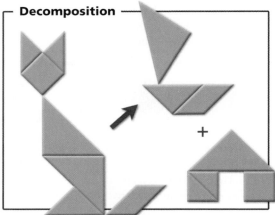

FIGURE 11
Types of Reactions
Three categories of chemical reactions are synthesis, decomposition, and replacement. **Making Models** *How do these different geometric shapes act as models for elements and compounds in reactions?*

Classifying Chemical Reactions

Substances may combine to make a more complex substance. They may break apart to make simpler substances. Or, they may even exchange parts. In each case, new substances form. **Many chemical reactions can be classified in one of three categories: synthesis, decomposition, or replacement.**

Synthesis Have you ever listened to music from a synthesizer? You can hear many different notes and types of sounds combined to make music. To synthesize is to put things together. In chemistry, when two or more elements or compounds combine to make a more complex substance, the process is called **synthesis** (SIN thuh sis). The reaction of hydrogen and oxygen to make water is a synthesis reaction.

Decomposition In contrast to a synthesis reaction, a process called **decomposition** breaks down compounds into simpler products. You may have a bottle of hydrogen peroxide (H_2O_2) in your house to clean cuts. If you keep such a bottle for a very long time, you'll have water instead. The hydrogen peroxide decomposes into water and oxygen gas.

$$2 H_2O_2 \longrightarrow 2 H_2O + O_2$$

Replacement When one element replaces another in a compound, or when two elements in different compounds trade places, the process is called **replacement.** Look at this example:

$$2 Cu_2O + C \longrightarrow 4 Cu + CO_2$$

Copper metal can be obtained by heating copper oxide with carbon. The carbon takes the place of copper.

Differentiated Instruction

Less Proficient Readers L1
Previewing Visuals Before students read about classifying chemical reactions, have them preview Figure 11. Tell them to read the caption and then to compare and contrast the three drawings. Call on students to explain how the drawings differ.

Then, have students answer the caption question. If necessary, explain that the individual shapes represent atoms and the combined shapes represent compounds. Point out how the arrows and plus signs are used to show chemical reactions involving the shapes. **learning modality: visual**

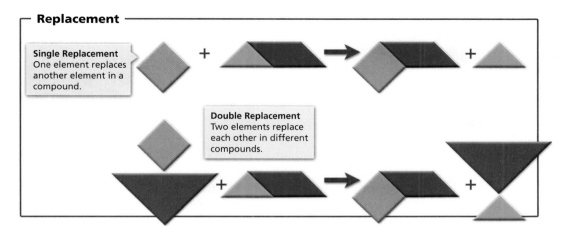

Replacement

Single Replacement One element replaces another element in a compound.

Double Replacement Two elements replace each other in different compounds.

The reaction between copper oxide and carbon is called a *single* replacement reaction because one element, carbon, replaces another element, copper, in the compound. In a *double* replacement reaction, elements in one compound appear to "trade places" with elements in another compound. The following reaction is an example of a double replacement:

$$FeS + 2\ HCl \longrightarrow FeCl_2 + H_2S$$

Use Figure 11 to help you track what happens to elements in different types of chemical reactions.

Section 2 Assessment

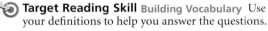 **Target Reading Skill** Building Vocabulary Use your definitions to help you answer the questions.

Reviewing Key Concepts

1. a. Identifying What do the formulas, arrow, and plus signs in a chemical equation tell you?
   b. Comparing and Contrasting How are reactants and products treated the same in a chemical reaction? How are they treated differently?
2. a. Summarizing In your own words, state the meaning of the principle of conservation of mass.
   b. Applying Concepts If the total mass of the products of a reaction is 250 g, what was the total mass of the reactants?

3. a. Reviewing What are three types of chemical reactions?
   b. Inferring What is the smallest possible number of products in a decomposition reaction?
   c. Classifying Classify the following reaction:
   $$P_4O_{10} + 6\ H_2O \longrightarrow 4\ H_3PO_4$$

Math Practice

Balance the following equations:

4. $Fe_2O_3 + C \longrightarrow Fe + CO_2$

5. $SO_2 + O_2 \longrightarrow SO_3$

Math Practice

Math Skill Formulas and equations

Answers
4. $2\ Fe_2O_3 + 3\ C \rightarrow 4\ Fe + 3\ CO_2$
5. $2\ SO_2 + O_2 \rightarrow 2\ SO_3$

Lab zone Chapter Project

Keep Students on Track Check that students' reaction chambers have been tested for leaks before they begin the chemical reaction. Remind students to carefully measure and record both reactants and products when they burn sugar in their reaction chambers.

Technology and Society

Air Bags

Key Concept
Air bags save lives by protecting people in collisions, but they can pose a serious danger for children and small adults.

Build Background Knowledge

Experience With Air Bags
Ask if anyone has ever been in a collision in which an air bag deployed. If they have, urge them to describe to the class what happened. Otherwise, have students look at the inflated air bag in the van in the picture. Ask: **What would have happened to the dummy's head if the air bag had not deployed?** (*It would have hit the steering wheel.*)

Introduce the Debate
After students have read about air bags in the feature, point out that air bags can be dangerous as well as protect people from death or injury in a crash. Explain that the bags inflate so rapidly and with such force that a child or small adult sitting too close to the air bag may be injured as much by the bag as by the collision itself. State that the potential danger of air bags is the major reason why there is debate over their use.

Facilitate the Debate
- Have students research and answer the Weigh the Impact questions.
- After students have finished their research and answers, divide the class into two groups. Arbitrarily assign one group to argue that air bags should be required in all cars because they do more good than harm. Assign the other group to argue the opposite position.
- Give members of each group a chance to meet and discuss the issue. Each group should prepare a statement of their views and a list of supporting evidence. Groups should also elect one of their members to present the group's views in the debate.
- Provide class time for the debate. Give each group a chance to present its views. Also give each group time to rebut the views of the other group.
- After the debate, take a vote to see where the class stands on the issue and whether the debate changed students' minds about air bags.

AIR BAG & SEAT BELT SAFETY CAMPAIGN

Air Bags

What moves faster than 300 km/h, inflates in less than a second, and saves lives? An air bag, of course! When a moving car is suddenly stopped in a crash, objects inside the car keep moving forward. Death or serious injury can result when passengers hit the hard parts of the car's interior. Air bags, working with seat belts, can slow or stop a person's forward motion in a crash.

How Do Air Bags Increase Safety?
Before front air bags became a requirement in the 1990s, seat belts were the only restraints for passengers in cars. Seat belts do a great job of keeping people from flying forward in a crash, but even with seat belts, some movement takes place. Air bags were designed as a second form of protection. They provide a buffer zone between a person and the steering wheel, dashboard, or windshield.

$$2\ NaN_3 \longrightarrow 2\ Na + 3\ N_2$$

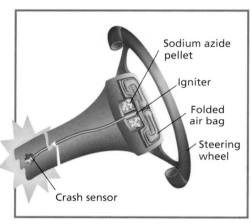

Collision Detected
The crash sensor is located toward the front of the car. The sensor detects an impact and sends a signal to the air bag igniter to start the chemical reaction.

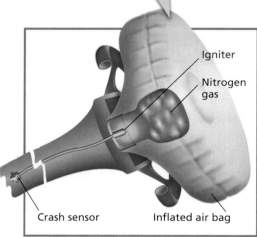

Air Bag Inflates
Pellets of a compound called sodium azide (NaN_3) are heated, causing a rapid decomposition reaction. This reaction releases sodium metal (Na) and nitrogen gas (N_2), which inflate the air bag in about 30 milliseconds.

Background

History of Science Air bags were invented in 1968 by Allen Breed. They were first used in 1973, when Ford and General Motors installed them in some government vehicles. In 1975, auto makers began offering air bags to the public as an option on some of their cars. In 1988, Chrysler became the first company to offer air bags as standard equipment on their vehicles.

Within a few years, dozens of people, mostly children, had been killed by air bags. Child deaths rose as passenger-side air bags became more common. By 1997, only 57% of consumers considered air bags an important factor in deciding on a car, down from 82% the year before. By then, auto makers started developing "smart" air bags that they hoped would be less dangerous.

During a crash test, the air bag should inflate upon impact.

Cushion or Curse?

Air bags save hundreds of lives each year. However, if your body is too close to the air bag when it inflates, the impact of the expanding bag may do more harm than good. Since 1990, more than 200 people, including 140 children, have been killed by air bags inflating close to them. Air bags are designed for adults but pose a risk to smaller, lightweight adults and children. That is why children should never ride in a front seat. They are safer in the back seat without air bags than in the front seat with air bags.

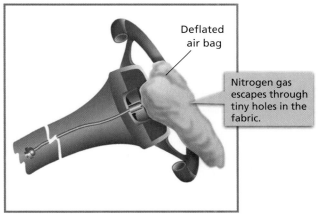

Deflated air bag

Nitrogen gas escapes through tiny holes in the fabric.

Air Bag Deflates
Tiny holes in the fabric of the air bag allow some of the nitrogen gas to escape, so the bag starts to deflate by the time a person makes contact with it. In this way, the air bag provides a deflating cushion that slows forward movement.

▲ Car manufacturers must test their vehicles to verify that they meet minimum government safety standards. New cars are required to have air bags on both the driver and passenger sides.

Weigh the Impact

1. Identify the Need
Air bags are called supplemental restraint systems. Why is it so important to restrain people in a collision?

2. Research
Use the Internet to learn how air bags are being changed, added, and redesigned to improve their safety and effectiveness.

3. Write
Choose one type of new air bag technology and summarize it in a few short paragraphs.

Go Online
PHSchool.com

For: More on air bags
Visit: PHSchool.com
Web Code: cgh-2020

Chapter 2 L ◆ 65

Weigh the Impact

1. It is important to restrain people in a collision because death or serious injury can result when passengers hit the hard parts of the car's interior during a collision.

2. Students may learn that front air bags have been added to the passenger side of many cars and that some cars also have side air bags, which help protect people in rollovers. In addition, students may learn that air bags are being improved to make them sensitive to the size and/or mass of riders. This should make air bags safer for children and small adults.

3. Possible types of new air bag technology students might write about include scales in seats, dashboard ultrasound units, electrical field systems, and seat sensors that read tags attached to infant safety seats. Students' paragraphs might summarize how the technology works, its stage of development, how well it protects people from injury, and any drawbacks of the technology.

For: More on air bags
Visit: PHSchool.com
Web Code: cgh-2020

Students can research air bags online.

Extend

Point out the equation for the chemical reaction that occurs inside an airbag. Have students identify the reactant and products and the type of reaction that occurs. Ask them to explain what causes the air bag to inflate.

Background

Facts and Figures Car makers are trying to make "smart" air bags that can take into account the passenger's size and/or mass when they deploy. One technology for "smart" air bags uses a scale in the seat to weigh the occupant. It directs the air bag to deploy only if the occupant is above a certain weight. Another technology uses an ultrasound unit on the dashboard. The unit produces high frequency sounds and reads the echoes to determine the size of the occupant of the seat. An electrical field system uses antennas in the car seat to create a weak electrical field. This system can determine the occupant's size and mass.

Section
3
Controlling Chemical Reactions

Objectives

After this lesson, students will be able to

L.2.3.1 Explain how activation energy is related to chemical reactions.

L.2.3.2 Identify factors that affect the rate of a chemical reaction.

Target Reading Skill

Relating Cause and Effect Explain that cause is the reason for what happens. The effect is what happens because of the cause. Relating cause and effect helps students relate the reasons for what happens to what happens as a result.

Answers

Students' graphic organizers should show that the factors that can cause an increased rate of reaction include increase in surface area, increase in temperature, increase in concentration of reactants, and use of a catalyst.

All in One Teaching Resources

• Transparency L22

Preteach

Build Background Knowledge   L2

Slowing Down Reactions

Ask: **Why do we keep some foods in a refrigerator?** *(To keep them from spoiling)* As you ask how refrigeration helps prevent food from spoiling, lead students to infer that low temperatures slow down the rate of decomposition reactions that spoil food. Tell students that in this section they will learn how temperature and other factors slow down or speed up chemical reactions.

Reading Preview

Key Concepts

• How is activation energy related to chemical reactions?

• What factors affect the rate of a chemical reaction?

Key Terms

• activation energy
• concentration • catalyst
• enzyme • inhibitor

Target Reading Skill

Relating Cause and Effect As you read, identify the factors that can cause the rate of a chemical reaction to increase. Write the information in a graphic organizer like the one below.

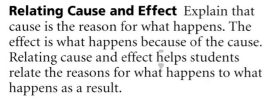

Causes

| Increase in surface area |

Effect

Increased rate of reaction

Lab zone Discover **Activity**

Can You Speed Up or Slow Down a Reaction?

1. Put on your safety goggles and lab apron.

2. Obtain three 125-mL solutions of vitamin C and water—one at room temperature, one at about 75°C, and one chilled to between 5°C and 10°C.

3. Add 3 drops of iodine solution to each container and stir each with a clean spoon. Compare changes you observe in the solutions.

4. Clean up your work area and wash your hands.

Think It Over

Inferring What conclusion can you make about the effect of temperature on the reaction of iodine and vitamin C?

With a splintering crash, a bolt of lightning strikes a tree in the forest. The lightning splits the tree and sets fire to the leaves on the ground below it. The leaves are dry and crisp from drought. The crackling fire burns a black patch in the leaves. The flames leap to nearby dry twigs and branches on the ground. Soon, the forest underbrush is blazing, and the barks of trees start burning. Miles away in an observation tower, a ranger spots the fire and calls in the alarm—"Forest fire!"

Forest fires don't just happen. Many factors contribute to them—lightning and drought to name just two. But, in general, wood does not always burn easily. Yet, once wood does begin to burn, it gives off a steady supply of heat and light. Why is it so hard to start and maintain some chemical reactions?

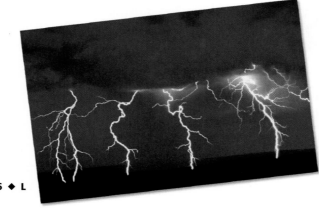

◀ Lightning can supply enough energy to ignite a forest fire.

Lab zone Discover **Activity**

Skills Focus Inferring   L1

Materials safety goggles, lab apron, 125 mL vitamin C solution at three temperatures, iodine, 3 clear plastic cups, spoon

Time 10 minutes

Tips Prepare vitamin C solution by adding 1 crushed vitamin C tablet to every 480 mL of water. Each group will need 125 mL of solution at each temperature. Chill one third of the total solution in an ice bath and heat one third in a beaker on a hot plate to 75°C. Caution students that iodine can stain skin and clothing.

Expected Outcome Vitamin C reacts with iodine and turns it colorless.

Think It Over At higher temperatures, vitamin C and iodine react faster.

FIGURE 12
Modeling Activation Energy
The rock at the top of this hill cannot roll down the hill until a small push gets it going.
Making Models How is this cartoon a kind of model for the role of activation energy in a chemical reaction?

Energy and Reactions

To understand why it can be hard to start some chemical reactions, look at Figure 12. The rock at the top of the hill can fall over the cliff, releasing energy when it crashes into the rocks at the bottom. Yet it remains motionless until it's pushed over the small hump.

Activation Energy Every chemical reaction is like that rock. A reaction won't begin until the reactants have enough energy to push them "over the hump." The energy is used to break the chemical bonds of the reactants. Then, the atoms begin to form the new chemical bonds of the products. The **activation energy** is the minimum amount of energy needed to start a chemical reaction. **All chemical reactions need a certain amount of activation energy to get started.**

Consider the reaction in which hydrogen and oxygen form water. This reaction gives off a large amount of energy. But if you just mix the two gases together, they can remain unchanged for years. For the reaction to start, a tiny amount of activation energy is needed—even just an electric spark. Once a few molecules of hydrogen and oxygen react, the rest will quickly follow because the first few reactions provide activation energy for more molecules to react. Overall, the reaction releases more energy than it uses. Recall from Section 1 that this type of reaction is described as exothermic.

 Reading Checkpoint What is the function of a spark in a reaction between hydrogen gas and oxygen gas?

DISCOVERY CHANNEL SCHOOL

Chemical Reactions

Video Preview
▶ Video Field Trip
Video Assessment

Differentiated Instruction

Gifted and Talented L3
Modeling Activation Energy Challenge students to think of a way they could use dominoes to model the role of activation energy in a chemical reaction. Encourage them to share their ideas with the class.
learning modality: kinesthetic

Less Proficient Readers L1
Previewing Visuals Have students look at the figures and read the captions before they read the section. This will give them an overview of what they are about to read and help them place it in context. This may improve their reading comprehension.
learning modality: visual

Energy and Reactions

Teach Key Concepts L2
Activation Energy

Focus State that all chemical reactions need a certain amount of energy to get started.

Teach Point out that reactions that release energy, and those that require energy, need activation energy. Use the example of hydrogen and oxygen, which combine to produce water and energy. Ask: **In terms of energy, what type of reaction is this?** *(Exothermic)* Explain that the reaction will not begin without activation energy.

Apply Say that a spark can provide enough energy for a few molecules of hydrogen and oxygen to react. Ask: **What provides the energy for the other molecules to react?** *(Energy released by the reaction of the first few molecules)* **learning modality: verbal**

All in One Teaching Resources
• Transparency L23

Chemical Reactions

Show the Video Field Trip to give students a chance to see energy-producing chemical reactions. Discussion question: **What chemical reaction takes place inside fireworks?** *(Powder containing potassium nitrate burns quickly and produces gas.)*

Independent Practice L2
All in One Teaching Resources
• Guided Reading and Study Worksheet: *Controlling Chemical Reactions*

⊙ **Student Edition on Audio CD**

Monitor Progress L2
Answers
Figure 12 By showing that a certain amount of initial energy is needed to start the rock falling over the hill

 Reading Checkpoint To start the reaction

Classifying Chemical Reactions

Time 5 minutes

Focus Have students classify chemical reactions as endothermic or exothermic.

Teach Review the difference between endothermic and exothermic reactions. Then, name several chemical reactions, and have students decide whether they are endothermic or exothermic. Ask: **Is the baking of bread an endothermic or exothermic reaction?** *(Endothermic)* **The burning of wood?** *(Exothermic)* **The mixing of baking soda and vinegar?** *(Endothermic)* **The rusting of iron?** *(Exothermic)*

Apply Ask: **What endothermic and exothermic reactions have you used today?** *(For an endothermic reaction, students might say that they cooked food. For an exothermic reaction, they might say that they burned fuel while traveling to school by car or bus.)*
learning modality: verbal

Use Visuals: Figure 13

Energy Changes in Chemical Reactions

Focus Have students compare and contrast the graphs in Figure 13 for a better understanding of energy changes in exothermic and endothermic reactions.

Teach Tell students to read the caption and look at the graphs in Figure 13. Ask: **How are the two graphs the same?** *(Both graphs plot energy against time for chemical reactions. In both graphs, the reaction begins when energy rises to a peak, the activation energy, which is about the same for both reactions.)* **How are the two graphs different?** *(The graph on the left is for an exothermic reaction, and the graph on the right is for an endothermic reaction. In the exothermic reaction, heat is released, and the products have less energy than the reactants. In the endothermic reaction, heat is absorbed, and the products have more energy than the reactants.)*

Apply Ask: **If the energy level for the exothermic reaction had started out as low as the energy level for the endothermic reaction, would the activation energy also be lower? Why?** *(No, because the activation energy is the minimum amount of energy required to start the reaction)* **learning modality: visual**

Exothermic and Endothermic Reactions Every chemical reaction needs activation energy to get started. Whether or not a reaction needs still more energy from the environment to keep going depends on if it is exothermic or endothermic.

Exothermic reactions follow the pattern you can see in the first diagram in Figure 13. The dotted line marks the energy of the reactants before the reaction begins. The peak in the graph shows the activation energy. Notice that at the end of the reaction, the products have less energy than the reactants. This difference results in a release of heat. The burning of fuel, such as wood, natural gas, or oil, is an example of an exothermic reaction. People can make use of the heat that is released to warm their homes and cook food.

Now look at the graph of an endothermic reaction on the right of Figure 13. Endothermic reactions also need activation energy to get started. But, in addition, they need energy to keep going. Notice that the energy of the products is higher than that of the reactants. This difference tells you that the reaction must absorb energy to continue.

When you placed baking soda in vinegar in the Discover activity in Section 1, the thermal energy already present in the solution was enough to start the reaction. The reaction continued by drawing energy from the solution, making the solution feel colder. But most endothermic reactions require a continuous source of heat to occur. For example, baking bread requires added heat until the baking process is completed.

 Reading Checkpoint **In what type of reaction do the reactants have less energy than the products?**

FIGURE 13
Energy Changes in Chemical Reactions
Both exothermic and endothermic reactions need energy to get started. **Reading Graphs** *What does the peak in the curve in each graph represent?*

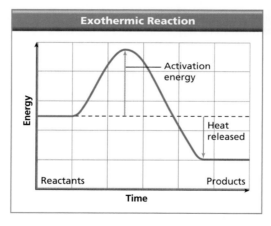

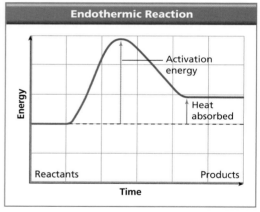

All in One Teaching Resources

• Transparency L24

Rates of Chemical Reactions

Chemical reactions don't all occur at the same rate. Some, like explosions, are very fast. Others, like the rusting of metal, are much slower. Also, a particular reaction can occur at different rates depending on the conditions.

If you want to make a chemical reaction happen faster, you need to get more reactant particles together more often and with more energy. To slow down a reaction, you need to do the opposite. **Chemists can control rates of reactions by changing factors such as surface area, temperature, and concentration, and by using substances called catalysts and inhibitors.**

Surface Area Look at Figure 14. The wreckage used to be a grain elevator. It exploded when grain dust ignited in the air above the stored grain. Although the grain itself doesn't react violently in air, the grain dust can. This difference is related to surface area. When a chunk of solid substance reacts with a liquid or gas, only the particles on the surface of the solid come into contact with the other reactant. But if you break the solid into smaller pieces, more particles are exposed and the reaction happens faster. Sometimes, speeding up a reaction this way is dangerous. Other times, increasing surface area can be useful. For example, chewing your food breaks it into smaller pieces that your body can digest more easily and quickly.

FIGURE 14
Surface Area and Reaction Rate
Grain dust reacts explosively with oxygen. Minimizing grain dust in a grain elevator can help prevent an accident like the one shown here.

Chapter 2 L ◆ 69

Lab zone Skills **Activity**

Interpreting Data

1. Measure the length and width of a face of a gelatin cube.
2. Calculate the area of that face of the cube.
   Area = length × width
3. Repeat for each of the other five faces. Then add the six values to get the total surface area.
4. Using a plastic knife, cut the cube in half. Add the surface areas of the two pieces to get a new total.

5. How did the original total surface area compare with the total area after the cube was cut?
6. Predict the total surface area if you cut each cube in two again. If you have time, test your prediction.

L ● 69

Affect of Temperature on Chemical Reactions

Materials two antacid tablets, two plastic cups, cold tap water, hot tap water

Time 10 minutes

Focus Give students a chance to observe how increasing temperature speeds up a reaction.

Teach Divide the class into small groups. Give each group two antacid tablets and two plastic cups. Have groups fill one cup with cold tap water and the other cup with hot tap water. Ask: **Do you think the antacid will react faster in hot water or cold water?** *(Sample answer: Hot water)* Have students drop a tablet into each cup of water and observe what happens. Ask: **How did the two reactions differ?** *(The antacid reacted faster in the cup of hot water.)*

Apply Ask: **Why did the reaction occur faster in the hot water?** *(Sample answer: The greater temperature gave the particles more energy to move rapidly and come into contact with other particles, as well as more energy to get over the activation energy "hump.")*
learning modality: visual

Integrating Life Science L2

Remind students that a catalyst is a material that increases the rate of a reaction by lowering the activation energy. Point out that the human body has thousands of different catalysts, called enzymes, and each one affects just one kind of chemical reaction. Tell students that human body temperature is normally around 37°C. Ask: **How might our normal body temperature be related to our dependence on catalysts?** *(Our body temperature is too low for many chemical reactions to take place without the help of catalysts.)* **learning modality: verbal**

Temperature Another way to increase the rate of a reaction is to increase its temperature. When you heat a substance, its particles move faster. Faster-moving particles increase the reaction rate in two ways. First, the particles come in contact more often, which means there are more chances for a reaction to happen. Second, faster-moving particles have more energy. This increased energy causes more particles of the reactants to get over the activation energy "hump."

In contrast, reducing temperature slows down reaction rates. For example, milk contains bacteria, which carry out thousands of chemical reactions as they live and reproduce. At room temperature, those reactions happen faster and milk spoils more quickly. You store milk and other foods in the refrigerator because keeping foods cold slows down those reactions, so your foods stay fresh longer.

Concentration A third way to increase the rate of a chemical reaction is to increase the concentration of the reactants. **Concentration** is the amount of a substance in a given volume. For example, adding a small spoonful of sugar to a glass of lemonade will make it sweet. But adding a large spoonful of sugar makes the lemonade sweeter. The glass with more sugar has a greater concentration of sugar molecules.

Increasing the concentration of reactants supplies more particles to react. Compare the two reactions of acid and magnesium metal in Figure 15. The test tube on the left has a lower concentration of acid. This reaction is slower than the one on the right, where the acid concentration is higher. You see evidence for the increased rate of reaction in the greater amount of gas bubbles produced.

Reading Checkpoint **Why may an increase in temperature affect the rate of a chemical reaction?**

FIGURE 15
Concentration and Reaction Rate
Bubbles of hydrogren gas form when magnesium reacts with acid.
Relating Cause and Effect *What makes the reaction faster in the test tube on the right?*

70 ◆ **L**

Catalysts Another way to control the rate of a reaction is to change the activation energy needed. A **catalyst** (KAT uh list) is a material that increases the rate of a reaction by lowering the activation energy. Although catalysts affect a reaction's rate, they are not permanently changed by a reaction. For this reason catalysts are not considered reactants.

Many chemical reactions happen at temperatures that would kill living things. Yet, some of these reactions are necessary for life. The cells in your body (as in all living things) contain biological catalysts called **enzymes** (EN zymz). Your body has thousands of different enzymes. Each one is specific—it affects only one chemical reaction.

As shown in Figure 16, enzymes provide a surface on which reactions can take place. By bringing reactant molecules close together, the enzyme lowers the activation energy needed. In this way, enzymes make chemical reactions that are necessary for life happen at a low temperature.

Inhibitors Sometimes a reaction is more useful when it can be slowed down rather than speeded up. A material used to decrease the rate of a reaction is an **inhibitor.** Most inhibitors work by preventing reactants from coming together. Usually they combine with one of the reactants either permanently or temporarily. Inhibitors include preservatives added to food products to prevent them from becoming stale or spoiling.

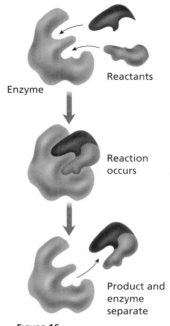

Reactants

Enzyme

Reaction occurs

Product and enzyme separate

FIGURE 16
Enzyme Action
After a reaction, an enzyme molecule is unchanged.

Section 3 Assessment

🎯 **Target Reading Skill** Relating Cause and Effect Use the information in your graphic organizer about speeding up chemical reactions to help you answer Question 2 below.

Reviewing Key Concepts

1. **a.** Defining What is activation energy?
   b. Describing What role does activation energy play in chemical reactions?
   c. Making Generalizations Look at the diagram in Figure 13, and make a generalization about activation energy in exothermic and endothermic reactions.
2. **a.** Identifying What are four ways that chemists can control the rates of chemical reactions?
   b. Applying Concepts Which would react more quickly in a chemical reaction: a single sugar cube or an equal mass of sugar crystals? Explain.

Lab zone **At-Home Activity**

Comparing Reaction Rates Place an iron nail in a plastic cup. Add enough water to almost cover the nail. Place a small piece of fine steel wool in another cup and add the same amount of water. Ask family members to predict what will happen overnight. The next day, examine the nail and steel wool. Compare the amount of rust on each. Were your family's predictions correct? Explain how surface areas affect reaction rates.

All in One Teaching Resources
• Transparency L25

Monitor Progress _____ L2

Answers
Figure 15 A greater concentration of acid makes the reaction faster in the test tube on the right.

✓ **Reading Checkpoint** An increase in temperature may allow particles to have more energy so they are more likely to come into contact with each other and to reach the activation energy level.

Assess

Reviewing Key Concepts

1. a. The minimum amount of energy needed to start a chemical reaction **b.** All chemical reactions need a certain amount of activation energy to get started. **c.** Students might say that both endothermic and exothermic reactions need a similar level of activation energy in order to begin.
2. a. Chemists can control the rates of chemical reactions by changing factors such as surface area, temperature, and concentration, and by using substances called catalysts and inhibitors. **b.** Sugar crystals, because more particles of sugar are exposed than in a sugar cube

Reteach L1
Call on students to define each of the key terms in the section.

Performance Assessment L2
Skills Check Have students draw a graph showing the general relationship between the concentration of reactants and the speed of a chemical reaction.
Students can keep their graphs in their portfolios. **Portfolio**

All in One Teaching Resources
• Section Summary: *Controlling Chemical Reactions*
• Review and Reinforce: *Controlling Chemical Reactions*
• Enrich: *Controlling Chemical Reactions*

Lab zone **At-Home Activity**

Comparing Reaction Rates L2
Students should use a non-galvanized nail. Point out that steel wool is made of iron mixed with carbon. Family members might predict correctly that the steel wool will rust more than the nail. Students are expected to explain that the steel wool has more rust because it has a greater surface area.

Lab zone **Chapter Project**

Keep Students on Track Remind students to interpret their results from the sugar-burning reaction to determine whether the results support the principle of conservation of mass. Tell students to start summarizing their findings and thinking of ways to present their results to the class.

Temperature and Enzyme Activity

Prepare for Inquiry

Key Concept
Temperature affects the rate at which chemical reactions occur. Students will determine the effect of temperature on catalyzed reactions.

Skills Objective
After this lab, students will be able to
- calculate the time it takes for a reaction to occur
- interpret data to determine how temperature affects the rate of a reaction
- draw conclusions about how the activity of a catalyst is affected by temperature

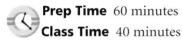 **Prep Time** 60 minutes

Class Time 40 minutes

Advance Planning
- Prepare the catalase solution by placing fresh liver in a blender and blending until soupy. Add twice the volume of distilled water and mix.
- Make about a dozen disks for each group by using a paper punch to make disks of filter paper. Place the disks in the liver solution and stir gently.
- Divide the disks and solution into fourths and place in beakers. Keep one beaker at room temperature. Place one beaker in an ice water ($0°C$) bath, one in a bath of $37°C$ water, and one in a boiling water ($100°C$) bath.
- Prepare the 0.1% hydrogen peroxide solution by adding 500 mL of distilled water to 25 mL of 3% hydrogen peroxide.

Safety
Caution students to be careful around the boiling water bath. You may want to distribute the disks from the boiling water so students do not have to handle hot equipment. Make sure students wash their hands after performing the experiment. Review the safety guidelines in Appendix A.

All in One Teaching Resources
- Lab Worksheet: *Temperature and Enzyme Activity*

Temperature and Enzyme Activity

Problem
Catalase is an enzyme that speeds up the breakdown of hydrogen peroxide into water and oxygen gas. Hydrogen peroxide is a poisonous waste product of reactions in living things. How does temperature affect the action of the enzyme catalase?

Skills Focus
calculating, interpreting data, drawing conclusions

Materials
- forceps
- stopwatch
- test tube with a one-hole stopper
- 0.1% hydrogen peroxide solution
- filter paper disks soaked in liver preparation (catalase enzyme) and kept at four different temperatures (room temperature, 0–4°C, 37°C, and 100°C)
- container to hold water (beaker or bowl)

Procedure
1. Form a hypothesis that predicts how the action of the catalase enzyme will differ at the different temperatures to be tested.

Data Table		
Temperature (°C)	Time (sec)	Average Time for Class (sec)

2. Fill a container with water. Then fill a test tube with 0.1% hydrogen peroxide solution until the test tube is overflowing. Do this over a sink or the container of water.
3. Make a data table similar to the one shown.
4. Moisten the small end of a one-hole stopper with water.
5. Using forceps, remove a filter paper disk soaked in liver preparation (catalase enzyme) that has been kept at room temperature. Stick it to the moistened end of the one-hole stopper.
6. Your partner should be ready with the stopwatch for the next step.
7. Place the stopper firmly into the test tube, hold your thumb over the hole, and quickly invert the test tube. Start the stopwatch. Put the inverted end of the test tube into the container of water, as shown in the photograph, and remove your thumb.

Guide Inquiry

Invitation
Ask: **What happens when you use hydrogen peroxide to clean a cut or scrape?** (*The hydrogen peroxide bubbles.*) Explain that the bubbling is caused by the release of oxygen in a reaction between hydrogen peroxide and catalase. Add that catalase is an enzyme found in many organisms. In humans, it is found in blood.

Introduce the Procedure
Tell students they will measure the rate at which small paper disks soaked with catalase collect oxygen bubbles and float to the top of an inverted test tube of hydrogen peroxide. Have students look at the picture to see how they will hold the inverted test tube.

◄ Catalase from blood reacts with hydrogen peroxide.

8. Observe what happens to the filter paper inside the test tube. Record the time it takes for the disk to rise to the top. If the disk does not rise within 2 minutes, record "no reaction" and go on to Step 9.

9. Rinse the test tube and repeat the procedure with catalase enzyme disks kept at 0°C, 37°C, and 100°C. **CAUTION:** *When you remove the disk kept in the hot water bath, do not use your bare hands. Avoid spilling the hot water.*

Analyze and Conclude

1. Observing What makes the disk float to the top of the inverted test tube?

2. Calculating Calculate the average time for each temperature based on the results of the entire class. Enter the results in your data table.

3. Graphing Make a line graph of the data you collected. Label the horizontal axis (x-axis) "Temperature" with a scale from 0°C to 100°C. Label the vertical axis (y-axis) "Time" with a scale from 0 to 30 seconds. Plot the class average time for each temperature.

4. Interpreting Data What evidence do you have that your hypothesis from Step 1 is either supported or not supported?

5. Interpreting Data How is the time it takes the disk to rise to the top of the inverted tube related to the rate of the reaction?

6. Drawing Conclusions What can you conclude about the activity of the enzyme at the various temperatures you tested? (*Hint:* Enzyme activity is greater when the rate of reaction is faster.)

7. Predicting Make a prediction about how active the enzyme would be at 10°C, 60°C, and 75°C. Give reasons to support your prediction.

8. Communicating A buildup of hydrogen peroxide in living things can damage cells. The normal human body temperature is 37°C. Write a paragraph relating your results to the body's temperature and its need to break down hydrogen peroxide.

Design an Experiment

The activity of an enzyme also depends upon the concentration of the enzyme. Design an experiment that explores the relationship between enzyme activity and enzyme concentration. (Your teacher can give you disks soaked with different enzyme concentrations.) *Obtain your teacher's permission before carrying out your investigation.*

Go Online
PHSchool.com
For: Data sharing
Visit: PHSchool.com
Web Code: cgd-2023

Troubleshooting the Experiment

- Monitor the temperature of the baths. It is important to keep the disks in the warm water close to 37°C to duplicate normal body temperature.
- Remind students that they must invert the test tube quickly and begin timing the rise of the disk immediately after inverting the test tube.

Expected Outcome

The catalase at 37°C is the fastest, followed by room-temperature catalase, and then by catalase at 0°C. At 100°C, there is no reaction.

Analyze and Conclude

1. Oxygen bubbles cling to the disk and cause it to float.

2. Average times should decrease from 0°C through room temperature to 37°C, with no reaction at 100°C.

3. Check that students have correctly labeled both axes and used appropriate scales. Data from the third column of their data table should be plotted in the graph.

4. Answers will vary depending on students' hypotheses. The data will show that the reaction is fastest at 37°C. Students may have predicted that the reaction would occur fastest at the highest temperature, 100°C.

5. A slower reaction rate will result in a longer time for the disk to rise to the top of the inverted tube.

6. Students might conclude that the enzyme shows a little activity at 0°C, more activity at room temperature, the greatest activity at normal body temperature of 37°C, and no activity at 100°C.

7. Students are likely to predict that at 10°C, the enzyme would show more activity than at 0°C but less activity than at room temperature. They might predict that at 60°C the enzyme would show less activity than at body temperature and at 70°C it would show less activity than at 60°C.

8. Catalase is most effective at breaking down hydrogen peroxide at 37°C, which is normal body temperature. As a result, hydrogen peroxide does not build up and damage cells.

Extend Inquiry

Design an Experiment Students can design a procedure, similar to the one in this lab, to test disks treated with varying concentrations of enzyme. The expected outcome is that the activity will be greater for the higher enzyme concentration.

Go Online
PHSchool.com
For: Data sharing
Visit: PHSchool.com
Web Code: cgd-2023

Students can go online to pool and analyze their data with students nationwide.

Objectives

After this lesson, students will be able to
L.2.4.1 List the three things necessary to maintain a fire.
L.2.4.2 Explain why you should know about the causes of fire and how to prevent a fire.

Target Reading Skill

Using Prior Knowledge Explain that using prior knowledge helps students connect what they already know to what they are about to read.

Answers

Samples answers:

What You Know
1. A fire needs fuel to burn.
2. A fire needs oxygen to burn
3. All homes should have smoke detectors.

What You Learned
1. Fire is the result of a combustion reaction.
2. The most deadly fires start with cigarettes.
3. Baking soda can be used to put out small fires.

All in One Teaching Resources

• Transparency L26

Preteach

Build Background Knowledge L2

Experience With Fire
Encourage students to share experiences they may have had involving fire. Ask them to describe the properties of things that burn and things that do not. Call on volunteers to explain how to put out different kinds of fires. Ask: **What fire safety rules have you learned?** (*Students may describe the stop, drop, and roll rule for reacting when clothing is on fire, or they may say that every family should have a fire escape plan for their home.*)

Reading Preview

Key Concepts
• What are the three things necessary to maintain a fire?
• Why should you know about the causes of fire and how to prevent a fire?

Key Terms
• combustion • fuel

Target Reading Skill
Using Prior Knowledge Before you read, write what you know about fire safety in a graphic organizer like the one below. As you read, continue to write in what you learn.

What You Know
1. A fire needs fuel to burn.
2.

What You Learned
1.
2.

Firefighters battle a blaze. ▼

Lab zone · Discover **Activity**

How Does Baking Soda Affect a Fire?

1. Put on your safety goggles.
2. Secure a small candle in a holder or a ball of clay. After instructions from your teacher, use a match to light the candle.
3. Place a beaker next to the candle. Measure 1 large spoonful of baking soda into the beaker. Add about 100 mL of water and stir. Add about 100 mL of vinegar.
4. As soon as the mixture stops foaming, tip the beaker as if you are pouring something out of it onto the flame. **CAUTION:** *Do not pour any liquid on the candle.*
5. Observe what happens to the flame.

Think It Over
Developing Hypotheses The gas produced in the beaker was carbon dioxide, CO_2. Based on the results of this experiment, develop a hypothesis to explain what you observed in Step 5.

The call comes in. Fire! A blaze has been spotted in a warehouse near gasoline storage tanks. Firefighters scramble aboard the ladder truck and the hose truck. Lights flash, sirens blare, and traffic swerves to clear a path for the trucks. The firefighters know from their training that fire is a chemical reaction that can be controlled—but only if they reach it in time.

74 ◆ L

Lab zone · Discover **Activity**

Skills Focus Developing hypotheses L1

Materials safety goggles, small candle, clay or candle holder, match, beaker, large spoon, baking soda, water, vinegar

Time 15 minutes

Tip Show students how to "pour out" the gas from the beaker in Step 4 without pouring out any liquid.

Expected Outcome The carbon dioxide gas produced by the reaction will extinguish the candle flame.

Think It Over Students may say that the carbon dioxide gas produced by the chemical reaction smothered the candle flame by depriving it of oxygen.

Understanding Fire

Fire is the result of **combustion,** a rapid reaction between oxygen and a substance called a fuel. A **fuel** is a material that releases energy when it burns. Common fuels include oil, wood, gasoline, natural gas, and paper. Combustion of these types of fuel always produces carbon dioxide and water. When fuels don't burn completely, products such as smoke and poisonous gases may be produced.

The Fire Triangle Although a combustion reaction is very exothermic and fast, a fire cannot start unless conditions are right. **The following three things are necessary to start and maintain a fire—fuel, oxygen, and heat.**

You probably know that oxygen is one of the gases in air. About 20 percent of the air around you is composed of oxygen gas. If air can reach the fuel, so can oxygen. A large fire can create a strong draft that pulls air toward it. As the air around the flame is heated, it rises rapidly. Cooler air flows toward the fire, replacing the heated air and bringing a fresh supply of oxygen. If you stand in front of a fire in a fireplace, you can feel the air flow toward the fire.

Heat is a part of the fire triangle. Fuel and oxygen can be together, but they won't react until something provides the activation energy to start combustion. This energy can come from a lighted match, an electric spark, or the heat from a stove. Once combustion starts, the heat released supplies more activation energy to keep the reaction going.

Once started, a fire can continue burning as long as all components of the fire triangle are available. Coal in abandoned mines under the town of Centralia, Pennsylvania, started burning in 1962. The coal is still burning. Many old airshafts lead into the tunnels. Because some airshafts cannot be located and sealed, air continues to flow into the mines, supporting the fire. Heat and poisonous gases coming up from the fire through cracks in the ground made living in Centralia difficult. Everyone eventually moved away. No one knows how long this fire will continue to burn.

 Reading Checkpoint What is heat's role in starting a fire?

FIGURE 17
The Fire Triangle
The fire triangle can be controlled in the grill below. If any point of the fire triangle is missing, a fire will not continue.
Applying Concepts How would closing the lower air vents affect the fire?

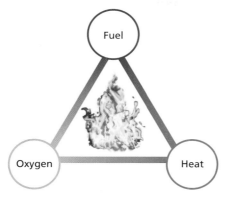

Fuel

Oxygen   Heat

Escaping gases

Heat   Air vent

Air vent   Charcoal fuel

Oxygen in air

Understanding Fire

Teach Key Concepts L2
The Fire Triangle

Focus Use the fire triangle to show students what every fire needs in order to burn.

Teach Draw a large triangle on the board, like the one in Figure 17. Inside the triangle write the word *Fire*. Draw a large circle at each angle of the triangle, as in the figure. Then, ask: **What does every fire need to burn?** (*Fuel, oxygen, and heat*) Write each term in one of the circles as students name it.

Apply Tell the class that if you put a candle inside a glass jar, light the candle, and then cover the jar, the candle will soon go out. Ask: **Why will the candle go out?** (*The candle cannot to continue to burn after the oxygen in the jar is used up.*) **learning modality: visual**

All in One Teaching Resources
• Transparency L27

Independent Practice L2
All in One Teaching Resources
• Guided Reading and Study Worksheet: *Fire and Fire Safety*

💿 **Student Edition on Audio CD**

Monitor Progress _____ L2

Oral Presentation Call on students to name the reactants and products in a combustion reaction involving wood or paper. Call on another student to say whether the reaction is endothermic or exothermic.

Answers
Figure 17 Closing the lower air vents would cause the fire to go out because it would deprive the fire of oxygen.

✓ **Reading Checkpoint** Heat's role in starting a fire is to provide the activation energy needed to begin the combustion reaction.

Differentiated Instruction

**English Learners/Intermediate L1
Comprehension: Use Visuals** Make copies of Figure 17 with the circles blank. Give students copies of the figure, and have them fill in the circles with the missing terms. Tell them to write the terms in their own language as well as in English. Urge them to save the diagram for a study guide. **learning modality: verbal**

**English Learners/Intermediate L2
Comprehension: Use Visuals** Make enlarged copies of Figure 18, and pass them out to students. Have students translate the labels in the figure into their own language. Urge them to use the figure with the translated labels to explain to their families the features of a fire-safe house. **learning modality: verbal**

Home Fire Safety

Teach Key Concepts
Fighting and Preventing Fires

Focus State that controlling fire involves both fighting and preventing fires.

Teach First, review methods for fighting fires. Explain that water is useful for putting out fires involving wood, paper, or other dry fuels. Stress that fires involving electricity or liquids such as oil or gasoline cannot be put out with water but must be put out with carbon dioxide gas or other smothering agent. Ask: **If a fire is growing as you fight it, what should you do?** (*Get away from the fire, and call the fire department*) Then, call students' attention to the fire-safe house in Figure 18. Ask: **What are some ways to prevent fires or to prevent injuries and deaths from fires?** (*Sample answers: Keep matches out of the reach of children. Make sure that flammable items are stored safely away from sources of flames, such as the kitchen stove. Install smoke detectors and safety ladders. Keep fire extinguishers and emergency phone numbers handy.*)

Apply Ask: **Why is it a good idea to keep a box of baking soda near the kitchen stove?** (*Because it can be used to put out small fires*) **learning modality: verbal**

Controlling Fire Use your knowledge of chemical reactions to think of ways to control a fire. What if you remove one part of the fire triangle? For example, you can get the fuel away from the flames. You can also keep oxygen from getting to the fuel. Finally, you can cool the combustion reaction.

How do firefighters usually fight fires? They use hoses to spray huge amounts of water on the flames. Water removes two parts of the fire triangle. First, water covers the fuel, which keeps it from coming into contact with oxygen. Second, evaporation of the water uses a large amount of heat, causing the fire to cool. Without heat, there isn't enough energy to continue the combustion. Therefore, the reaction stops.

Home Fire Safety

Every year, fire claims thousands of lives in the United States. **If you know how to prevent fires in your home and what to do if a fire starts, you are better prepared to take action.** You may save your home or even your life! The most common sources of home fires are small heaters, cooking, and faulty electrical wiring. The fires that cause the most deaths start from carelessness with cigarettes.

Fighting Fires You can fight a small fire by using what you know about the fire triangle. For example, carbon dioxide gas can smother a fire by preventing contact between the fuel and oxygen in the air. Therefore, you can put out a small fire on the stove by throwing baking soda on it. Baking soda decomposes when heated and releases carbon dioxide gas. Or, you can use the cover of a saucepan to cut off the flow of oxygen.

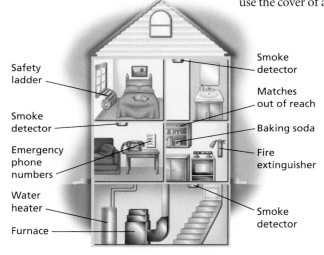

Safety ladder
Smoke detector
Emergency phone numbers
Water heater
Furnace
Smoke detector
Matches out of reach
Baking soda
Fire extinguisher
Smoke detector

FIGURE 18
A Fire-Safe House
This fire-safe house has many fire-prevention and fire safety features. *Inferring Why are smoke detectors located on every floor?*

A small fire is easy to control. You can cool a match enough to stop combustion just by blowing on it. A small fire in a trash can may be doused with a pan of water. If the fire spreads to the curtains, however, even a garden hose might not deliver enough water to put it out.

One of the most effective ways to fight a small fire is with a fire extinguisher. But a fire that is growing as you fight it is out of control. If a fire is out of control, there is only one safe thing to do—get away from the fire and call the fire department.

Preventing Trouble The best form of fire safety is prevention. Figure 18 shows some features of a fire-safe house. You can also check your home to be sure that all flammable items are stored safely away from sources of flames, such as the kitchen stove. Fires can be dangerous and deadly, but many fires can be prevented if you are careful. Understanding the chemistry of fire gives you a way to reduce risk and increase your family's safety.

 Reading Checkpoint How does baking soda put a fire out?

FIGURE 19
Fire-Prevention Devices
Fire extinguishers and baking soda can be used to interrupt the fire triangle. Smoke detectors can help you identify a fire and escape to safety.

Section 4 Assessment

Target Reading Skill Previewing Visuals Review your graphic organizer and revise it based on what you just learned in the section.

Reviewing Key Concepts

1. a. **Listing** What three things are required for combustion?
   b. **Explaining** How does the fire triangle help you control fire?
   c. **Applying Concepts** To stop a forest fire, firefighters may remove all the trees in a strip of land that lies in the path of the fire. What part of the fire triangle is affected? Explain.
2. a. **Reviewing** Why is it important to know about the causes of fire and how to prevent fires?
   b. **Identifying** What are the three most common causes of home fires?
   c. **Problem Solving** Choose one common cause of home fires. Describe measures that can be taken to prevent fires of this type.

Lab zone At-Home **Activity**

Family Safety Plan Work with your family to formulate a fire safety plan. How can fires be prevented in your home? How can fires be put out if they occur? Is there a functioning smoke detector on each floor of the home, especially near the bedrooms? How can the fire department be contacted in an emergency? Design a fire escape route. Make sure all family members know the route as well as a meeting place outside.

Lab zone At-Home **Activity**

Family Safety Plan L2 A fire safety plan should include installing and maintaining the fire-prevention and fire safety features shown in Figure 20. It also should include planning and rehearsing an escape route and deciding on a meeting place outside.

Lab zone Chapter **Project**

Keep Students on Track You may want to give students some class time to finish preparing their presentations. Tell them to be prepared to use examples from their data to support their conclusions.

Monitor Progress _____ L2

Answers
Figure 18 Smoke detectors are located on every floor because fire can start on any floor and the closer the smoke detector is to the source of the smoke, the sooner it will go off.

Reading Checkpoint Baking soda puts out a fire by producing carbon dioxide gas, which smothers the fire.

Assess

Reviewing Key Concepts

1. **a.** Fuel, oxygen, and heat **b.** The triangle shows you that removing any one of the three things needed for fire allows you to put out or prevent a fire. **c.** Removing the trees interrupts the supply of fuel needed for the fire.
2. **a.** Knowing what causes fire and how to prevent fires gives you a way to reduce risk and increase your family's safety. **b.** Small heaters, cooking, and faulty electrical wiring **c.** Students should describe measures that can be taken to prevent fires caused by small heaters, cooking, or faulty electrical wiring. For example, they might say having electrical wiring done by a professional electrician may help prevent fires caused by faulty electrical wiring.

Reteach L1

Ask students to name fire-prevention and fire safety features of a fire-safe house.

Performance Assessment L2

Oral Presentation Call on students to list the three things that fires need. Call on other students to describe a fire and how it could be put out by removing one of the three things.

All in One Teaching Resources

- Section Summary: *Fire and Fire Safety*
- Review and Reinforce: *Fire and Fire Safety*
- Enrich: *Fire and Fire Safety*

Chapter 2
Study Guide

interactive
Textbook

- Complete student edition
- Section and chapter self-assessment
- Assessment reports for teachers

Help Students Read   L1

Building Vocabulary

Word Origins Remind students that synthesis refers to a chemical reaction in which reactants combine to make new products. State that the term *synthesis* comes from a Greek word meaning "to put together." Explain that, like some other Greek-origin words, synthesis has *es* for a plural ending. In other words, one reaction is a synthesis, but two or more reactions are syntheses.

Paraphrase Have students paraphrase each of the boldface sentences in the chapter. They should try to state the ideas in the sentences as accurately as possible in their own words. This will require them to know the meaning of the terms in the most important concepts in the chapter and improve their grasp of chapter vocabulary.

Connecting Concepts

Concept Maps Help students develop one way to show how the information in this chapter is related. Matter has physical and chemical properties and undergoes physical and chemical changes. In chemical reactions, substances are broken down, built up, or changed in other ways. Fire is a chemical reaction that can be dangerous unless steps are taken to prevent and control it. Have students brainstorm to identify the key concepts, key terms, details, and examples. Then, write each one on a self-sticking note, and attach it at random to chart paper or the board.

Tell students that this concept map will be organized in hierarchical order, beginning at the top with the key concepts. Ask students these questions to guide them in organizing the information on the self-sticking notes: **What happens to chemical bonds when chemical changes occur?**

① Observing Chemical Change

Key Concepts

- Matter can be described in terms of two kinds of properties—physical properties and chemical properties. Changes in matter can be described in terms of physical changes and chemical changes.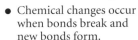
- Chemical changes occur when bonds break and new bonds form.
- Chemical reactions involve two main kinds of changes that you can observe—formation of new substances and changes in energy.

Key Terms

matter	chemical reaction
chemistry	precipitate
physical property	endothermic reaction
chemical property	exothermic reaction
physical change	

② Describing Chemical Reactions

Key Concepts

- Chemical equations use chemical formulas and other symbols instead of words to summarize a reaction.
- The principle of conservation of mass states that, in a chemical reaction, the total mass of the reactants must equal the total mass of the products.
- To describe a reaction accurately, a chemical equation must show the same number of each type of atom on both sides of the equation.
- Many chemical reactions can be classified in one of three categories: synthesis, decomposition, or replacement.

Key Terms

chemical equation	open system
reactant	coefficient
product	synthesis
conservation of mass	decomposition
closed system	replacement

③ Controlling Chemical Reactions

Key Concepts

- All chemical reactions need a certain amount of activation energy to get started.
- Chemists can control rates of reactions by changing factors such as surface area, temperature, and concentration, and by using substances called catalysts and inhibitors.

Key Terms

activation energy
concentration
catalyst
enzyme
inhibitor

④ Fire and Fire Safety

Key Concepts

- The following three things are necessary to start and maintain a fire—fuel, oxygen, and heat.
- If you know how to prevent fires in your home and what to do if a fire starts, you are better prepared to take action.

Key Terms

combustion
fuel

What are the two main kinds of changes you can observe when chemical reactions occur? What is the principle of conservation of mass? What are three categories of chemical reactions? What is activation energy? What factors control rates of chemical reactions? What is the fire triangle? Prompt students by using connecting words, such as "includes," "involve," "can be classified as," and "such

as," to indicate the basis for the organization of the map. The phrases should form a sentence between or among a set of concepts.

Answer

Accept logical presentations by students.

All in One Teaching Resources

- Key Terms Review: *Chemical Reactions*
- Connecting Concepts: *Chemical Reactions*

Review and Assessment

Go Online
PHSchool.com
For: Self-Assessment
Visit: PHSchool.com
Web Code: cga-2020

Organizing Information

Concept Mapping Copy the chemical reactions concept map onto a separate sheet of paper. Then complete it and add a title. (For more on Concept Mapping, see the Skills Handbook.)

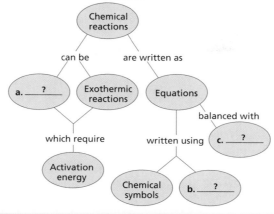

Reviewing Key Terms

Choose the letter of the best answer.

1. Which of the following is *not* a physical property?
  a. flexibility
  b. ability to catch fire
  c. melting point
  d. ability to conduct electricity

2. A chemical reaction that gives off heat is likely to be
  a. endothermic.
  b. a precipitate.
  c. a physical change.
  d. exothermic.

3. You can balance a chemical equation by changing the
  a. subscripts.
  b. coefficients.
  c. reactants.
  d. products.

4. A chemical reaction in which two elements combine to form a compound is called a
  a. synthesis reaction.
  b. replacement reaction.
  c. decomposition reaction.
  d. precipitation reaction.

5. The activation energy of a chemical reaction
  a. is supplied by a catalyst.
  b. is released at the end.
  c. starts the reaction.
  d. changes with time.

6. A chemical reaction in which a fuel combines rapidly with oxygen is a (an)
  a. inhibited reaction.
  b. combustion reaction.
  c. enzyme reaction.
  d. endothermic reaction.

Writing in Science

Explanation You are a writer for a children's book about chemistry. Write a paragraph that young children would understand that explains the concept of "activation energy." Be sure to use examples, such as the burning of wood or gas.

Chemical Reactions
Video Preview
Video Field Trip
▶ Video Assessment

Chapter 2 L ◆ 79

Review and Assessment

Organizing Information
a. Endothermic reactions
b. Other symbols (or Arrows and plus signs)
c. Coefficients

Reviewing Key Terms
1. b **2.** d **3.** b **4.** a **5.** c **6.** b

Writing in Science

Writing Mode Explanation
Scoring Rubric
4 Exceeds criteria; includes a simply written explanation that clearly and correctly explains the concept with several relevant examples
3 Meets criteria
2 Includes an explanation and at least one example but contains some errors
1 Includes a general description only and/or contains serious errors

Video Assessment

Chemical Reactions

Show the Video Assessment to review chapter content and as a prompt for the writing assignment. Discussion question: **What are the results of the chemical reactions that take place in fireworks?** *(The reactions release energy as heat and light.)*

Go Online
PHSchool.com
For: Self-Assessment
Visit: PHSchool.com
Web Code: cga-2020

Students can take a practice test online that is automatically scored.

All in One Teaching Resources
- Transparency L29
- Chapter Test
- Performance Assessment Teacher Notes
- Performance Assessment Student Worksheet
- Performance Assessment Scoring Rubric

ExamView® Computer Test Bank CD-ROM

Checking Concepts

7. Two kinds of changes are physical changes and chemical changes. A physical change does not change a substance into another substance. A chemical change does change a substance into another.

8. You cannot change the subscripts, because they are the numbers of particular atoms in molecules, and molecular formulas cannot be changed. It is the number of molecules of each substance that must be changed by using coefficients.

9. It does not violate the principle of conservation of matter. Not all of the reactants and products were measured, so it is impossible to tell if the total amount of mass changed or remained the same.

10. Enzymes lower the activation energy required for chemical reactions in your body to take place. Because of this, the reactions take place at normal body temperatures that are safe for you.

11. Water covers the fuel, which keeps it from coming into contact with oxygen. In addition, the evaporation of water uses a large amount of heat, causing the fire to cool.

12. Inhibitors decrease the rate of a reaction, such as the spoiling of food. Most inhibitors work by preventing reactants from coming together.

Thinking Critically

13. Students may say that they would paint the steel or cover it with some other protective coating to prevent the steel from coming into contact with water and salt.

14. a. Replacement **b.** Synthesis
c. Decomposition **d.** Synthesis

15. Sample answer: Opening the door suddenly lets oxygen into the room. The added oxygen allows the fire to flare up.

16. Sample answer: Detailed carvings provide more surface area for the acid rain to react with.

Math Practice

17. $MgO + 2\,HBr \rightarrow MgBr_2 + H_2O$

18. $2\,N_2 + 5\,O_2 \rightarrow 2\,N_2O_5$

19. $C_2H_4 + 3\,O_2 \rightarrow 2\,CO_2 + 2\,H_2O$

20. $Fe + 2HCl \rightarrow FeCl_2 + H_2$

Review and Assessment

Checking Concepts

7. What are the two kinds of changes that occur in matter? Describe how you can tell one from the other.

8. Why can't you balance a chemical equation by changing the subscripts of the reactants or the products?

9. You find the mass of a piece of iron metal, let it rust, and measure the mass again. The mass has increased. Does this violate the principle of conservation of mass? Explain.

10. How do enzymes in your body make chemical reactions occur at safe temperatures?

11. Why does spraying water on a fire help to put the fire out?

12. How are inhibitors useful in controlling chemical reactions?

Thinking Critically

13. Problem Solving Steel that is exposed to water and salt rusts quickly. If you were a shipbuilder, how would you protect a new ship? Explain why your solution works.

14. Classifying The following are balanced equations for chemical reactions. Classify each of the equations as synthesis, decomposition, or replacement.

a. $2\,Al + Fe_2O_3 \rightarrow 2\,Fe + Al_2O_3$
b. $2\,Ag + S \rightarrow Ag_2S$
c. $CaCO_3 \rightarrow CaO + CO_2$
d. $2\,NO + O_2 \rightarrow 2\,NO_2$

15. Relating Cause and Effect Firefighters open doors very carefully because sometimes a room will burst violently into flames when the door is opened. Based on your knowledge of the fire triangle, explain why this happens.

16. Inferring Some statues are made of materials that can react in acid rain and begin to dissolve. It has been observed that statues with smooth surfaces are dissolved by acid rain much slower than statues with very detailed carvings. Explain this observation.

Math Practice

Balance the chemical equations in Questions 17–20.

17. $MgO + HBr \longrightarrow MgBr_2 + H_2O$

18. $N_2 + O_2 \longrightarrow N_2O_5$

19. $C_2H_4 + O_2 \longrightarrow CO_2 + H_2O$

20. $Fe + HCl \longrightarrow FeCl_2 + H_2$

Applying Skills

Use the energy diagram to answer Questions 21–23.

The two graphs below represent the same chemical reaction under different conditions.

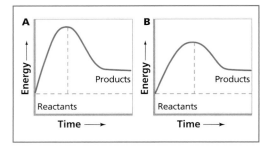

21. Interpreting Data How does the energy of the products compare with the energy of the reactants?

22. Classifying Tell whether this reaction is exothermic or endothermic.

23. Applying Concepts What change in condition might account for the lower "hump" in the second graph? Explain.

Lab zone Chapter **Project**

Performance Assessment Make a poster of your test results. Display your reaction chamber for the class. Discuss how your chamber was built to the specifications agreed upon by the class. Describe its safety features. Based on your results, rate how effectively your chamber works as a closed system.

Applying Skills

21. The energy of the products is greater than the energy of the reactants.

22. The reaction is endothermic.

23. The use of a catalyst might account for the lower "hump" in the second graph, because a catalyst is a material that lowers the activation energy.

 Chapter **Project** L3

Test-Taking Tip

Watching for Qualifiers

Many multiple-choice questions use qualifiers such as the words *best, except for, most,* and *least.* For example, you might be asked what is the *best* method for determining the density of a liquid. When you answer that kind of question, you need to read all the answer choices very carefully. Some of the answers may be correct, but not the best answer. In another question you may be told that a particular condition is satisfied by all the answer choices *except for* one. If you read the question too quickly, you may miss this two-word qualifier. In this type of question, the incorrect statement is actually the correct answer choice.

Sample Question

Each chemical equation below is correctly balanced *except for*

A $NaOH + HCl \longrightarrow NaCl + H_2O$
B $SO_3 + H_2O \longrightarrow H_2SO_4$
C $AgNO_3 + H_2S \longrightarrow Ag_2S + HNO_3$
D $Fe + H_2SO_4 \longrightarrow FeSO_4 + H_2$

Answer

The correct answer is **C.** A balanced chemical equation shows the same number of each type of atom on both sides of the equation. The left side of the equation shows a total of 1 Ag, 1 N, 3 O, 2 H, and 1 S. The right side shows 1 N and 3 O, but 2 Ag and only 1 H, so the equation is not balanced.

Choose the letter of the best answer.

1. Which of the following is the *best* evidence for a chemical reaction?
   A gas bubbles
   B formation of a new substance
   C change of state
   D change in temperature

2. Which shows a balanced chemical equation for the decomposition of aluminum oxide (Al_2O_3)?
   F $Al_2O_3 \longrightarrow 2 Al + O_2$
   G $Al_2O_3 \longrightarrow 2 Al + 3 O_2$
   H $2 Al_2O_3 \longrightarrow 4 Al + O_2$
   J $2 Al_2O_3 \longrightarrow 4 Al + 3 O_2$

Base your answers to Questions 3 and 4 on the diagram below. The diagram represents molecules of two different elements that are gases. The elements react chemically to produce a third gas.

3. The diagram represents a(n)
   A endothermic reaction in which energy is released.
   B exothermic reaction in which energy is absorbed.
   C exothermic reaction in which energy is released.
   D reaction in which energy is destroyed.

4. What can be inferred from the diagram?
   F Matter is not created or destroyed in a chemical reaction.
   G The rate of a reaction depends on the surface area of the reactants.
   H A gas molecule always consists of two identical atoms.
   J The product is carbon monoxide gas.

Constructed Response

5. Zinc metal (Zn) reacts with hydrochloric acid (HCl) to produce hydrogen gas (H_2) and zinc chloride ($ZnCl_2$). A scientist has powdered zinc and a chunk of zinc of equal mass. Available in the lab are dilute HCl and concentrated HCl. Which combination of zinc and acid would react most quickly? Explain why the combination you chose would make the reaction occur most quickly.

Performance Assessment Students' presentations should include a description of the design process they went through to construct and test their reaction chambers. Students can use posters, overhead transparencies, or handouts of tables or graphs to show the masses of reactants and products in the chemical reaction they undertook in their chambers. Students are expected to explain whether their data support the principle of conservation of mass. Urge students to make comparisons between their data and those of their classmates. Ask them to try to explain any discrepancies.

Standardized Test Prep

1. B   **2.** J   **3.** C   **4.** F
5. Powdered zinc should be chosen because it has more surface area than solid zinc, and increasing the surface area increases the rate of the reaction. Concentrated hydrochloric acid should be chosen because more concentrated reactants react more quickly than less concentrated reactants.

Chapter at a Glance

PRENTICE HALL
Teacher**EXPRESS**™
Plan • Teach • Assess

 Chapter **Project** *Make Your Own Indicator*

Technology

Local Standards

All in One Teaching Resources
- Chapter Project Teacher Notes, pp. 178–179
- Chapter Project Student Overview, pp. 180–181
- Chapter Project Student Worksheets, pp. 182–183
- Chapter Project Scoring Rubric, p. 184

Discovery CHANNEL
SCHOOL
Video Preview

 Section 1

3–4 periods
1–2 blocks

Understanding Solutions
L.3.1.1 State the characteristics of solutions, colloids, and suspensions.
L.3.1.2 Describe what happens to the particles of a solute when a solution forms.
L.3.1.3 Explain how solutes affect the freezing point and boiling point of a solvent.

Discovery CHANNEL
SCHOOL
Video Field Trip

Go Online
active art

 Section 2

2–3 periods
1–1 1/2 blocks

Concentration and Solubility
L.3.2.1 Describe how concentration is measured.
L.3.2.2 Explain why solubility is useful in identifying substances.
L.3.2.3 Identify factors that affect the solubility of a substance.

Go Online
SCLINKS
NSTA

 Section 3

2–3 periods
1–1 1/2 blocks

Describing Acids and Bases
L.3.3.1 Name the properties of acids and bases.
L.3.3.2 Identify where acids and bases are commonly used.

Go Online
SCLINKS
NSTA

 Section 4

3–4 periods
1–2 blocks

Acids and Bases in Solution
L.3.4.1 State what kinds of ions acids and bases form in water.
L.3.4.2 Explain what pH tells you about a solution.
L.3.4.3 Describe what happens in a neutralization reaction.

Go Online
PHSchool.com

 Section 5

1–2 periods
1/2–1 block

Digestion and pH
L.3.5.1 Explain why the body must digest food.
L.3.5.2 Describe how pH affects digestion.

Go Online
SCLINKS
NSTA

Review and Assessment

Test Preparation

All in One Teaching Resources
- Key Terms Review, p. 224
- Transparency L41
- Performance Assessment Teacher Notes, p. 233
- Performance Assessment Scoring Rubric, p. 234
- Performance Assessment Student Worksheet, p. 235
- Chapter Test, pp. 236–239

Discovery CHANNEL
SCHOOL
Video Assessment

Test Preparation
Blackline Masters

Chapter Activities Planner

For more activities

LAB ZONE
Easy Planner
CD-ROM

Student Edition	Inquiry	Time	Materials	Skills	Resources
Chapter Project, p. 83	Open-ended	Ongoing (2–3 weeks)	**All in One** Teaching Resources See p. 178	Designing experiments, controlling variables, comparing and contrasting, communicating	**Lab zone Easy Planner** **All in One** Teaching Resources Support pp. 178–179
Section 1					
Discover Activity, p. 84	Guided	10 minutes	Water, graduated cylinder, 2 plastic cups, small spoon, pepper, table salt	Observing	**Lab zone Easy Planner**
Try This Activity, p. 86	Directed	15 minutes	50 mL gelatin-and-water mixture, 2 beakers, 50 mL saltwater solution, flashlight	Inferring	**Lab zone Easy Planner**
Skills Activity, p. 88	Directed	15 minutes	Table salt or other solute, water, balance, hot plate, thermometer	Designing experiments	**Lab zone Easy Planner**
At-Home Activity, p. 89	Guided	Home		Applying concepts, communicating	**Lab zone Easy Planner**
Design Your Own Lab, pp. 90–91	Open-ended	40 minutes	Spoon; solid stoppers, #4; thermometers; hot plate; balance; stirring rods; ice; timer or watch; test tube rack; test tubes, 25 × 150 mm; coarse, rock, and table salt; graduated cylinders and beakers, various sizes	Controlling variables, drawing conclusions, designing experiments	**Lab zone Easy Planner Lab Activity Video** **All in One** Teaching Resources Design Your Own Lab: *Speedy Solutions*, pp. 192–194
Section 2					
Discover Activity, p. 92	Guided	15 minutes	Spoon, small plastic cup, water, soap flakes, salt, sugar, vinegar, pepper, powdered chalk, vegetable oil	Drawing conclusions	**Lab zone Easy Planner**
Skills Activity, p. 94	Directed	15 minutes	Baking soda, cool water, small spoon, graduated cylinder, beaker, warm water	Predicting	**Lab zone Easy Planner**
Section 3					
Discover Activity, p. 98	Guided	15 minutes	Red and blue litmus paper, plastic dropper, plastic cups, lemon juice, orange juice	Classifying	**Lab zone Easy Planner**
Section 4					
Discover Activity, p. 104	Guided	15 minutes	Plastic dropper, red cabbage juice, 3 plastic cups, lemon juice, ammonia cleaner	Forming operational definitions	**Lab zone Easy Planner**
Try This Activity, p. 106	Directed	15 minutes	Red and blue litmus paper, plastic dropper, plastic cup, orange juice, soda water, coffee, antacid, tea	Interpreting data	**Lab zone Easy Planner**
At-Home Activity, p. 109	Guided	Home		Applying concepts, communicating	**Lab zone Easy Planner**
Consumer Lab, pp. 110–111	Guided	40 minutes	3 plastic droppers; small plastic cups; dilute hydrochloric acid (HCl), 50 mL; methyl orange solution, 1 mL; liquid antacid, 30 mL of each brand tested	Designing experiments, interpreting data, measuring	**Lab zone Easy Planner Lab Activity Video** **All in One** Teaching Resources Consumer Lab: *The Acid Test*, pp. 214–217
Section 5					
Discover Activity, p. 112	Guided	5 minutes	Piece of crusty bread	Inferring	**Lab zone Easy Planner**

Section Lesson Plans

Section 1 **Understanding Solutions**

⏱ *3–4 periods, 1–2 blocks*

Objectives

L.3.1.1 State the characteristics of solutions, colloids, and suspensions.

L.3.1.2 Describe what happens to the particles of a solute when a solution forms.

L.3.1.3 Explain how solutes affect the freezing point and boiling point of a solvent.

Key Terms

• solution • solvent • solute • colloid • suspension

Local Standards

Preteach

Build Background Knowledge

Students think of a way to distinguish a familiar solution from plain water.

 **Discover Activity** *What Makes a Mixture a Solution?* L1

Targeted Print and Technology Resources

All in One Teaching Resources

L2 Reading Strategy Transparency L30: Identifying Main Ideas

⊙ **Presentation-Pro CD-ROM**

Instruct

What Is a Solution? Explain what a solution is and which substance in a solution is the solute and which is the solvent.

Colloids and Suspensions Define colloids and suspensions, and challenge students to explain how they could separate a solute from a suspension.

Particles in a Solution Compare and contrast solutions of ionic compounds and molecular compounds.

Effects of Solutes on Solvents Use differences in taste to introduce the concept that solutes affect the properties of solvents.

 **Design Your Own Lab** *Speedy Solutions* L2

Targeted Print and Technology Resources

All in One Teaching Resources

L2 Guided Reading, pp. 187–189
L2 Transparency L31
L2 Design Your Own Lab: *Speedy Solutions,* pp. 192–194

📼 **Lab Activity Video/DVD**
Design Your Own Lab: *Speedy Solutions*

PHSchool.com Web Code: cgp-2031

⊙ **Student Edition on Audio CD**

Assess

Section Assessment Questions

↩ Have students use their completed graphic organizers with their lists of what they know and what they learned to answer the questions.

Reteach

Students fill in details in an outline of the section.

Targeted Print and Technology Resources

All in One Teaching Resources

• Section Summary, p. 186
L1 Review and Reinforce, p. 190
L3 Enrich, p. 191

Section 2 Concentration and Solubility

🕐 *2–3 periods, 1–1 1/2 blocks*

ABILITY LEVELS
L1 Basic to Average
L2 For All Students
L3 Average to Advanced

Objectives

L.3.2.1 Describe how concentration is measured.

L.3.2.2 Explain why solubility is useful in identifying substances.

L.3.2.3 Identify factors that affect the solubility of a substance.

Key Terms

• dilute solution • concentrated solution • solubility • saturated solution
• unsaturated solution • supersaturated solution

Local Standards

Preteach

Build Background Knowledge

Students recall what they already know about concentration using a familiar example.

 **Discover Activity** *Does It Dissolve?*   **L1**

Targeted Print and Technology Resources

All in One Teaching Resources

L2   Reading Strategy:
Building Vocabulary

💿 **Presentation-Pro CD-ROM**

Instruct

Concentration Define and discuss concentration.

Solubility Introduce and explain solubility.

Factors Affecting Solubility Describe how solubility may be affected by pressure, type of solvent, and temperature.

Targeted Print and Technology Resources

All in One Teaching Resources

L2   Guided Reading, pp. 197–198

L2   Transparency L32

www.SciLinks.org Web Code:
scn-1232

💿 **Student Edition on Audio CD**

Assess

Section Assessment Questions

 Have students use their completed sentences using key terms to answer the questions.

Reteach

Students fill in the blanks in sentences in which key terms are defined.

Targeted Print and Technology Resources

All in One Teaching Resources

• Section Summary, p. 196

L1   Review and Reinforce, p. 199

L3   Enrich, p. 200

Section Lesson Plans

Section 3 Describing Acids and Bases

🕐 *2–3 periods, 1–1 1/2 blocks*

ABILITY LEVELS
L1 Basic to Average
L2 For All Students
L3 Average to Advanced

Objectives

L.3.3.1 Name the properties of acids and bases.
L.3.3.2 Identify where acids and bases are commonly used.

Local Standards

Key Terms

• acid • corrosive • indicator • base

Preteach

Build Background Knowledge

Students identify sour taste as a common property of acids in lemons and vinegar.

 **Discover Activity** *What Colors Does Litmus Paper Turn?* L1

Targeted Print and Technology Resources

 Teaching Resources
L2 Reading Strategy Transparency
L33: Asking Questions

⊙ **Presentation-Pro CD-ROM**

Instruct

Properties of Acids Introduce properties of acids, and give students examples of acids that demonstrate the properties.

Properties of Bases Guide students in inferring the properties of bases, based on the description of bases as the "opposite" of acids.

Uses of Acids and Bases Use Figures 15 and 16 to help students identify uses of specific acids and bases.

Targeted Print and Technology Resources

All in One Teaching Resources
L2 Guided Reading, pp. 203–204

www.SciLinks.org Web Code: scn-1233

⊙ **Student Edition on Audio CD**

Assess

Section Assessment Questions

🔄 Have students use their completed graphic organizers with their questions and answers to answer the questions.

Reteach

Students help make a concept map showing the properties and uses of acids and bases.

Targeted Print and Technology Resources

All in One Teaching Resources
• Section Summary, p. 202
L1 Review and Reinforce, p. 205
L3 Enrich, p. 206

Section 4 Acids and Bases in Solution

 3–4 periods, 1–2 blocks

Objectives

L.3.4.1 State what kinds of ions acids and bases form in water.

L.3.4.2 Explain what pH tells you about a solution.

L.3.4.3 Describe what happens in a neutralization reaction.

Key Terms

- hydrogen ion (H^+) • hydroxide ion (OH^-) • pH scale
- neutralization • salt

Local Standards

Preteach

Build Background Knowledge

Students answer questions about a common acid solution as an introduction to acids and bases in solution.

 **Discover Activity** *What Can Cabbage Juice Tell You?* **L1**

Targeted Print and Technology Resources

 **Teaching Resources**

L2 Reading Strategy Transparency L34: Previewing Visuals

Presentation-Pro CD-ROM

Instruct

Acids and Bases in Solution Guide students in understanding how acids and bases produce ions in water.

Strength of Acids and Bases Use a questioning strategy to help students recognize what determines the strength of acids and bases.

Acid-Base Reactions Define and discuss neutralization.

 **Consumer Lab** *The Antacid Test* **L2**

Targeted Print and Technology Resources

 **Teaching Resources**

L2 Guided Reading, pp. 209–211
L2 Transparencies L35, L36, L37, L38
L2 Consumer Lab: *The Antacid Test,* pp. 214–217

Lab Activity Video/DVD
Consumer Lab: *The Antacid Test*

PHSchool.com Web Code: cgd-2034

Student Edition on Audio CD

Assess

Section Assessment Questions

Have students use their completed graphic organizers of questions and answers to answer the questions.

Reteach

Students use the key terms in sentences.

Targeted Print and Technology Resources

Teaching Resources

- Section Summary, p. 208
L1 Review and Reinforce, p. 212
L3 Enrich, p. 213

Section 5 Digestion and pH

 1–2 periods, 1/2–1 block

ABILITY LEVELS
L1 Basic to Average
L2 For All Students
L3 Average to Advanced

Objectives

L.3.5.1 Explain why the body must digest food.

L.3.5.2 Describe how pH affects digestion.

Key Terms

• digestion • mechanical digestion • chemical digestion

Local Standards

Preteach

Build Background Knowledge

Students use their knowledge of hydrochloric acid to predict its role in digestion.

 **Discover Activity** *Where Does Digestion Begin?* L1

Targeted Print and Technology Resources

 **Teaching Resources**

L2 Reading Strategy Transparency L39: Sequencing

⊙ **Presentation-Pro CD-ROM**

Instruct

What Is Digestion? Work with students to compare and contrast mechanical and chemical digestion.

pH in the Digestive System Use Figure 25 to show how pH changes in the digestive system, and help students infer why pH changes.

Targeted Print and Technology Resources

 Teaching Resources

L2 Guided Reading, pp. 220–221
L2 Transparency L40

www.SciLinks.org Web Code: scn-1235

⊙ **Student Edition on Audio CD**

Assess

Section Assessment Questions

⟳ Have students use their completed flowcharts to answer the questions.

Reteach

Students fill in the missing information in an overhead transparency of Figure 25 without the labels.

Targeted Print and Technology Resources

Teaching Resources

• Section Summary, p. 219
L1 Review and Reinforce, p. 222
L3 Enrich, p. 223

Chapter 3 Content Refresher

Section 1 Understanding Solutions

Solutions, Colloids, and Suspensions Solutions are a type of mixture of two or more substances in which the dissolved particles are distributed evenly throughout. One of the substances in a solution is called the *solvent*. The solvent is the substance that is present in greater amount than any other component. The most common liquid solvent is water. Solutions in which water is the solvent are called *aqueous solutions*.

A substance present in lesser amount in a solution is called a *solute*. Adding solute to a solvent changes some of the solvent's properties. Generally, a solution has a higher boiling point, lower freezing point, and lower vapor pressure than a pure solvent. Adding some solutes also changes the temperature of the solution. Heat is released and the temperature increases if more energy is required to hold the solute together than to form the solution. Heat is absorbed and the temperature decreases if less energy is required to hold the solute together than to form the solution.

Solutes and solvents can be liquids, gases, or solids. Generally, the state of the solvent determines the state of the solution. Examples of solutions include carbonated water, which is a gas dissolved in a liquid, and salt water, which is a solid dissolved in a liquid.

Colloids and suspensions are also mixtures of two or more substances. They differ from solutions and from each other mainly in the size of their particles. Solutions have the smallest particles, followed by colloids, with suspensions having the largest particles. Many of the other distinctive properties of these three types of mixtures are related to the differences in particle size. In a solution, the dissolved particles are individual molecules or ions. They are too small to be seen even with a microscope. They also cannot be filtered or centrifuged out of the solution, and they do not settle out.

In a colloid, the particles are very large molecules or tiny pieces of the dissolved substance. The particles range from about 10^{-7} cm to 10^{-5} cm in diameter. The particles are too small to be seen directly with a regular microscope, but they can be detected with an electron microscope or by their deflection of a beam of light. Because the particles are so small, they are unaffected by gravity. Therefore, they will remain suspended in the medium indefinitely. The constant bombardment of dispersed particles by molecules of the medium keeps the particles in continual random motion, called *Brownian motion*.

The particles of a colloid cannot be filtered out. However, they can be separated by centrifuging, which increases the force of gravity on the particles. Colloids can be classified on the basis of the phases of the dispersed substance and of the medium of dispersion, as shown in the table.

Types of Colloids

Type	Dispersed Substance/ Medium of Dispersion	Example
Aerosol	Solid or liquid/gas	Fog
Foam	Gas/solid or liquid	Whipped cream
Emulsion	Liquid/liquid	Mayonnaise
Gel	Solid/liquid	Jelly
Sol	Solid/solid	Certain alloys

In a suspension, the particles are even larger than those in a colloid. Particles in a suspension are visible with a regular microscope and sometimes even with the unaided eye. The particles also readily settle out, or they can be filtered out. Examples of suspensions are dust or oil droplets in air and sand in water.

Professional Development

Section 2 Concentration and Solubility

Concentration and Solubility In a solution, concentration is a measure of the amount of solute relative to the amount of solvent or to the total amount of solution. It can be expressed in several different ways. Most simply, concentration is the percent by weight or volume of solute in solution. Concentration also may be given as the weight of solute in a given volume of solvent or solution. If the amount of solute in a solution is very small compared with the amount of solvent, concentration may be given in parts per million (ppm). In chemistry, concentration is often expressed in terms of the number of molecules or ions in solution. For example, molarity gives concentration as the moles of solute per liter of solution, where 1 mole equals the gram-molecular weight of the substance. For example, the gram-molecular weight of salt (NaCl) is 58.44 g. Therefore, a 1-molar solution of salt in water would contain 58.44 g of salt dissolved in 1 L of water.

The maximum concentration of a solute in a given solvent, at a particular temperature and pressure, is called *solubility*. A solution that has reached the maximum concentration is said to be *saturated*. At that concentration, no more solute can be dissolved in the solvent unless conditions change. If the temperature of the solvent increases, the solubility of a solid or liquid solute will increase. If the solute is a gas, the solubility will decrease with increasing temperature. An increase in pressure increases the solubility of a gas, but it has little effect on the solubility of a liquid or solid.

The solubility of a solute also depends on the nature of the solvent. Polar solutes tend to have higher solubility in polar solvents, and nonpolar solutes tend to have higher solubility in nonpolar solvents. For example, oil and detergent are nonpolar, so oil has relatively high solubility in detergent. However, oil has very low solubility in water, which is polar. In addition to water, alcohols are among the most widely used solvents (see table). Although alcohols are polar, they are only weakly polar compared with water. As a result, they can dissolve both polar and nonpolar solutes.

Alcohols Used as Solvents

Type of Alcohol	Used as solvent for
Methyl	Fats, oils, resins, nitrocellulose
Ethyl	Lacquers, paints, varnishes, glues, drugs, explosives
Isopropyl	Oils, gums, alkaloids, resins
Isobutyl	Castor-oil-based brake fluids
Tertiary butyl	Drugs, cleaning compounds
Ethylene glycol	Stains, oils, resins, enamels, inks, dyes

Section 3 Describing Acids and Bases

Definitions and Examples of Acids and Bases In the 1880s, a Swedish chemist named Svante Arrhenius defined acids as substances that dissolve in water to produce hydrogen ions (H^+). Similarly, he defined bases as substances that dissolve in water to produce hydroxyl ions (OH^-). Arrhenius received the Nobel prize in chemistry in 1903 for his definitions of acids and bases. However, these definitions apply only to acids and bases in aqueous solutions. A more general definition was proposed in 1923, independently by Danish chemist Johannes Brønsted and British chemist Thomas Lowry. These scientists defined acids as proton donors and bases as protons acceptors. The protons still must be hydrogen ions (H^+) but a water solution is not required. According to this definition, water itself can be considered as either an acid or a base, because a water molecule can lose a proton to form a hydroxide ion or gain a proton to form a hydronium ion.

A commonly known acid is hydrochloric acid, which is produced when hydrogen chloride (HCl) is dissolved in water. It is one of the strongest acids. It is used in the manufacture of other chemicals and also to clean metals and to process some foods. Hydrochloric acid secreted by the stomach plays an important role in digestion.

A well-known base is formed when sodium hydroxide (NaOH) dissolves in water. Commonly known as lye, sodium hydroxide is inexpensive and used in many processes that require a strong base. These uses include textile production and paper making.

Address Misconceptions

Students may think that only acids, not bases, can cause physical injury. For a strategy for overcoming this misconception, see **Address Misconceptions** in Section 3, *Describing Acids and Bases*.

Section 4 Acids and Bases in Solution

pH pH is the negative logarithm of the hydrogen ion concentration, in moles per liter, of a solution. Pure water, which is neutral, has a hydrogen ion concentration of 10^{-7} moles per liter, so its pH is 7. Adding an acid to pure water increases the hydrogen ion concentration and lowers the pH. Adding a base to pure water decreases the hydrogen ion concentration and raises the pH. Acids range in pH from 0 up to, but not including, 7. The lower the number, the stronger the acid. Bases range in pH from 14 down to, but not including, 7. The higher the number, the stronger the base. The table lists pH values of some common substances other than those listed in Figure 20 in the text.

pH of Some Common Substances

Substance	pH
Gastric juice	1.0
Black coffee	5.0
Acid rain	5.6
Urine	6.0
Borax solution	9.2
Milk of magnesia	9.9
Toothpaste	10.5
Limewater	11.0

Although litmus paper and similar indicators can be used to determine whether a substance is an acid or a base, such indicators do not give the pH value of the substance. An approximate pH value can be determined using liquid or paper pH indicators. A more exact value can be determined using titration. To find the pH of an acid using titration, measured volumes of a base of known pH and concentration are added to a measured volume of the acid until the acid is neutralized. The amount of base that was needed to neutralize the acid can then be used to determine the pH of the acid.

Section 5 Digestion and pH

Digestive Enzymes pH is important in human digestion because digestive enzymes require a certain pH in order to function. In the mouth, the most important digestive enzyme is amylase, which is found in saliva. Salivary amylase breaks starches and complex sugars into simpler sugars. It requires a neutral pH.

In the stomach, the most important digestive enzyme is pepsin. Pepsin begins the breakdown of proteins. It is secreted by cells in the innermost layer of the stomach, along with hydrochloric acid, which lowers the pH of the stomach to about 2, the ideal level of acidity for pepsin to function. Hydrochloric acid also kills microorganisms that may be present in food. Other digestive enzymes in the stomach include rennin, which curdles milk, and lipase, which begins the breakdown of fats. Both require an acidic environment. In contrast to the strongly acidic gastric juice from the stomach, secretions of the small intestine and pancreas as well as liver bile are all basic. These secretions contribute to the slightly alkaline environment of the small intestine, which has a pH of about 8. The pancreas secretes digestive enzymes that enter the small intestine through the pancreatic duct. These enzymes include pancreatic lipase, which helps digest fats, and pancreatic amylase, which continues the digestion of sugars. The pancreas also secretes bicarbonate, which helps neutralize the acidity of partially digested food entering from the stomach. In addition, the small intestine secretes enzymes of its own, including trypsin and chymotrypsin, which complete the digestion of proteins and require a basic environment in order to function.

Help Students Read

Relating Cause and Effect
Neutralization Reactions

Strategy Use leading questions to guide students through an ordered sequence so they can more easily identify cause and effect relationships, such as how a reaction between an acid and a base can produce a neutral product.

Example
1. Have students study the equation of an acid-base reaction.
2. Ask them to identify the reactants in the equation.
3. Challenge students to identify the ions that give the acid and base their properties.
4. Have students identify and describe how the ions recombine to produce a neutral product.
5. Ask students to generalize from this example and state what causes the neutralization of an acid and base
See Section 4, *Acids and Bases in Solution,* for a script using the Relating Cause and Effect strategy with students.

Chapter 3
Acids, Bases, and Solutions

Interactive Textbook

Solutions containing transition metal compounds are often very colorful. ▶

Chapter Project L3

Objectives
In this Chapter Project, students will make their own acid-base indicators from foods, plants, or other materials and use them, along with pH test papers, to test readily available acids and bases. After completing this Chapter Project, students will be able to
• design experiments to determine which foods or other materials are acid-base indicators
• control variables to test several substances with acid-base indicators
• compare and contrast test results using their own indicators with test results using pH test papers and a standard pH scale
• communicate their findings to the class

Skills Focus
Designing experiments, controlling variables, comparing and contrasting, communicating

Project Time Line 2–3 weeks

All in One Teaching Resources
• Chapter Project Teacher Notes
• Chapter Project Worksheet 1
• Chapter Project Worksheet 2
• Chapter Project Scoring Rubric

Developing a Plan
Spend about half of one class period launching the project. Give students a week to test and select materials to use as indicators. Allow them another week to test a variety of substances using their indicators and pH test papers. In the final week, students can compile and interpret their test results and present them to the class.

Possible Materials
• Substances that make good indicators include: red cabbage, tea, beets, rose petals, red grapes, red onion skin, blueberries, tomato skin, grass, and greens (such as collard, kale, or spinach).
• Substances students might test include: vinegar, milk, lemon juice, apple juice, carbonated drinks, soapy water, salt water, ammonia, bleach, household cleaners, and shampoo.

Lab zone™ Chapter Project

Make Your Own Indicator

As you learn about acids and bases in this chapter, you can make your own solutions that will tell you if something is an acid or a base. Then you can use your solutions to test for acids and bases among substances found in your home.

Your Goal To make acid-base indicators from flowers, fruits, vegetables, or other common plant materials

To complete the project, you must
- make one or more indicators that will turn colors in acids and bases
- use your indicators to test a number of substances
- compare your indicators to a standard pH scale
- rank the tested substances according to their pH
- follow the safety guidelines in Appendix A

Plan It! Brainstorm with your classmates about foods, spices, flowers, or other plant materials that have definite, deep colors. Think about fruits and vegetables you may find in a supermarket. These materials may make good candidates for your indicators.

Acids, Bases, and Solutions

Show the Video Preview to introduce solutions and concentration. Discussion question: **How does the flapping of bees' wings ensure that the concentration of sugar in the honey cells increases?** (*The moving air causes water inside the open cells to evaporate. As the amount of water decreases, the concentration of sugar in the fluid increases.*)

could use tea as an acid-base indicator. Point out that substances with deep colors usually make the best indicators. Lead the class in brainstorming other materials that might make good acid-base indicators.

Performance Assessment

The Chapter Project Scoring Rubric will help you evaluate how well students complete the Chapter Project. You may want to share the scoring rubric with your students so they will know what is expected. Students will be assessed on
- the effectiveness of their acid-base indicators
- the number of materials they tested using their indicators and pH test paper, and the accuracy of their test results
- the logic and completeness of their comparisons of test results
- the thoroughness and organization of their presentations

Students can keep their summaries of test results in their portfolios. **Portfolio**

- For extracting dye, students will need equipment such as electric blenders, mortars and pestles, cheesecloth, and strainers.
- They will need clean, empty bottles with screw-top lids for storing their finished indicators.
- Provide pH test papers.

Launching the Project

Have students read the project overview in the text. Then, show students a glass of tea. Explain that tea is one of many naturally occurring compounds that can be used to identify substances as acids or bases. Have test tubes of vinegar solution and ammonia solution prepared in advance. Use pH test paper to find the pH of the two solutions, and show the results to the class. Then, add two drops of tea to each test tube, and tell students to observe the changes. Ask them to use their observations to decide how they

Objectives

After this lesson, students will be able to

L.3.1.1 State the characteristics of solutions, colloids, and suspensions.

L.3.1.2 Describe what happens to the particles of a solute when a solution forms.

L.3.1.3 Explain how solutes affect the freezing point and boiling point of a solvent.

Target Reading Skill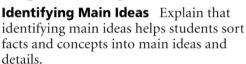

Identifying Main Ideas Explain that identifying main ideas helps students sort facts and concepts into main ideas and details.

Answer

Sample answer: The solvent is the substance present in the largest amount. A solute is a substance present in smaller amounts than the solvent. A solution has the same properties throughout. A solution contains particles that are too small to see.

All in One Teaching Resources

• Transparency L30

Preteach

Build Background Knowledge   L2

Identifying Solutions

Have students imagine mixing a spoon of sugar in a glass of water until the sugar dissolves. Ask: **Would you be able to see a difference between the sugar water solution and plain water?** *(No; they would appear the same.)* **How could you tell the sugar water from plain water?** *(Sample answer: By taste)* Tell students that in this section they will learn more about solutions and how they differ from pure substances.

Reading Preview

Key Concepts

• What are the characteristics of solutions, colloids, and suspensions?

• What happens to the particles of a solute when a solution forms?

• How do solutes affect the freezing point and boiling point of a solvent?

Key Terms

• solution • solvent • solute
• colloid • suspension

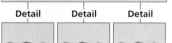 Target Reading Skill

Identifying Main Ideas As you read the *What is a Solution?* section, write the main idea in a graphic organizer like the one below. Then write supporting details that further explain the main idea.

Main Idea

A solution consists of at least one solute in a well-mixed . . .

Detail	Detail	Detail

Lab zone — Discover Activity

What Makes a Mixture a Solution?

1. Put about 50 or 60 milliliters of water into a plastic cup. Add a spoonful of pepper and stir well.

2. To a similar amount of water in a second cup, add a spoonful of table salt. Stir well.

3. Compare the appearance of the two mixtures.

Think It Over

Observing What is the difference between the two mixtures? What other mixtures have you seen that are similar to pepper and water? That are similar to table salt and water?

Imagine a hot summer day. You've been outdoors and now you're really thirsty. A tall, cool glass of plain tap water would taste great. But exactly what is tap water?

Tap water is more than just water. It's a mixture of pure water (H_2O) and a variety of other substances, such as chloride, fluoride, and metallic ions. Gases, such as oxygen and carbon dioxide, are also dissolved in tap water. The dissolved substances give tap water its taste.

What Is a Solution?

Tap water is one example of a mixture called a solution. A **solution** is a well-mixed mixture that contains a solvent and at least one solute. The **solvent** is the part of a solution present in the largest amount. It dissolves the other substances. The **solute** is the substance that is present in a solution in a smaller amount and is dissolved by the solvent. **A solution has the same properties throughout. It contains solute particles (molecules or ions) that are too small to see.**

Solutions With Water In many common solutions, the solvent is water. Sugar in water, for example, is the starting solution for flavored soft drinks. Adding food coloring gives the drink color. Dissolving carbon dioxide gas in the mixture produces a fizzy soda. Water dissolves so many substances that it is often called the "universal solvent."

Lab zone — Discover Activity

Skills Focus Observing   L1

Materials water, graduated cylinder, 2 plastic cups, small spoon, pepper, table salt

Time 10 minutes

Tip Tell students to wash the spoon before making their second mixture.

Expected Outcome The pepper will not dissolve in the water, but the salt will.

Think It Over In the first mixture, the pepper is visible. In the second mixture, the salt dissolves and forms a clear mixture. Students might say that sand and water are similar to pepper and water and that sugar and water are similar to salt and water. Accept any other appropriate responses.

Life depends on water solutions. Nutrients used by plants are dissolved in water in the soil. Sap is a solution that carries sugar dissolved in water to tree cells. Water is the solvent in blood, saliva, and tears. Reactions in cells take place in solution. To keep cells working, you must replace the water you lose in sweat and urine—two other water solutions.

Solutions Without Water Many solutions are made with solvents other than water, as you can see in Figure 1. For example, gasoline is a solution of several different liquid fuels. You don't even need a liquid solvent to make solutions. A solution may be made of any combination of gases, liquids, or solids.

 Reading Checkpoint What solvent is essential to living things?

Discovery CHANNEL SCHOOL

Acids, Bases, and Solutions

Video Preview
▶ Video Field Trip
Video Assessment

Examples of Common Solutions

Solute	Solvent	Solution
Gas	Gas	Air (oxygen and other gases in nitrogen)
Gas	Liquid	Soda water (carbon dioxide in water)
Liquid	Liquid	Antifreeze (ethylene glycol in water)
Solid	Liquid	Dental filling (silver in mercury)
Solid	Liquid	Ocean water (sodium chloride and other compounds in water)
Solid	Solid	Brass (zinc and copper)

FIGURE 1
Solutions can be made from any combination of solids, liquids, and gases.
Interpreting Photos *What are the solutes and solvent for stainless steel?*

The air in these gas bubbles is a solution of oxygen and other gases in nitrogen.

Salt water is a solution of sodium chloride and other compounds in water.

Stainless steel is a solution of chromium, nickel, and carbon in iron.

Chapter 3 L ◆ 85

Instruct

What Is a Solution?

Teach Key Concepts L2
Solutions, Solvents, and Solutes

Focus Define solution as a well-mixed mixture that contains at least two substances.

Teach On the board, write *solvent* and *solute*. Tell students that the terms apply to substances in a solution. Explain that the solvent is always the substance that there is more of.

Apply Describe a solution of two liquids, in which there are 10 mL of liquid A and 12 mL of liquid B. Ask: **Which substance is the solvent, and which is the solute?** *(Substance B is the solvent, and A is the solute.)* **learning modality: verbal**

Acids, Bases, and Solutions

Show the Video Field Trip to give students a chance to see how temperature affects concentration. Discussion question: **How do syrup makers increase the sugar concentration of maple syrup?** *(By boiling it; most of the water evaporates.)*

Independent Practice L2

 **Teaching Resources**

• Guided Reading and Study Worksheet: *Understanding Solutions*

⊙ Student Edition on Audio CD

Monitor Progress _____ L2

Oral Presentation Call on students to define *solution, solvent,* and *solute.*

Answers
Figure 1 Solutes are chromium, nickel, and carbon; the solvent is iron.

Reading Checkpoint Water

⌐ Differentiated Instruction

English Learners/Beginning Comprehension: Modified Cloze L1
Rewrite the first paragraph under the heading *What Is a Solution?* Leave blank the terms *solution, solvent,* and *solute.* Show students how to fill in the blanks with a sample sentence on the board. Then, have them fill in the blanks in the paragraph.
learning modality: verbal

English Learners/Intermediate Comprehension: Ask Questions L2 Check students' comprehension of the most important concepts on these two pages. Change the boldface sentences and the sentences containing boldface terms into questions, and have students answer them. **learning modality: verbal**

Colloids and Suspensions

Teach Key Concepts L2
Colloids and Suspensions

Focus Tell students that not all mixtures are solutions. Some are colloids or suspensions.

Teach Define colloids and suspensions. Ask: **What are some examples of colloids?** *(Sample answers: Milk, gelatin)* **What are some examples of suspensions?** *(Sample answers: Pepper and water, "snow" and water in a snow globe)* Explain that particles in suspensions are larger than particles in colloid. Unlike the particles in a colloid, particles in suspensions can be separated out of the solvent.

Apply Ask: **How could you separate pepper from a suspension of pepper and water?** *(Sample answer: Pour the suspension through a filter.)* **learning modality: verbal**

Use Visuals: Figure 2 L2
Particles in Different Types of Mixtures

Focus Use Figure 2 to compare and contrast particles in solutions, colloids, and suspensions.

Teach Call students' attention to the figure, and have them read the caption and labels. Ask: **Why can you see through glass cleaner but not through milk?** *(Particles in glass cleaner are too small to scatter light, whereas particles in milk are large enough to scatter light.)* **Why can you see particles in a snow globe but not in milk?** *(Particles in a snow globe are larger than particles in milk.)*

Apply Call on a volunteer to go to the board and write the names of the three different types of mixtures in order of decreasing particle size. *(Suspensions, colloids, solutions)* **learning modality: visual**

FIGURE 2
Comparing Three Mixtures
Solutions are different from colloids and suspensions.
Interpreting Photographs In which mixture can you see the particles?

Solution
In a solution of glass cleaner, particles are uniformly distributed and too small to scatter light.

Colloid
Fats and proteins in milk form globular particles that are big enough to scatter light, but are too small to be seen.

Suspension
Suspended particles of "snow" in water are easy to see.

Colloids and Suspensions

Not all mixtures are solutions. Colloids and suspensions are mixtures that have different properties than solutions.

Colloids Have you ever made a gelatin dessert? To do so, you stir powdered gelatin in hot water until the two substances are uniformly mixed. The liquid looks like a solution, but it's not. Gelatin is a colloid. A **colloid** (KAHL oyd) is a mixture containing small, undissolved particles that do not settle out.

Solutions and colloids differ in the size of their particles and how they affect the path of light. **A colloid contains larger particles than a solution. The particles are still too small to be seen easily, but are large enough to scatter a light beam.** For example, fog—a colloid that consists of water droplets in air—scatters the headlight beams of cars. In addition to gelatin and fog, milk, mayonnaise, shaving cream, and whipped cream are examples of colloids.

Suspensions If you did the Discover Activity, you noticed that no matter how much you stir pepper and water, the two never really seem to "mix" completely. When you stop stirring, you can still see pepper flakes floating on the water's surface and collecting at the bottom of the cup. Pepper and water make a suspension. A **suspension** (suh SPEN shun) is a mixture in which particles can be seen and easily separated by settling or filtration. **Unlike a solution, a suspension does not have the same properties throughout. It contains visible particles that are larger than the particles in solutions or colloids.**

 Reading Checkpoint Which kind of mixture has the largest particles?

Lab zone Try This Activity

Scattered Light

1. Pour 50 mL of a gelatin-and-water mixture into a small, clean glass beaker.
2. Pour 50 mL of a saltwater solution into another clean beaker that is about the same size.
3. Compare the appearance of the two liquids.
4. In a darkened room, shine a small flashlight through the side of the beaker that contains gelatin. Repeat this procedure with the saltwater solution.
5. Compare the appearance of the light inside the two beakers.

Inferring What evidence tells you that gelatin is a colloid?

Lab zone Try This Activity

Skills Focus Inferring L2

Materials 50 mL gelatin-and-water mixture, 2 beakers, 50 mL saltwater solution, flashlight

Time 15 minutes

Tip Make sure students stir the mixtures thoroughly to dissolve all the salt and gelatin.

Expected Outcome Light will shine through the saltwater solution but it will be scattered by the larger particles in the gelatin.

Extend Have students repeat the procedure using other mixtures and decide whether the other mixtures are solutions or colloids based on whether or not they scatter light. **learning modality: visual**

Particles in a Solution

Why do solutes seem to disappear when you mix them with a solvent? If you had a microscope powerful enough to look at the mixture's particles, what would you see? **When a solution forms, particles of the solute leave each other and become surrounded by particles of the solvent.**

Ionic and Molecular Solutes Figure 3 shows what happens when an ionic solid mixes with water. The positive and negative ions are attracted to the polar water molecules. Water molecules surround each ion as it leaves the surface of the crystal. As each layer of the solid is exposed, more ions can dissolve.

However, not every substance breaks into ions when it dissolves in water. A molecular solid, such as sugar, breaks up into individual neutral molecules. The polar water molecules attract the slightly polar sugar molecules. This causes the sugar molecules to move away from each other. But covalent bonds within the molecules are not broken.

Solutes and Conductivity You have a water solution, but you don't know if the solute is salt or sugar. How could you find out? Think about what you learned about the electrical conductivity of compounds. A solution of ionic compounds in water conducts electricity, but a water solution of molecular compounds may not. You could test the conductivity of the solution. If no ions are present (as in a sugar solution), electricity will not flow.

 Reading Checkpoint Which kind of solution conducts electricity?

Go Online
active art

For: Salt Dissolving in Water activity
Visit: PHSchool.com
Web Code: cgp-2031

FIGURE 3
Salt Dissolving in Water
When an ionic solid—like table salt—dissolves, water molecules surround and separate the positive and negative ions. Notice that the sodium ions attract the oxygen ends of the water molecules.

 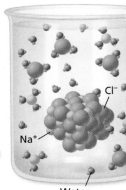 

Na⁺   Cl⁻   Water
Na⁺   Cl⁻   Water
Cl⁻   Na⁺   Water

Differentiated Instruction

Special Needs L1
Observing Solutions Suggest that students make or obtain at home some of the solutions described in the text, such as glass cleaner, milk, gelatin, mayonnaise, sugar water, and salt water. Tell students to examine each solution and write a brief description of it. **learning modality: visual**

Gifted and Talented L3
Making Models of Solutions Challenge students to use Legos® or other small objects to create models of saltwater and sugar water solutions to show the chemical differences between ionic and molecular solutes dissolved in water. Encourage students to share their models with the class. **learning modality: kinesthetic**

Particles in a Solution

Teach Key Concepts L2
Ionic vs. Molecular Compounds in Solution

Focus Compare and contrast solutions of ionic compounds and molecular compounds.

Teach Review differences between ionic and molecular compounds. Remind students that salt is an ionic compound. Have students look at Figure 3 to observe what happens when salt dissolves in water. Point out that the ionic bonds between sodium and chloride are broken due to the attraction of the polar water molecules for the oppositely charged ions. Then, tell students that sugar is a molecular compound. Explain that when sugar dissolves in water, the sugar molecules move away from each other, but the individual sugar molecules do not break apart.

Apply Ask: **Why do sugar molecules not break apart as salt ions do when they are dissolved in water?** *(Sample answer: because sugar's covalent bonds do not break; and the nearly neutral sugar molecules are less attracted by the polar water molecules)*
learning modality: verbal

Go Online
active art

For: Salt Dissolving in Water activity
Visit: PHSchool.com
Web Code: cgp-2031

Students can investigate solutes and solutions in an activity online.

All in One Teaching Resources
• Transparency L31

Monitor Progress L2

Skills Check Have students make a Venn diagram comparing and contrasting colloids and suspensions.

Answers
Figure 2 In the suspension

 Reading Checkpoint A suspension

 Reading Checkpoint A solution of ionic compounds in water

Effects of Solutes on Solvents

Teach Key Concepts
How Solutes Affect Solvents

Focus Use differences in taste to introduce the concept that solutes affect the properties of solvents.

Teach Ask: **How does the taste of sugar water compare with the taste of plain water?** (*Sugar water tastes sweet; plain water has little or no taste.*)

Apply Ask: **What are some other non-visible properties, besides taste, that might change when you add a solute to a solvent?** (*Students might list properties such as freezing and boiling points and ability to conduct electricity.*) **learning modality: verbal**

Lab zone Build **Inquiry** L2

Making Inferences About Antifreeze

Focus Have students read the last paragraph under the subheading *Higher Boiling Points*, describing the boiling point and freezing points of water and antifreeze.

Teach Ask: **Would a car be better protected by pure antifreeze or a mixture of half antifreeze and half water? Why?** (*Half antifreeze and half water, because the mixture has a lower freezing point and a higher boiling point than either water or antifreeze alone*) **learning modality: logical/mathematical**

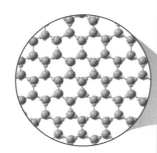

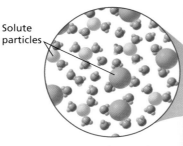
Solute particles

Lab zone Skills **Activity**

Designing Experiments

How does the mass of a solute affect the boiling temperature of a given volume of water? Design an experiment using a solute, water, a balance, a hot plate, and a thermometer.

What variables should remain constant in your experiment? What is the manipulated variable? What will be the responding variable?

With approval from your teacher, do the experiment.

Freshwater lake ▶

Saltwater bay ▶

FIGURE 4
Salt's Effect on Freezing Point
Fresh water on the surface of a lake is frozen. At the same temperature, salt water is not frozen.

Effects of Solutes on Solvents

The freezing point of water is 0°C, and the boiling point is 100°C. These statements are true enough for pure water under everyday conditions, but the addition of solutes to water can change these properties. **Solutes lower the freezing point and raise the boiling point of a solvent.**

Lower Freezing Points Solutes lower the freezing point of a solvent. When liquid water freezes, water molecules join together to form crystals of solid ice. Pure water is made only of water molecules that freeze at 0°C. In a salt solution, solute particles are present in the water when it freezes. The solute particles make it harder for the water molecules to form crystals. The temperature must drop lower than 0°C for the solution to freeze. Figure 4 shows how solutes can affect the freezing point of water.

Lab zone Skills **Activity**

Skills Focus Designing experiments L3

Materials table salt or other solute, water, balance, hot plate, thermometer

Time 15 minutes

Tip Check students' designs before they begin.

Expected Outcome Sample design: Make two samples of solution that differ only in mass of solute; bring them to a boil; measure the temperature when boiling begins. Quantity of water, type of solute, and amount of heat should remain constant. The manipulated variable is mass of solute. The responding variable is boiling point. Increasing the mass of the solute will raise the boiling point.

Extend Have students design an experiment to determine the effect of the solute on the freezing point of water. **learning modality: logical/mathematical**

Higher Boiling Points Solutes raise the boiling point of a solvent. To see why, think about the difference between the molecules of a liquid and those of a gas of the same substance. In a liquid, molecules are moving close to each other. In a gas, they are far apart and moving more rapidly. As the temperature of a liquid rises, the molecules gain energy and escape into the air. In pure water, all the molecules are water. But in a solution, some of the particles are water molecules and others are particles of solute. The presence of the solute makes it harder for the water molecules to escape, so more energy is needed. The temperature must go higher than 100°C for the water to boil.

Car manufacturers make use of the effects of solutes to protect engines from heat and cold. The coolant in a car radiator is a solution of water and another liquid called antifreeze. (Often the antifreeze is ethylene glycol.) The mixture of the two liquids has a higher boiling point and lower freezing point than water alone. Because this solution can absorb more of the heat given off by the running engine, risk of damage to the car from overheating is greatly reduced. The risk of damage from freezing in very cold weather is also reduced.

FIGURE 5
Calling Solutes to the Rescue?
This couple might have prevented their car from overheating by using the proper coolant in the radiator.
Relating Cause and Effect Explain how coolant works.

 Reading Checkpoint **Does salt water have a lower or higher freezing point than pure water?**

Section 1 Assessment

 **Target Reading Skill** Identifying Main Ideas Use your graphic organizer to help you answer Question 1 below.

Reviewing Key Concepts

1. a. **Defining** What is a solution?
   b. **Comparing and Contrasting** How are solutions different from colloids and suspensions?
   c. **Inferring** Suppose you mix food coloring in water to make it blue. Have you made a solution or a suspension? Explain.
2. a. **Reviewing** What happens to the solute particles when a solution forms?
   b. **Sequencing** Describe as a series of steps what happens to sugar molecules when they dissolve in water.
3. a. **Summarizing** What effects do solutes have on a solvent's freezing and boiling points?

   b. **Relating Cause and Effect** Why is the temperature needed to freeze ocean water lower than the temperature needed to freeze the surface of a freshwater lake?
   c. **Applying Concepts** Why does salt sprinkled on icy roads cause the ice to melt?

Lab zone **At-Home Activity**

Passing Through With a family member, mix together a spoonful each of sugar and pepper in about 100 mL of warm water in a plastic container. Pour the mixture through a coffee filter into a second container. Ask your family member what happened to the sugar. Let the water evaporate overnight. Describe the difference between a solution and a suspension.

Chapter 3 L ◆ 89

Lab zone **At-Home Activity**

Passing Through L2 The pepper, but not the sugar, will be filtered out. After the water evaporates, the sugar will remain. Students can explain that a solution contains small particles that cannot be seen or easily separated, whereas a suspension contains larger particles that can be seen and easily separated.

Lab zone **Chapter Project**

Keep Students on Track Make sure students have properly tested and selected workable acid-base indicators. Check that they have correctly prepared the indicators by extracting the dye. Tell them to keep their prepared indicators refrigerated. Encourage them to start testing the pH of a variety of substances.

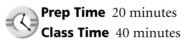
Speedy Solutions L2

Prepare for Inquiry

Key Concept
The speed at which salt dissolves in water depends on several variables. Students will design an experiment to find out how a chosen variable affects this speed.

Skills Objective
After this lab, students will be able to
- design an experiment to determine how a chosen variable affects the speed of salt dissolving in water
- control other variables that also might affect this speed
- draw conclusions about how the chosen variable affects the speed of salt dissolving

Prep Time 20 minutes

Class Time 40 minutes

Safety
Caution students to be careful working around the hot plate. Remind them that the test tubes and thermometers are fragile. Review the safety guidelines in Appendix A.

All in One Teaching Resources
- Lab Worksheet: *Speedy Solutions*

Guide Inquiry

Invitation
Show students a test tube containing some water. Drop a few grains of salt into the tube and swirl. Ask: **How do you know when the salt is completely dissolved?** (*No more crystals are visible in the bottom of the tube.*) Ask: **How could you make the salt dissolve faster?** (*Sample answers: Increase the temperature or volume of water, use smaller grains of salt, shake the test tube faster*) Lead a discussion of how these changes could be measured. For example, ask: **How could you measure the speed at which you shake the test tube?** (*Sample answer: By counting the number of shakes per second*)

Speedy Solutions

Problem
How can you control the rate at which certain salts dissolve in water?

Skills Focus
controlling variables, drawing conclusions, designing experiments

Materials
- spoon
- solid stoppers, #4
- thermometers
- hot plate
- balance
- stirring rods
- ice
- timer or watch
- test tube rack
- test tubes, 25 × 150 mm
- coarse, rock, and table salt
- graduated cylinders and beakers, various sizes

Design a Plan

1. Make a list of all the variables you can think of that could affect the speed at which sodium chloride dissolves in water.

2. Compare your list with your classmates' lists, and add other variables.

3. Choose one variable from your list to test.

4. Write a hypothesis predicting the effect of your chosen variable on the speed of dissolving.

5. Decide how to work with your choice.
   - If you choose temperature, you might perform tests at 10°C, 20°C, 30°C, 40°C, and 50°C.
   - If you choose stirring, you might stir for various amounts of time.

6. Plan at least three tests for whichever variable you choose. Remember to control all other variables.

7. Write down a series of steps for your procedure and safety guidelines for your experiment. Be quite detailed in your plan.

8. As part of your procedure, prepare a data table in which to record your results. Fill in the headings on your table that identify the manipulated variable and the responding variable. (*Hint:* Remember to include units.)

Data Table			
Manipulated Variable	Dissolving Time		
	Test 1	Test 2	Test 3

9. Have your teacher approve your procedure, safety guidelines, and data table.

10. Perform the experiment.

Introduce the Procedure
Have students read through the procedure, and answer any questions they may have. Tell them to select just one variable to test. Guide them in formulating hypotheses regarding their variables. For example, if students choose to test rate of stirring, ask: **What do you think will happen if you do not stir or if you stir at a rate of three times per second?** Have students express their hypotheses as "If…then…" statements.

Expected Outcome
Results will vary, but most students will find that salt dissolves more quickly with higher water temperature, greater water volume, finer grains of salt, or faster stirring or shaking.

Analyze and Conclude

1. **Controlling Variables** Which is the manipulated variable in your experiment? Which is the responding variable? How do you know which is which?

2. **Controlling Variables** List three variables you held constant in your procedure. Explain why controlling these variables makes your data more meaningful.

3. **Graphing** Make a line graph of your data. Label the horizontal axis with the manipulated variable. Label the vertical axis with the responding variable. Use an appropriate scale for each axis and label the units.

4. **Drawing Conclusions** Study the shape of your graph. Write a conclusion about the effect of the variable you tested on the speed at which salt dissolves in water.

5. **Drawing Conclusions** Does your conclusion support the hypothesis you wrote in Step 4 of your Plan? Explain.

6. **Designing Experiments** What advantage would there be in running your tests a second or third time?

7. **Predicting** If you switched procedures with another student who tested the same variable as you, do you think you would get the same results? Explain why or why not.

8. **Communicating** Write an e-mail to a friend explaining how your results relate to what you have learned about particles and solubility.

More to Explore

Choose another variable from the list you made in Steps 1 and 2 of your Plan. Repeat the process with that variable. Of the two variables you chose, which was easier to work with? Explain.

Troubleshooting the Experiment

• Evaluate all student designs for safety. Also, make sure the designs control all but the manipulated variable. In addition, check that designs describe how the manipulated and responding variables will be measured.

• No more than 36 g of salt per 100 mL of water should be used, because this is the solubility of salt in water at 0°C.

Analyze and Conclude

1. Manipulated variables will vary. The responding variable is the time it takes the salt to dissolve. The manipulated variable is the variable that is changed by the experimenter. The responding variable is the variable that is changed as a result.

2. Students should correctly identify at least three variables that are held constant and explain that controlling them avoids confusion about which variable causes the observed effect.

3. Students' graphs should accurately reflect the data collected. All graphs should have the time required for the salt to dissolve on the y-axis and the chosen variable on the x-axis.

4. Answers will vary depending on the variables students chose. Sample answer: Decreasing the grain size of salt increases the rate at which salt dissolves in water.

5. Students' answers will depend on their hypotheses. Make sure students correctly interpret their conclusions with respect to their hypotheses.

6. More than one trial would provide evidence that the data are accurate and that procedures are being followed consistently.

7. Sample answer: Valid procedures, even if different, should produce data that support the same conclusions.

8. Sample answer: Smaller grains of salt have greater surface area, so more solute ions are in contact with water molecules at any given time.

Extend Inquiry

More to Explore Answers will vary depending on which variables were chosen. For example, if students chose temperature and grain size, they may say that they found it easier to measure water temperature than size of salt grains. Accept all logical explanations.

Objectives
After this lesson, students will be able to
L.3.2.1 Describe how concentration is measured.
L.3.2.2 Explain why solubility is useful in identifying substances.
L.3.2.3 Identify factors that affect the solubility of a substance.

Target Reading Skill 🔄

Building Vocabulary Explain that knowing the definitions of key terms helps students understand what they read.

Answers
Sample sentences: A **dilute solution** is a mixture that has only a little solute dissolved in a certain amount of solvent. A **concentrated solution** is one that has a lot of solute dissolved in the same amount of solvent. **Solubility** is a measure of how much solute can dissolve in a solvent at a given temperature. A **saturated solution** contains so much solute that no more dissolves. An **unsaturated solution** can continue to dissolve more solute. A **supersaturated solution** has more dissolved solute than is predicted by its solubility at the given temperature.

Preteach

Build Background Knowledge L2
Concentration
Use a familiar example to help students recall what they already know about concentration. Call on a volunteer to describe how to make orange juice by adding water to frozen concentrate. Point out that the amount of orange juice relative to the amount of water decreases as more water is added. In other words, the concentration of orange juice decreases. Ask: **How does the appearance of the orange juice change as it becomes less concentrated?** (*Sample answer: It becomes more watery and lighter in color.*)

Reading Preview

Key Concepts
- How is concentration measured?
- Why is solubility useful in identifying substances?
- What factors affect the solubility of a substance?

Key Terms
- dilute solution
- concentrated solution
- solubility
- saturated solution
- unsaturated solution
- supersaturated solution

🔄 Target Reading Skill
Building Vocabulary As you read, carefully note the definition of each Key Term. Also note other details in the paragraph that contains the definition. Use all this information to write a meaningful sentence using the Key Term.

Making Maple Syrup ▼

Collecting sap

Boiling sap

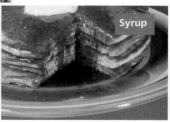
Syrup

Lab zone Discover **Activity**

Does It Dissolve?
1. 🧤 Put half a spoonful of soap flakes into a small plastic cup. Add about 50 mL of water and stir. Observe whether the soap flakes dissolve.
2. Clean out the cup. Repeat the test for a few other solids and liquids provided by your teacher.
3. Classify the items you tested into two groups: those that dissolved easily and those that did not.

Think It Over
Drawing Conclusions Based on your observations, does the physical state (solid or liquid) of a substance affect whether or not it dissolves in water? Explain.

Have you ever had syrup on your pancakes? You probably know that it's made from the sap of maple trees. Is something that sweet really made in a tree? Well, not exactly.

Concentration
The sap of a maple tree and pancake syrup differ in their concentrations. That is, they differ in the amount of solute (sugar) dissolved in a certain amount of solvent (water). The sap is a **dilute solution,** a mixture that has only a little solute dissolved in a certain amount of solvent. The syrup, on the other hand, is a **concentrated solution**—one that has a lot of solute dissolved in the same amount of solvent.

Lab zone Discover **Activity**

Skills Focus Drawing conclusions L1

Materials spoon, small plastic cup, water, soap flakes, salt, sugar, vinegar, pepper, powdered chalk, vegetable oil

Time 15 minutes

Tips Put chalk pieces in a plastic bag and crush them. Label and set out the materials for the students.

Expected Outcome Soap flakes, salt, sugar, and vinegar dissolve easily. Pepper, chalk, and vegetable oil do not.

Think It Over The ability to dissolve is not related to whether a substance is solid or liquid. Some solids and liquids dissolved readily, but other solids and liquids did not.

Changing Concentration You can change the concentration of a solution by adding more solute. You can also change it by adding or removing solvent. For example, fruit juices are sometimes packaged as concentrates, which are concentrated solutions. In making the concentrate, water was removed from the natural juice. When you make juice from the concentrate, you add water, making a dilute solution.

Measuring Concentration You know that maple syrup is more concentrated than maple sap. But you probably do not know the actual concentration of either solution. **To measure concentration, you compare the amount of solute to the amount of solvent or to the total amount of solution.**

Often, the method used to describe concentration depends on the type of solution. For example, you might measure the mass of a solute or solvent in grams. Or you might measure the volume of a solute or solvent in milliliters or liters. You can report concentration as the percent of solute in solution by volume or mass.

 Reading Checkpoint How can you change the concentration of a solution?

Solubility

If a substance dissolves in water, a question you might ask is, "How much can dissolve?" Suppose you add sugar to a glass of iced tea. Is there a limit to how "sweet" you can make the tea? The answer is yes. At the temperature of iced tea, several spoonfuls of sugar are about all you can add. At some point, no matter how much you stir the tea, no more sugar will dissolve. **Solubility** is a measure of how much solute can dissolve in a solvent at a given temperature.

When you've added so much solute that no more dissolves, you have a **saturated solution.** If you add more sugar to a saturated solution of iced tea, the extra sugar just settles to the bottom of the glass. On the other hand, if you can continue to dissolve more solute, you still have an **unsaturated solution.**

FIGURE 6
Dissolving Sugar in Tea
At some point, this boy will not be able to dissolve any more sugar in his tea.
Applying Concepts *What term describes how much sugar can dissolve in a solvent?*

L ◆ 93

Solubility of Compounds

Focus Use Figure 7 to help students visualize the concept of solubility and to compare the solubility of some common compounds.

Teach Have students look at the solubility values listed in the table in Figure 7. Explain that the values refer to the maximum mass of solute that can dissolve in 100 grams of water at $0°$ Celsius. Point out the solubility of baking soda (6.9 g) and sugar (180 g). Then, call students' attention to the piles of baking soda and sugar pictured on the left. Explain that the piles represent the amounts given in the table.

Apply Ask: **How large a pile of table salt would dissolve in 100 g of water at 0°C? Explain.** (*Sample answer: The solubility of table salt is greater than that of baking soda, but less than that of sugar. Therefore, the pile of table salt would be larger than the pile of baking soda but smaller than the pile of sugar.*) **learning modality: visual**

Factors Affecting Solubility

Teach Key Concepts `L2`
Conditions That Affect Solubility

Focus State that the solubility of a substance is a characteristic property of the substance. Add, however, that solubility may be affected by such factors as pressure, type of solvent, and temperature.

Teach Describe how pressure affects the solubility of a gas: the more pressure a gas is under, the more of it that dissolves. Explain how the nature of the solvent affects how well a solute dissolves. For example, explain why vinegar is soluble in water but not in oil. Ask: **How do you think temperature affects solubility?** (*Students are likely to predict correctly that increasing temperature increases solubility.*) Explain how the effect of temperature varies with different materials.

Apply Refer students to the values in the table in Figure 7. Ask: **What might the solubility of table sugar be in 100 g of water at 50°C?** (*Accept any answer greater than 180 g, which is the solubility of table sugar at 0°C.*) **learning modality: logical/ mathematical**

Solubility in 100 g of Water at 0°C	
Compound	Solubility (g)
Carbon dioxide (CO_2)	0.348
Baking soda ($NaHCO_3$)	6.9
Table salt ($NaCl$)	35.7
Table sugar ($C_{12}H_{22}O_{11}$)	180

Baking Soda 6.9 g   **Sugar 180 g**

FIGURE 7
Each compound listed in the table dissolves in water, but in different amounts.
Interpreting Tables *Which compound is the most soluble? Which is the least soluble?*

Working With Solubility The solubility of a substance tells you how much solute you can dissolve before a solution becomes saturated. Solubility is given for a specific solvent (such as water) under certain conditions (such as temperature). Look at the table in Figure 7. It compares the solubility of some familiar compounds. In this case, the solvent is water and the temperature is 0°C. From the table, you can see that 6.9 grams of baking soda will dissolve in 100 grams of water at 0°C. But the same mass of water at the same temperature will dissolve 180 grams of table sugar!

Using Solubility Solubility can be used to help identify a substance because it is a characteristic property of matter. Suppose you had a white powder that looked like table salt or sugar. You wouldn't know for sure whether the powder is salt or sugar. And you wouldn't use taste to identify it. Instead, you could measure its solubility in water at 0°C and compare the results to the data in Figure 7.

 What does the solubility of a substance tell you?

Factors Affecting Solubility

Which dissolves more sugar: iced tea or hot tea? You have already read that there is a limit to solubility. An iced tea and sugar solution quickly becomes saturated. Yet a hot, steaming cup of the same tea can dissolve much more sugar before the limit is reached. The solubilities of solutes change when conditions change. **Factors that affect the solubility of a substance include pressure, the type of solvent, and temperature.**

Lab zone Skills Activity

Predicting
Make a saturated solution of baking soda in water. Add one small spoonful of baking soda to about 250 mL of cool water. Stir until the baking soda dissolves. Continue adding baking soda until no more dissolves. Keep track of how much baking soda you use. Then predict what would happen if you used warm water instead. Make a plan to test your prediction. With approval from your teacher, carry out your plan. Did your results confirm your prediction? Explain.

 Lab zone Skills Activity

Skills Focus Predicting `L3`

Materials baking soda, cool water, small spoon, graduated cylinder, beaker, warm water

Time 15 minutes

Tip Tell students to add a small amount of baking soda at a time so they can make a more accurate estimate of solubility.

Expected Outcome Students are likely to predict that more baking soda will dissolve in warm water than in cool water.

Extend Let students test their predictions by measuring how much baking soda dissolves in warm water and comparing it to the amount that dissolved in cool water. **learning modality: kinesthetic**

Pressure Pressure affects the solubility of gases. The higher the pressure of the gas over the solvent, the more gas can dissolve. To increase the carbon dioxide concentration in soft drinks, the gas is added under high pressure. Opening the bottle or can reduces the pressure. The escaping gas makes the sound you hear.

Scuba divers are aware of the effect of pressure on gases. Air is about 80 percent nitrogen. When divers breathe from tanks of compressed air, nitrogen from the air dissolves in their blood in greater amounts as they descend. This occurs because the pressure underwater increases with depth. If divers return to the surface too quickly, nitrogen bubbles come out of solution and block blood flow. Divers double over in pain, which is why this condition is sometimes called "the bends."

Solvents Sometimes you just can't make a solution because the solute and solvent are not compatible. Have you ever tried to mix oil and vinegar, which is mostly water, to make salad dressing? If you have, you've seen how the dressing quickly separates into layers after you stop shaking it. Oil and water separate because water is a polar compound and oil is nonpolar. Polar compounds and nonpolar compounds do not mix very well.

For liquid solutions, the solvent affects how well a solute dissolves. The expression "like dissolves like" gives you a clue to which solutes are soluble in which solvents. Ionic and polar compounds usually dissolve in polar solvents. Nonpolar compounds do not usually dissolve in polar solvents. If you work with paints, you know that water-based (latex) paints can be cleaned up with just soap and water. But cleaning up oil-based paints may require a nonpolar solvent, such as turpentine.

FIGURE 8
Pressure Changes Solubility
Opening a shaken bottle of soda water may produce quite a spray as dissolved gas comes out of solution.

 Just after ▶ shaking...

 ...a little ▶ while later

FIGURE 9
Solvents and Solubility
Try as she might, this girl cannot get oil and vinegar to stay mixed. Nonpolar and polar compounds don't form solutions with each other.

Chapter 3 L ◆ 95

L ● 95

Math Skill Making and interpreting graphs

Focus Remind students that solids have greater solubility in water at higher temperatures.

Teach Call students' attention to the graph, and have them read the labels on the axes. Inform students that potassium nitrate is a crystalline salt that is used in fertilizer and gunpowder.

Answers

1. KNO₃ is least soluble at 0°C.

2. Approximately 65 g of KNO₃ are needed to saturate a water solution at 40°C.

3. KNO₃ is about twice as soluble at 40°C as it is at 20°C.

4. No; the curve shows that solubility increases more with each 20°C increase in temperature.

All in One Teaching Resources

• Transparency L32

Lab zone Build Inquiry L2

Effect of Temperature on Solubility of Gas

Materials 2 bottles of carbonated beverages, 1 at room temperature and 1 chilled

Time 10 minutes

Focus Have students predict the effect of temperature on the solubility of carbon dioxide in a bottled beverage.

Teach Tell students that one of the bottles of carbonated beverage is cold and the other is warm. Give students a chance to feel the difference in temperature between the two bottles. Then, ask: **Which bottle will lose less gas when I open it?** *(Students are likely to predict accurately that the chilled bottle will lose less gas than the bottle at room temperature.)* Have students watch while you open the bottles. They will notice the fizz of escaping gas from the room temperature bottle and little or no fizz from the chilled bottle. Explain that, unlike solids, gases become less soluble at higher temperatures.

Apply Have students look at the graph in the Math Analyzing Data feature. Then, ask: **If you made a graph for the solubility of carbon dioxide in water at different**

Temperature and Solubility

The solubility of the compound potassium nitrate (KNO₃) varies in water at different temperatures.

1. **Reading Graphs** At which temperature shown in the graph is KNO₃ least soluble in water?
2. **Reading Graphs** Approximately what mass of KNO₃ is needed to saturate a water solution at 40°C?
3. **Calculating** About how much more soluble is KNO₃ at 40°C than at 20°C?
4. **Interpreting Data** Does solubility increase at the same rate with every 20°C increase in temperature? Explain.

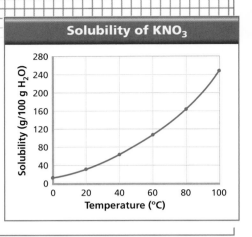

Solubility of KNO₃

(graph: Solubility (g/100 g H₂O) vs Temperature (°C))

Temperature For most solids, solubility increases as the temperature increases. That is why the temperature is reported when solubilities are listed. For example, the solubility of table sugar in 100 grams of water changes from 180 grams at 0°C to 231 grams at 25°C to 487 grams at 100°C.

Cooks use this increased solubility of sugar when they make desserts such as rock candy, fudge, or peanut brittle. To make peanut brittle, you start with a mixture of sugar, corn syrup, and water. At room temperature, not enough of the required sugar can dissolve in the water. The mixture must be heated until it begins to boil. Nuts and other ingredients are added before the mixture cools. Some recipes call for temperatures above 100°C. Because the exact temperature can affect the result, cooks use a candy thermometer to check the temperature.

Unlike most solids, gases become less soluble when the temperature goes up. For example, more carbon dioxide will dissolve in cold water than in hot water. Carbon dioxide makes soda water fizzy when you pour it into a glass. If you open a warm bottle of soda water, carbon dioxide escapes the liquid in greater amounts than if the soda water had been chilled. Why does warm soda taste "flat"? It contains less gas. If you like soda water that's very fizzy, open it when it's cold!

FIGURE 10
Temperature Changes Solubility
Some hard candy is made by cooling a sugar water solution. *Interpreting Photographs Why does sugar precipitate on the string when the solution is cooled?*

---

temperatures, what would the curve look like? *(Students should describe a curve showing the solubility of carbon dioxide decreasing with increasing temperature.)*
learning modality: logical/mathematical

FIGURE 11
A Supersaturated Solution
Dropping a crystal of solute into a supersaturated solution (left) causes the excess solute to rapidly come out of solution (center). Soon, the precipitation is complete (right).

Go Online
SCLINKS
For: Links on solubility
Visit: www.SciLinks.org
Web Code: scn-1232

Download a worksheet that will guide students' review of Internet sources on solubility.

When heated, a solution can dissolve more solute than it can at cooler temperatures. If a heated, saturated solution cools slowly, sometimes the extra solute will remain dissolved. A **supersaturated solution** has more dissolved solute than is predicted by its solubility at the given temperature. When you disturb a supersaturated solution by dropping in a crystal of the solute, the extra solute will come out of solution.

Go Online
SCLINKS
For: Links on solubility
Visit: www.SciLinks.org
Web Code: scn-1232

Reading Checkpoint As temperature increases, what happens to the solubility of a gas?

Section 2 Assessment

Target Reading Skill Building Vocabulary Use your sentences about the Key Terms to help answer the questions.

Reviewing Key Concepts

1. a. Reviewing What is concentration?
   b. Describing What quantities are compared when the concentration of a solution is measured?
   c. Applying Concepts Solution A contains 50 g of sugar. Solution B contains 100 g of sugar. Can you tell which solution has a higher sugar concentration? Explain.
2. a. Defining What is solubility?
   b. Explaining How can solubility help you identify a substance?
   c. Calculating Look back at the table in Figure 7. At 0°C, about how many times more soluble in water is sugar than salt?

3. a. Listing What are three factors that affect solubility?
   b. Summarizing How does temperature affect the solubility of most solids?
   c. Relating Cause and Effect When you heat water and add sugar, all of the sugar dissolves. When you cool the solution, some sugar comes out of solution. Explain.

Math Practice

4. Calculating a Concentration What is the concentration of a solution that contains 45 grams of sugar in 500 grams of solution?
5. Calculating a Concentration How much sugar is dissolved in 500 grams of a solution if the solution is 70 percent sugar by mass?

Math Practice

Math Skill Calculating percentage

Answers
4. 9%
5. 350 g

Lab zone Chapter Project

Keep Students on Track As students use their own acid-base indicators and also pH papers to test a variety of substances, remind them to record their test results. Advise them to make a data table for this purpose.

Go Online
SCLINKS NSTA
For: Links on solubility
Visit: www.SciLinks.org
Web Code: scn-1232

Monitor Progress L2

Answers
Figure 10 Sugar precipitates because sugar is less soluble at lower temperatures.

 Reading Checkpoint It decreases.

Assess

Reviewing Key Concepts

1. a. The amount of solute dissolved in a certain amount of solvent or solution **b.** The amount of solute is compared to the amount of solvent or the total amount of solution. **c.** No, because you do not know the amount of solvent or the total amount of solution

2. a. Solubility is a measure of how much solute can dissolve in a solvent at a given temperature. **b.** Because solubility is a characteristic property of matter, you may be able to identify an unknown substance by comparing its solubility with the solubility of known substances. **c.** Sugar is about five times more soluble.

3. a. Three factors that affect solubility are pressure, type of solvent, and temperature. **b.** The solubility of most solids is greater at higher temperatures. **c.** At a lower temperature, sugar has lower solubility, so some of the sugar comes out of solution.

Reteach L1
Read the sentences containing key terms, but leave the key terms blank. Call on students to fill in the blanks.

Performance Assessment L2
Writing Have students explain how they could dissolve more salt in a saturated salt solution.

All in One Teaching Resources
• Section Summary: *Concentration and Solubility*
• Review and Reinforce: *Concentration and Solubility*
• Enrich: *Concentration and Solubility*

Objectives

After this lesson, students will be able to

L.3.3.1 Name the properties of acids and bases.

L.3.3.2 Identify where acids and bases are commonly used.

Target Reading Skill

Asking Questions Explain that changing a head into a question helps students anticipate the ideas, facts, and events they are about to read.

Answers

Sample questions and answers:
Describing Acids and Bases

What is an acid? (*An acid is a substance that tastes sour, reacts with metals and carbonates, and turns blue litmus paper red.*) **What is a base?** (*A base is a substance that tastes bitter, feels slippery, and turns red litmus paper blue.*) **What are uses of acids and bases?** (*Uses of acids include cleaning products, fertilizers, and car batteries; uses of bases include cleaning products, baking ingredients, and cement manufacturing.*)

All in One Teaching Resources

• Transparency L33

Preteach

Build Background Knowledge L2

Recalling the Taste of Acids

Ask: **What do lemons and vinegar have in common?** (*Students are likely to say a sour taste.*) Explain that they have a sour taste because they are acids and a sour taste is a property of acids. Tell students that in this section they will learn more about acids, and they will also learn about other types of compounds called bases.

Reading Preview

Key Concepts

• What are the properties of acids and bases?

• Where are acids and bases commonly used?

Key Terms

• acid • corrosive • indicator
• base

Target Reading Skill

Asking Questions Before you read, preview the red headings. In a graphic organizer like the one below, ask a *what* question for each heading. As you read, write the answers to your questions.

Describing Acids and Bases

Question	Answer
What is an acid?	An acid is . . .

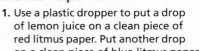
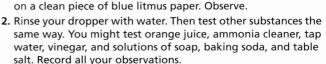

Lab zone Discover Activity

What Colors Does Litmus Paper Turn?

1. Use a plastic dropper to put a drop of lemon juice on a clean piece of red litmus paper. Put another drop on a clean piece of blue litmus paper. Observe.
2. Rinse your dropper with water. Then test other substances the same way. You might test orange juice, ammonia cleaner, tap water, vinegar, and solutions of soap, baking soda, and table salt. Record all your observations.
3. Wash your hands when you are finished.

Think It Over

Classifying Group the substances based on how they make the litmus paper change color. What other properties do the items in each group have in common?

Did you have any fruit for breakfast today—perhaps an orange, an apple, or fruit juice? If so, an acid was part of your meal. The last time you washed your hair, did you use shampoo? If your answer is yes, then you may have used a base.

You use many products that contain acids and bases. In addition, the chemical reactions of acids and bases even keep you alive! What are acids and bases—how do they react, and what are their uses?

Properties of Acids

What is an acid, and how do you know when you have one? In order to identify an acid, you can test its properties. **Acids** are compounds whose characteristic properties include the kinds of reactions they undergo. **An acid is a substance that tastes sour, reacts with metals and carbonates, and turns blue litmus paper red.** Some common acids you may have heard of are hydrochloric acid, nitric acid, sulfuric acid, carbonic acid, and acetic acid.

◀ Lemons are acidic.

Lab zone Discover Activity

Skills Focus Classifying L1

Materials red and blue litmus paper, plastic dropper, plastic cups, lemon juice, orange juice, ammonia cleaner, tap water, vinegar, and solutions of soap, baking soda, and table salt

Time 15 minutes

Tips Students must rinse droppers after each test. Students must not taste the substances.

Expected Outcome Acids turn blue litmus paper red. Bases turn red litmus paper blue.

Think It Over Lemon juice, orange juice, and vinegar turn blue litmus paper red. Ammonia cleaner, soap, and baking soda turn red litmus paper blue. Tap water and salt water have no effect. Students may say that the acids taste sour and the bases feel slippery.

Sour Taste If you've ever tasted a lemon, you've had first-hand experience with the sour taste of acids. Can you think of other foods that sometimes taste sour, or tart? Citrus fruits—lemons, grapefruits, oranges, and limes—are acidic. They all contain citric acid. Other fruits (cherries, tomatoes, apples) and many other types of foods contain acids, too.

Although sour taste is a characteristic of many acids, it is not one you should use to identify a compound as an acid. Scientists never taste chemicals in order to identify them. Though acids in sour foods may be safe to eat, many other acids are not.

Reactions With Metals Do you notice the bubbles in Figure 12? Acids react with certain metals to produce hydrogen gas. Not all metals react this way, but magnesium, zinc, and iron do. When they react, the metals seem to disappear in the solution. This observation is one reason acids are described as **corrosive,** meaning they "eat away" at other materials.

The metal plate in Figure 12 is being etched with acid. Etching is one method of making printing plates that are then used to print works of art on paper. To make an etching, an artist first coats a metal plate with an acid-resistant material—often bees-wax. Then the design is cut into the beeswax with a sharp tool, exposing some of the metal. When the plate is treated with acid, the acid eats away the design in the exposed metal. Later, ink applied to the plate collects in the grooves made by the acid. The ink is transferred to the paper when the etching is printed.

FIGURE 12
Etching With Acid
Metal etching takes advantage of the reaction of an acid with a metal. Lines are cut in a wax coating on a plate. Here, hydrochloric acid eats away at the exposed zinc metal, forming bubbles you can see in the close-up. **Applying Concepts** *What gas forms in this reaction?*

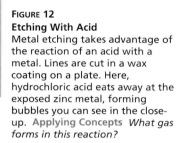

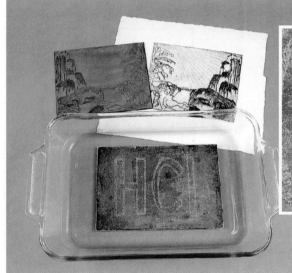

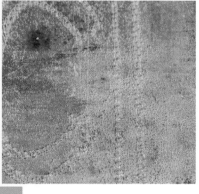

Chapter 3 **L** ◆ **99**

L ● 99

Testing for Limestone

Materials 1.0 *M* muriatic acid (hydrochloric acid), dropper, 1 limestone rock, 1 non-limestone rock

Time 10 minutes

Focus Give students a chance to observe the limestone test described in the text.

Teach Explain that acids react with carbonates, which are compounds containing carbonate ions (CO_3^{2-}), and the reaction produces carbon dioxide gas. State that this characteristic reaction of acids can be used to identify rocks containing limestone, because limestone contains carbonates. Apply one or two drops of acid to each rock sample, and allow students to observe what happens. (Wear goggles and a lab apron and use caution when handling the acid.)

Apply Ask: **Based on your observations, which rock contains limestone?** (*Students should identify the rock that bubbled when acid was applied.*) **learning modality: visual**

Properties of Bases

Teach Key Concepts L2

Common Properties of Bases

Focus Guide students in inferring the properties of bases.

Teach Tell students that bases are a group of compounds that are often described as the "opposite" of acids. Ask: **What properties do you think characterize bases?** (*Students are expected to name properties that are "opposite" those of acids. For example, they might say correctly that bases do not taste sour, do not react with carbonates, and do not turn blue litmus paper red.*) Elaborate by telling students that bases taste bitter, feel slippery, and turn red litmus paper blue.

Apply Name products that contain bases, such as shampoo, soap, and tonic water. Point out how shampoo and soap feel slippery and tonic water tastes bitter.
learning modality: verbal

Reactions With Carbonates Acids also react with carbonate ions in a characteristic way. Recall that an ion is an atom or a group of atoms that has an electric charge. Carbonate ions contain carbon and oxygen atoms bonded together. They carry an overall negative charge (CO_3^{2-}). One product of an acid's reaction with carbonates is the gas carbon dioxide.

Geologists, scientists who study Earth, use this property of acids to identify rocks containing certain types of limestone. Limestone is a compound that contains the carbonate ion. If a geologist pours dilute hydrochloric acid on a limestone rock, bubbles of carbon dioxide appear on the rock's surface.

Reactions With Indicators If you did the Discover activity, you used litmus paper to test several substances. Litmus is an example of an **indicator,** a compound that changes color when in contact with an acid or a base. Look at Figure 13 to see what happens to litmus paper as it is dipped in a solution containing acid. Vinegar, lemon juice, and other acids turn blue litmus paper red. Sometimes chemists use other indicators to test for acids, but litmus is one of the easiest to use.

Properties of Bases

Bases are another group of compounds that can be identified by their common properties. **A base is a substance that tastes bitter, feels slippery, and turns red litmus paper blue.** Bases often are described as the "opposite" of acids. Common bases include sodium hydroxide, calcium hydroxide, and ammonia.

FIGURE 13
The Litmus Test
Litmus paper is an easy way to identify quickly whether an unknown compound is an acid or a base. *Inferring What can you infer about a liquid that does not change the color of blue litmus paper?*

Acids turn blue litmus paper red.
Acid

Bases turn red litmus paper blue.
Base

100 ◆ L

FIGURE 14
Slippery Feel of Bases
Most soaps contain bases, which make them feel slippery.

Bitter Taste Have you ever tasted tonic water? The slightly bitter taste is caused by the base quinine. Bases taste bitter. Soaps, some shampoos, and detergents taste bitter too, but you wouldn't want to identify these as bases by a taste test!

Slippery Feel Picture yourself washing a dog. As you massage the soap into the dog's fur, you notice that your hands feel slippery. This slippery feeling is another characteristic of bases. But just as you avoid tasting a substance to identify it, you wouldn't want to touch it. Strong bases can irritate or burn your skin. A safer way to identify bases is by their other properties.

Reactions With Indicators As you might guess, if litmus paper can be used to test acids, it can be used to test bases, too. Look at Figure 13 to see what happens to a litmus paper as it is dipped in a basic solution. Bases turn red litmus paper blue. Like acids, bases react with other indicators. But litmus paper gives a reliable, safe test. An easy way to remember which color litmus turns for acids or bases is to remember the letter *b*. **B**ases turn litmus paper **b**lue.

Other Reactions of Bases Unlike acids, bases don't react with carbonates to produce carbon dioxide. At first, you may think it is useless to know that a base doesn't react with certain chemicals. But if you know what a compound doesn't do, you know something about it. For example, you know it's not an acid. Another important property of bases is how they react with acids. You will learn more about these reactions in Section 4.

 Reading Checkpoint What is one safe way to identify a base?

For: Links on acids and bases
Visit: www.SciLinks.org
Web Code: scn-1233

Uses of Acids and Bases

Teach Key Concepts L2

Identifying Uses of Acids and Bases

Focus Use Figures 15 and 16 to help students identify uses of specific acids and bases.

Teach First, call students' attention to Figure 15. Ask: **What two acids do you need in your diet?** (*Ascorbic acid, or vitamin C, and folic acid*) **What is hydrochloric acid used for?** (*Cleaning bricks and metals*) **What acid is used in car batteries?** (*Sulfuric acid*) **What two acids might you find in fertilizer?** (*Nitric acid and phosphoric acid*) Next, call students' attention to Figure 16, and ask: **What base is found in drain cleaner?** (*Sodium hydroxide, or lye*) **What base would you add to garden soil to make it less acidic for plants?** (*Calcium oxide*) **Where might you find calcium hydroxide?** (*In mortar and cement*)

Apply Ask: **Why is baking soda used in baked goods?** (*It reacts with acids to produce carbon dioxide gas, which makes baked goods light and fluffy.*) **learning modality: visual**

Integrating Life Science L2

Point out that an acid called lactic acid is produced in muscles when they are active. Explain that lactic acid is formed when a carbohydrate called glycogen breaks down in muscles. The reaction produces the energy needed for muscle activity. The lactic acid that is produced builds up in the muscles, causing the burn you sometimes feel when you exercise and also the muscle soreness that is common after a hard workout. Challenge students to explain the phrase, sometimes used in reference to exercising, "Go for the burn." (*Sample answer: Exercise hard enough to build up lactic acid, which causes a burning sensation in the muscles.*)
learning modality: verbal

FIGURE 15
Uses of Acids

Acids play an important role in our nutrition and are also found in valuable products used in homes and industries.

Acids and Food ▼
Many of the vitamins in the foods you eat are acids.

Acids in the Home ▶
People often use dilute solutions of acids to clean brick and other surfaces. Hardware stores sell muriatic (hydrochloric) acid, which is used to clean bricks and metals.

Acids and Industry ▼
Farmers and manufacturers depend on acids for many uses.

Tomatoes and oranges contain ascorbic acid, or vitamin C.

Folic acid, needed for healthy cell growth, is found in green leafy vegetables.

Sulfuric acid is used in car batteries, to refine petroleum, and to treat iron and steel.

Nitric acid and phosphoric acid are used to make fertilizers for crops, lawns, and gardens.

Uses of Acids and Bases

Where can you find acids and bases? Almost anywhere. You already learned that acids are found in many fruits and other foods. In fact, many of them play important roles in the body as vitamins, including ascorbic acid, or vitamin C, and folic acid. Many cell processes also produce acids as waste products. For example, lactic acid builds up in your muscles when you make them work hard.

Manufacturers, farmers, and builders are only some people who depend on acids and bases in their work. **Acids and bases have many uses around the home and in industry.** Look at Figure 15 and Figure 16 to learn about a few of them. Many of the uses of bases take advantage of their ability to react with acids.

Reading Checkpoint What vitamin is an acid?

FIGURE 16
Uses of Bases

The reactions of bases make them valuable raw materials for a range of products.

Bases and Industry ▲
Mortar and cement are manufactured using the bases calcium oxide and calcium hydroxide. Gardeners sometimes add calcium oxide to soil to make the soil less acidic for plants.

Bases in the Home ▶
Ammonia solutions are safe to spray with bare hands, but gloves must be worn when working with drain cleaners.

Drain cleaners contain sodium hydroxide (lye).

You can't mistake the odor of household cleaning products made with ammonia.

Bases and Food ▼
Baking soda reacts with acids to produce carbon dioxide gas in baked goods. Without these gas bubbles, this delicious variety of breads, biscuits, cakes, and cookies would not be light and fluffy.

Section 3 Assessment

🎯 **Target Reading Skill** Asking Questions Work with a partner to check the answers in your graphic organizer.

Reviewing Key Concepts

1. a. Listing What are four properties of acids? Of bases?
  b. Describing How can you use litmus paper to distinguish an acid from a base?
  c. Applying Concepts How might you tell if a food contains an acid as one of its ingredients?
2. a. Reviewing What are three practical uses of an acid? Of a base?
  b. Making Generalizations Where are you most likely to find acids and bases in your own home? Explain.

c. Making Judgments Why is it wise to wear gloves when spreading fertilizer in a garden?

Writing in Science

Wanted Poster A bottle of acid is missing from the chemistry lab shelf! Design a wanted poster describing properties of the missing acid. Also include descriptions of tests a staff member from the chemistry lab could *safely* perform to determine if a bottle that is found actually contains acid. Add a caution on your poster that warns people *not* to touch any bottles they find. Instead, they should notify the chemistry lab.

Writing in Science

Writing Mode Description
Scoring Rubric
4 Exceeds criteria
3 Meets criteria
2 Includes a poster and describes properties and a test but contains some errors
1 Includes a general description only and/or contains serious errors

---

Monitor Progress _____ L2
Answer

✓ Reading Checkpoint Vitamin C is an acid.

Assess

Reviewing Key Concepts

1. a. Acids taste sour, react with metals, react with carbonates, and turn blue litmus paper red. Bases taste bitter, feel slippery, do not react with carbonates, and turn red litmus paper blue. **b.** An acid turns blue litmus paper red. A base turns red litmus paper blue. **c.** If a food contains an acid, it may taste sour.
2. a. Sample answer: Acids are found in foods, cleaners, and car batteries. Bases are used in cleaners, baked goods, and manufacturing cement. **b.** In your own home, you are most likely to find acids and bases in foods and cleaning and gardening products. **c.** Because fertilizer contains acids that can irritate the skin

Reteach L1
Work with the class to make a concept map on the board or an overhead transparency showing the properties and uses of acids and bases.

Performance Assessment L2
Writing Have students write a paragraph describing three ways you can tell acids and bases apart.
  Students can keep their paragraphs in their portfolios. 📁 Portfolio

All in One Teaching Resources
• Section Summary: *Describing Acids and Bases*
• Review and Reinforce: *Describing Acids and Bases*
• Enrich: *Describing Acids and Bases*

Objectives

After this lesson, students will be able to

L.3.4.1 State what kinds of ions acids and bases form in water.

L.3.4.2 Explain what pH tells you about a solution.

L.3.4.3 Describe what happens in a neutralization reaction.

Target Reading Skill

Previewing Visuals Explain that looking at the visuals before they read helps students activate prior knowledge and predict what they are about to read.

Answers

Sample questions and answers: Neutralization

What is a neutral solution? *(A neutral solution is one that has a pH close to 7.)*

What is neutralization? *(Neutralization is a reaction between an acid and a base.)*

All in One Teaching Resources

• Transparency L34

Preteach

Build Background Knowledge   L2

Acid Solutions

Ask: **What are the ingredients of lemonade?** *(Sugar, water, lemon juice)* **Does all lemonade taste the same?** *(No; it can be sweet or tart, weak or strong, depending on the relative amounts of the ingredients.)* **What would you add to lemonade to make it more tart?** *(More lemon juice)* Explain that lemonade is a solution of an acid in water. Tell students they will learn about solutions of acids and also solutions of bases in this section.

Section 4

Acids and Bases in Solution

Reading Preview

Key Concepts

• What kinds of ions do acids and bases form in water?

• What does pH tell you about a solution?

• What happens in a neutralization reaction?

Key Terms

• hydrogen ion (H⁺)
• hydroxide ion (OH⁻)
• pH scale   • neutralization   • salt

Target Reading Skill

Previewing Visuals When you preview, you look ahead at the material to be read. Preview Figure 21. Then write two questions that you have about the diagram in a graphic organizer like the one below. As you read, answer your questions.

Neutralization

Q. What is a neutral solution?
A.
Q.

Go Online
PHSchool.com

For: More on pH scale
Visit: PHSchool.com
Web Code: cgd-2034

Lab zone · Discover Activity

What Can Cabbage Juice Tell You?

1. Using a dropper, put 5 drops of red cabbage juice into each of three separate plastic cups.
2. Add 10 drops of lemon juice (an acid) to one cup. Add 10 drops of ammonia cleaner (a base) to another. Keep the third cup for comparison. Record the colors you see.
3. Now add ammonia, 1 drop at a time, to the cup containing lemon juice. Keep adding ammonia until the color no longer changes. Record all color changes you see.
4. Add lemon juice a drop at a time to the ammonia until the color no longer changes. Record the changes you see.

Think It Over

Forming Operational Definitions Based on your observations, what could you add to your definitions of acids and bases?

A chemist pours hydrochloric acid into a beaker. Then she adds sodium hydroxide to the acid. The mixture looks the same, but the beaker becomes warm. If she tested the solution with litmus paper, what color would the paper turn? Would you be surprised if it did not change color at all? If exactly the right amounts and concentrations of the acid and the base were mixed, the beaker would hold nothing but salt water!

Acids and Bases in Solution

How can two corrosive chemicals, an acid and a base, produce something harmless to the touch? To answer this question, you must know what happens to acids and bases in solution.

Acids What do acids have in common? Notice that each formula in the list of acids in Figure 17 begins with hydrogen. The acids you will learn about in this section produce one or more hydrogen ions and a negative ion in solution with water. A **hydrogen ion (H⁺)** is an atom of hydrogen that has lost its electron. The negative ion may be a nonmetal or a polyatomic ion. Hydrogen ions are the key to the reaction of acids.

Lab zone · Discover Activity

Skills Focus Forming operational definitions   L1

Materials dropper, red cabbage juice, 3 plastic cups, lemon juice, ammonia cleaner

Time 15 minutes

Tips To make cabbage juice, steep red cabbage leaves in hot water for 10 to

20 minutes until the water is deep red, and then discard the leaves. In Steps 3 and 4, lemon juice or ammonia should be added until the solution turns red or green.

Expected Outcome Cabbage juice will look red in an acid and green in a base. It may look light pink, purple, or blue in the transition between these two colors.

Think It Over Acids make red cabbage juice appear red. Bases turn red cabbage juice green.

Important Acids and Bases			
Acid	**Formula**	**Base**	**Formula**
Hydrochloric acid	HCl	Sodium hydroxide	$NaOH$
Nitric acid	HNO_3	Potassium hydroxide	KOH
Sulfuric acid	H_2SO_4	Calcium hydroxide	$Ca(OH)_2$
Carbonic acid	H_2CO_3	Aluminum hydroxide	$Al(OH)_3$
Acetic acid	$HC_2H_3O_2$	Ammonia	NH_3
Phosphoric acid	H_3PO_4	Calcium oxide	CaO

FIGURE 17
The table lists some commonly encountered acids and bases. **Making Generalizations** *What do all of the acid formulas in the table have in common?*

Acids in water solution separate into hydrogen ions (H^+) and negative ions. In the case of hydrochloric acid, for example, hydrogen ions and chloride ions form:

$$HCl \xrightarrow{\text{water}} H^+ + Cl^-$$

Now you can add to the definition of acids you learned in Section 3. **An acid is any substance that produces hydrogen ions (H^+) in water.** These hydrogen ions cause the properties of acids. For instance, when you add certain metals to an acid, hydrogen ions interact with the metal atoms. One product of the reaction is hydrogen gas (H_2). Hydrogen ions also react with blue litmus paper, turning it red. That's why every acid gives the same litmus test result.

Bases The formulas of bases give you clues to what ions they have in common. You can see in the table in Figure 17 that many bases are made of positive ions combined with hydroxide ions. The **hydroxide ion (OH^-)** is a negative ion, made of oxygen and hydrogen. When bases dissolve in water, the positive ions and hydroxide ions separate. Look, for example, at what happens to sodium hydroxide:

$$NaOH \xrightarrow{\text{water}} Na^+ + OH^-$$

Not every base contains hydroxide ions. For example, the gas ammonia (NH_3) does not. But in solution, ammonia is a base that reacts with water to form hydroxide ions.

$$NH_3 + H_2O \longrightarrow NH_4^+ + OH^-$$

Notice that in both reactions, there are negative hydroxide ions. **A base is any substance that produces hydroxide ions (OH^-) in water.** Hydroxide ions are responsible for the bitter taste and slippery feel of bases, and turn red litmus paper blue.

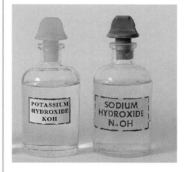

FIGURE 18
Comparing Bases
Many bases are made of positive ions combined with hydroxide ions.

Chapter 3 L ◆ 105

Instruct

Acids and Bases in Solution

Teach Key Concepts L2
Acids, Bases, and Ions

Focus Guide students in understanding how acids and bases produce ions in water.

Teach Read the boldface sentences on this page describing acids and bases. Remind students that ions are atoms or groups of atoms that have become electrically charged. Then, have students inspect the formulas for acids and bases in Figure 17. Point out that all the acids contain hydrogen. Ask: **What do all the bases—except ammonia and calcium oxide—contain?** *(OH)*. Explain that when an acid dissolves in water, positive hydrogen ions (H^+) are produced, and when a base dissolves in water, negative hydroxide ions (OH^-) are produced. Have students look at the equation for ammonia at the bottom of the page. Ask: **What does ammonia produce when it dissolves in water?** *(Hydroxide ions)*

Apply Ask: **What do you think explains the properties of acids?** *(Hydrogen ions)* **Of bases?** *(Hydroxide ions)* **learning modality: verbal**

All in One Teaching Resources
• Transparency L35

For: More on pH scale
Visit: PHSchool.com
Web Code: cgd-2034

Students can review the pH scale in an online interactivity.

Independent Practice L2
All in One Teaching Resources
• Guided Reading and Study Worksheet: *Acids and Bases in Solution*

O Student Edition on Audio CD

Monitor Progress L2

Writing Have students explain what causes the properties of acids and what causes the properties of bases.

Answer
Figure 17 All of the acid formulas start with hydrogen.

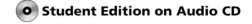

Differentiated Instruction

Less Proficient Readers L1
Developing Vocabulary Students may confuse hydrogen ions and hydroxide ions because the two terms look similar. Explain that *hydro-* in hydroxide refers to hydrogen and *-oxide* refers to oxygen. Emphasize this point by relating the two parts of the term *hydroxide* to the symbol for the hydroxide ion, OH^-. **learning modality: verbal**

Gifted and Talented L3
Writing Chemical Equations Challenge students to write a balanced chemical equation to show what is produced when calcium oxide dissolves in water. *($CaO + H_2O \rightarrow Ca^+ + 2\ OH^-$)* **learning modality: logical/mathematical**

Strength of Acids and Bases

Teach Key Concepts $\quad$ L2
Ions in Water

Focus Guide students in recognizing what determines the strength of acids and bases.

Teach Call students' attention to Figure 19. Ask: **Which acid shown in the figure, hydrogen chloride or acetic acid, produces more ions in water?** *(Hydrogen chloride)* **Which acid is stronger?** *(Hydrogen chloride)* Remind students that an acid's properties are determined by hydrogen ions. Then, ask: **What do you think determines the strength of an acid?** *(Sample answers: How well it produces hydrogen ions in water, or how many hydrogen ions it produces)* Remind students that the properties of a base are determined by hydroxide ions. Then, say that the base ammonia produces fewer hydroxide ions in water than does the base sodium hydroxide. Ask: **Which base do you think is a stronger base, ammonia or sodium hydroxide? Why?** *(Sodium hydroxide, because it produces more hydroxide ions)*

Apply Encourage students to state in a single sentence what determines the strength of acids and bases. *(Sample answer: The strength of acids and bases is determined by how well they produce ions in water.)* **learning modality: verbal**

All in One Teaching Resources
• Transparency L36

Help Students Read
Building Vocabulary: Word Origins The term *pH* may be confusing. Students generally do not know what the letters stand for or why the letter H is capitalized. Explain that the letter *p* in pH refers to the power (exponent) used in measuring ion concentrations. The letter *H* refers to hydrogen. Because it is the symbol for an element, H is always capitalized. Thus, pH literally means power of hydrogen. It refers to the hydrogen ion concentration in a solution. Lower numbers represent greater concentrations, that is, greater acidity.

Key
- Chloride ion (Cl⁻)
- Hydrogen ion (H⁺)
- Acetic acid (HC$_2$H$_3$O$_2$)
- Acetate ion (C$_2$H$_3$O$_2^-$)

Strong Acid

In a solution of a strong acid, all the acid molecules break up into ions.

Weak Acid

In a solution of a weak acid, fewer molecules break up into ions.

FIGURE 19
Acids in Solution
Strong acids and weak acids act differently in water. Hydrocloric acid (left) is a strong acid. Acetic acid (right) is a weak acid.

Strength of Acids and Bases

Acids and bases may be strong or weak. Strength refers to how well an acid or a base produces ions in water. As shown in Figure 19, the molecules of a strong acid react to form ions in solution. With a weak acid, very few molecules form ions. At the same concentration, a strong acid produces more hydrogen ions (H⁺) than a weak acid does. Examples of strong acids include hydrochloric acid, sulfuric acid, and nitric acid. Most other acids, such as acetic acid, are weak acids.

Strong bases react in a water solution in a similar way to strong acids. A strong base produces more hydroxide (OH⁻) ions than does an equal concentration of a weak base. Ammonia is a weak base. Lye, or sodium hydroxide, is a strong base.

Measuring pH Knowing the concentration of hydrogen ions is the key to knowing how acidic or basic a solution is. To describe the concentration of ions, chemists use a numeric scale called pH. The **pH scale** is a range of values from 0 to 14. It expresses the concentration of hydrogen ions in a solution.

Lab zone | Try This Activity

pHone Home

1. 🔬 🧴 Select materials such as fruit juices, soda water, coffee, tea, and antacids. If the sample is solid, dissolve some in a cup of water. Use a liquid as is.
2. Predict which materials are most acidic or most basic.
3. Using a plastic dropper, transfer a drop of one sample onto a fresh strip of pH test paper.
4. Compare the color of the strip to the pH test scale on the package.
5. Repeat for all your samples, rinsing the dropper between tests.

Interpreting Data List the samples from lowest to highest pH. Did any results surprise you?

Lab zone | Try This Activity

Skills Focus Interpreting data $\quad$ L2

Materials red and blue litmus paper, plastic dropper, plastic cup, orange juice, soda water, coffee, antacid, tea

Time 15 minutes

Tip Tell students that, in addition to strength of an acid or base, concentration of the acid or base in solution will affect its pH.

Expected Outcome Sample ranking of substances from lowest to highest pH: orange juice, coffee/tea, soda water, antacid. Students may be surprised by the high acidity of some foods.

Extend Have students predict and test whether soft drinks are basic or acidic. **learning modality: visual**

Figure 20 shows where some familiar substances fit on the pH scale. Notice that the most acidic substances are at the low end of the scale. The most basic substances are at the high end of the scale. You need to remember two important points about pH. **A low pH tells you that the concentration of hydrogen ions is high. In contrast, a high pH tells you that the concentration of hydrogen ions is low.** If you keep these ideas in mind, you can make sense of how the scale works.

You can find the pH of a solution by using indicators. The student in Figure 20 is using indicator paper that turns a different color for each pH value. Matching the color of the paper with the colors on the test scale tells how acidic or basic the solution is. A pH lower than 7 is acidic. A pH higher than 7 is basic. If the pH is 7, the solution is neutral. That means it's neither an acid nor a base. Pure water has a pH of 7.

Using Acids and Bases Safely Strength determines, in part, how safe acids and bases are to use. People often say that a solution is weak when they mean it is dilute. This could be a dangerous mistake! Even a dilute solution of hydrochloric acid can eat a hole in your clothing. An equal concentration of acetic acid, however, will not. In order to handle acids and bases safely, you need to know both their pH and their concentration.

Reading Checkpoint How would a weak base differ from an equal concentration of a strong base?

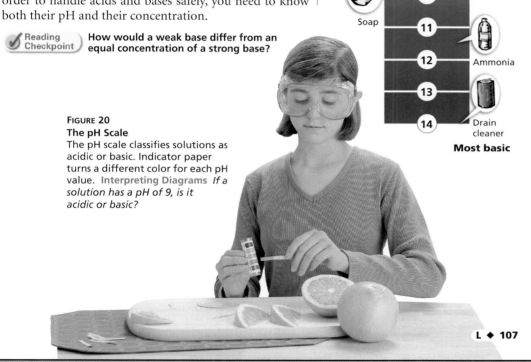

FIGURE 20
The pH Scale
The pH scale classifies solutions as acidic or basic. Indicator paper turns a different color for each pH value. *Interpreting Diagrams If a solution has a pH of 9, is it acidic or basic?*

Use Visuals: Figure 20 L2
The pH Scale

Focus Guide students in learning how to read and interpret the pH scale.

Teach Have students study the pH scale in Figure 20. Point out how the values go from 0, which is most acidic, to 14, which is most basic. Ask: **What value indicates a neutral substance?** *(7)* **Based on the results shown in the photo, where would you expect to find grapefruit juice on the pH scale?** *(Grapefruit juice has a pH of about 3.)* State that each unit of the pH scale represents a tenfold change in acidity. For example, an acid with a pH value of 2 has one tenth the acidity of an acid with a pH value of 1.

Apply Ask: **How much more acidic is an acid with a pH of 1 than an acid with a pH of 3?** *(100 times more acidic)* **learning modality: visual**

All in One Teaching Resources
• Transparency L37

Differentiated Instruction

Gifted and Talented L3
Investigating pH Students can research and add other common substances to the pH scale in Figure 20. Ask students to share their findings in an illustrated poster, based on the figure. **learning modality: logical/mathematical**

Less Proficient Readers L1
Visualizing Ion Concentration Students can use Figure 20 to visualize how pH values are related to hydrogen ions. Have students draw an inverted pyramid made by extending each color bar horizontally. The widest bar is pH=0, and the narrowest bar is pH=14. As the values go up, the bars get smaller, representing the fall in hydrogen ion concentration. **learning modality: visual**

Monitor Progress L2

Drawing Have students draw a simple pH scale showing the pH of neutral substances and the ranges of pH for acids and bases.

Answers
Figure 20 Basic

Reading Checkpoint The weak base would produce fewer hydroxide ions.

Acid-Base Reactions

Teach Key Concepts   L2
Neutralization

Focus Define and discuss neutralization.

Teach Tell students that neutralization is a reaction between an acid and a base. Add that the reaction produces a salt and water. Ask: **Why do you think the reaction is called neutralization?** *(Sample answer: Because it leads to a neutral product, salt water)*

Apply Ask: **Do you think the product would be neutral if much more HCl than NaOH were used in the reaction? Why or why not?** *(No; there would be more H⁺ than OH⁻ ions in the resulting solution, so it would be acidic.)* **learning modality: logical/mathematical**

All in One Teaching Resources
• Transparency L38

Help Students Read
Relating Cause and Effect Refer to the Content Refresher in this chapter, which provides guidelines for using the Relating Cause and Effect strategy.

Help students understand how a reaction between acids and bases can produce the neutral substance water. Refer students to the equation on this page. Remind them that an equation always has reactants on the left and products on the right. Ask: **What are the reactants in this neutralization reaction?** *(HCl and NaOH)* Tell students that HCl is a very strong acid, and NaOH is a very strong base. Ask: **What makes HCl an acid?** *(Hydrogen ions)* Have students identify the hydrogen ion in the equation. Repeat with the hydroxide ion, which gives NaOH its basic properties. Then, have students find the hydrogen atoms and oxygen atoms on the right side of the equation. Ask: **In what form are hydrogen and oxygen in the product?** *(Water)* Remind students that water is neutral. Guide students in generalizing, by asking: **What causes the neutralization of an acid and base?** *(Sample answer: Hydrogen ions and hydroxide ions are released and recombine as water.)*

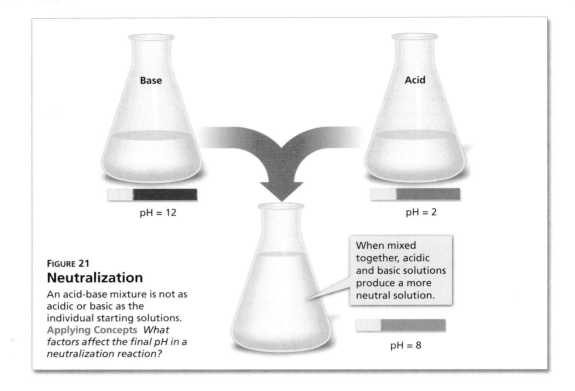

FIGURE 21
Neutralization
An acid-base mixture is not as acidic or basic as the individual starting solutions.
Applying Concepts *What factors affect the final pH in a neutralization reaction?*

Acid-Base Reactions

The story at the start of this section describes a chemist who mixed hydrochloric acid with sodium hydroxide. She got a solution of table salt (sodium chloride) and water.

$$HCl \ + \ NaOH \ \longrightarrow \ H_2O \ + \ Na^+ + \ Cl^-$$

If you tested the pH of the mixture, it would be close to 7, or neutral. In fact, a reaction between an acid and a base is called **neutralization** (noo truh lih ZAY shun).

Reactants After neutralization, an acid-base mixture is not as acidic or basic as the individual starting solutions were. Sometimes an acid-base reaction even results in a neutral solution. The final pH depends on such factors as the volumes, concentrations, and identities of the reactants. For example, some acids and bases react to form products that are not neutral. Also, common sense tells you that if only a small amount of strong base is reacted with a much larger amount of strong acid, the solution will remain acidic.

Products "Salt" may be the familiar name of the stuff you sprinkle on food. But to a chemist, the word refers to a specific group of compounds. A **salt** is any ionic compound that can be made from the neutralization of an acid with a base. A salt is made from the positive ion of a base and the negative ion of an acid.

Look at the equation for the reaction of nitric acid with potassium hydroxide:

$$HNO_3 + KOH \longrightarrow H_2O + K^+ + NO_3^-$$

One product of the reaction is water. The other product is potassium nitrate (KNO_3), a salt. **In a neutralization reaction, an acid reacts with a base to produce a salt and water.** Potassium nitrate is written in the equation as separate K^+ and NO_3^- ions because it is soluble in water. Some salts, such as potassium nitrate, are soluble. Others form precipitates because they are insoluble. Look at the table in Figure 22 to see a list of some common salts and their formulas.

Common Salts	
Salt	**Uses**
Sodium chloride NaCl	Food flavoring; food preservative
Potassium iodide KI	Additive in "iodized" salt that prevents iodine deficiency
Calcium chloride $CaCl_2$	De-icer for roads and walkways
Potassium chloride KCl	Salt substitute in foods
Calcium carbonate $CaCO_3$	Found in limestone and seashells
Ammonium nitrate NH_4NO_3	Fertilizer; active ingredient in cold packs

FIGURE 22
Each salt listed in this table can be formed by the reaction between an acid and a base.

 Reading Checkpoint What is a salt?

Section 4 Assessment

Target Reading Skill Previewing Visuals Refer to your questions and answers about Figure 21 to help you answer Question 3 below.

Reviewing Key Concepts

1. a. Identifying Which ion is found in the acids described in this section?
   b. Describing What kinds of ions do acids and bases form in water?
   c. Predicting What ions will the acid HNO_3 form when dissolved in water?

2. a. Reviewing What does a substance's pH tell you?
   b. Comparing and Contrasting If a solution has a pH of 6, would the solution contain more or fewer hydrogen ions (H^+) than an equal volume of solution with a pH of 3?
   c. Making Generalizations Would a dilute solution of HCl also be weak? Explain.

3. a. Reviewing What are the reactants of a neutralization reaction?
   b. Explaining What happens in a neutralization reaction?
   c. Problem Solving What acid reacts with KOH to produce the salt KCl?

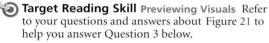 **At-Home Activity**

pH Lineup With a family member, search your house and refrigerator for the items found on the pH scale shown in Figure 20. Line up what you are able to find in order of increasing pH. Then ask your family member to guess why you ordered the substances in this way. Use the lineup to explain what pH means and how it is measured.

Chapter 3 L ◆ 109

Lab zone At-Home Activity

pH Lineup L2 Family members might guess that some of the substances at the lower end of the scale are acidic and that some at the higher end are basic. Students are expected to explain that pH refers to how acidic or basic a substance is and to describe the pH scale. Advise students to use Figure 20 to help them explain the pH scale.

Lab zone Chapter Project

Keep Students on Track Tell students to compare the results they obtained using their own acid-base indicators with the results they obtained using pH paper. Suggest that they try to correlate the color changes in their own indicators with the numbers in the standard pH scale.

Monitor Progress L2

Answers
Figure 21 The final pH is affected by the volumes, concentrations, and identities of the reactants.

Reading Checkpoint A salt is any ionic compound that can be made from the neutralization of an acid with a base.

Assess

Reviewing Key Concepts

1. a. Hydrogen ion **b.** Acids form hydrogen ions; bases form hydroxide ions. **c.** HNO_3 will form H^+ and NO_3^-.
2. a. How acidic or basic a solution is **b.** Fewer **c.** No; it would still be a strong acid because the concentration of H^+ ions remains high relative to the amount of HCl in the solution.
3. a. An acid and a base **b.** An acid reacts with a base to produce a salt and water. **c.** HCl

Reteach L1
Call on students to use the key terms in sentences.

Performance Assessment L2
Writing Have students write a chemical equation for the neutralization reaction involving HCl and NaOH. $(HCl + NaOH \rightarrow H_2O + NaCl)$

All in One Teaching Resources
• Section Summary: *Acids and Bases in Solution*
• Review and Reinforce: *Acids and Bases in Solution*
• Enrich: *Acids and Bases in Solution*

The Antacid Test L2

Prepare for Inquiry

Key Concept
The active ingredients in antacids are bases, which neutralize stomach acid. Different antacids neutralize different amounts of acid. Students will experiment to see if some antacids work better than others.

Skills Objective
After this lab, students will be able to
- design an experiment to determine which antacids neutralize more acid
- measure the amount of different antacids needed to neutralize a given amount of acid
- interpret the data to decide which antacid is most effective

 Prep Time 60 minutes
Class Time 40 minutes

Advance Planning
- Obtain methyl orange solution, or prepare the solution by dissolving 1 part (by mass) methyl orange powder in 99 parts water to give a 1% solution.
- Prepare 1.0 *M* HCl solution by carefully adding 83 mL of concentrated HCl to 1,000 mL of water. **CAUTION:** *Always add acid to water, never the other way around.*
- Purchase three different brands of liquid antacids.

Safety
Hydrochloric acid is corrosive. Students must wear lab aprons and safety goggles at all times to protect their clothing from the acid and from staining by indicators. If students get acid on their skin or clothes, they should rinse the affected area immediately with plenty of cool water and inform you at the same time. Review the safety guidelines in Appendix A.

 **Teaching Resources**
- Lab Worksheet: *The Antacid Test*

Consumer **Lab**

The Antacid Test

Problem
Which antacid neutralizes stomach acid with the smallest number of drops?

Skills Focus
designing experiments, interpreting data, measuring

Materials
- 3 plastic droppers • small plastic cups
- dilute hydrochloric acid (HCl), 50 mL
- methyl orange solution, 1 mL
- liquid antacid, 30 mL of each brand tested

Procedure

PART 1

1. Using a plastic dropper, put 10 drops of hydrochloric acid (HCl) into one cup.
   CAUTION: *HCl is corrosive. Rinse spills and splashes immediately with water.*

2. Use another plastic dropper to put 10 drops of liquid antacid into another cup.

3. In your notebook, make a data table like the one below. Record the colors of the HCl and the antacid.

Data Table		
Substance	Original Color	Color With Indicator
Hydrochloric Acid		
Antacid Brand A		
Antacid Brand B		

4. Add 2 drops of methyl orange solution to each cup. Record the colors you see.

5. Test each of the other antacids. Discard all the solutions and cups as directed by your teacher.

PART 2

6. Methyl orange changes color at a pH of about 4. Predict the color of the solution you expect to see when an antacid is added to a mixture of methyl orange and HCl.

7. Design a procedure for testing the reaction of each antacid with HCl. Decide how many drops of acid and methyl orange you need to use each time.

8. Devise a plan for adding the antacid so that you can detect when a change occurs. Decide how much antacid to add each time and how to mix the solutions to be sure the indicator is giving accurate results.

9. Make a second data table to record your observations.

10. Carry out your procedure and record your results.

11. Discard the solutions and cups as directed by your teacher. Rinse the plastic droppers thoroughly.

12. Wash your hands thoroughly when done.

Guide Inquiry

Invitation
Urge students to think of ads for antacids. Explain that antacids neutralize stomach acids that cause heartburn and indigestion. Ask: **How could you compare the effectiveness of different antacids?** (*Measure how much of each antacid is needed to neutralize a given amount of acid.*)

Introduce the Procedure
Have students read the procedure. Demonstrate how they will neutralize acid and observe changes in pH. Pour 3–4 mL of vinegar into a test tube. Add 2 drops of methyl orange solution. Add soap solution drop by drop until the solution changes from red to yellow. Explain that the solution is now neutral.

Analyze and Conclude

1. **Designing Experiments** What is the function of the methyl orange solution?

2. **Interpreting Data** Do your observations support your predictions from Step 6? Explain why or why not.

3. **Inferring** Why do you think antacids reduce stomach acid? Explain your answer, using the observations you made.

4. **Controlling Variables** Explain why it is important to use the same number of drops of HCl in each trial.

5. **Measuring** Which antacid neutralized the HCl with the smallest number of drops? Give a possible explanation for the difference.

6. **Calculating** If you have the same volume (number of drops) of each antacid, which one can neutralize the most acid?

7. **Drawing Conclusions** Did your procedure give results from which you could draw conclusions about which brand of antacid was most effective? Explain why or why not.

8. **Communicating** Write a brochure that explains to consumers what information they need to know in order to decide which brand of antacid is the best buy.

Design an Experiment

A company that sells a liquid antacid claims that its product works faster than tablets to neutralize stomach acid. Design an experiment to compare how quickly liquid antacids and chewable antacid tablets neutralize hydrochloric acid. *Obtain your teacher's permission before carrying out your investigation.*

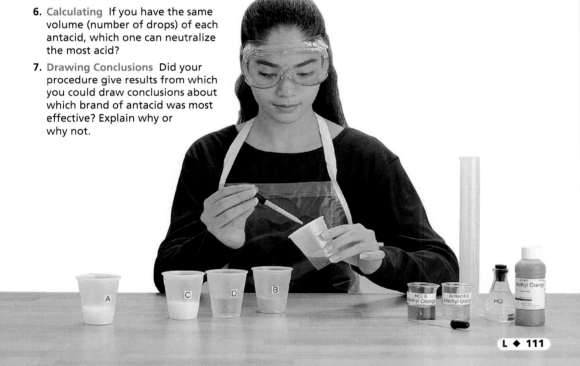

L ◆ 111

Troubleshooting the Experiment

- Have students stir or shake the antacids before dispensing them into cups.
- Advise students to add the antacids drop by drop. After each drop, they should gently swirl the cup and check for a color change. When the color change remains permanent for 15 seconds, they can record the number of drops used.

Expected Outcome

Methyl orange solution is red in acidic solutions and yellow in neutral solutions. Students should see a change from red to yellow as the antacids are added to the solutions. Different amounts of antacid may be needed, depending on the brands of antacids tested.

Analyze and Conclude

1. The methyl orange solution indicates whether a solution is acidic or neutral.

2. Answers may vary depending on students' predictions. If students predicted that methyl orange would change from red to yellow when antacid was added, then their prediction is likely to be supported by their observations.

3. Students might say that antacids are bases that react with acids to neutralize stomach acid.

4. The amount of acid must be controlled so you will know that any differences in resulting acidity must be due to the antacids.

5. Answers will vary depending on the antacids tested. Students may say that the antacid that neutralized the acid with the fewest drops contained a stronger or more concentrated base.

6. The antacid that neutralized HCl with the fewest drops can neutralize the most acid.

7. If students found differences in the number of drops of different antacids needed to neutralize the acid, they might conclude that the one that needed the fewest drops was the most effective. However, some students might say that antacids could work differently in the body, making it hard to draw conclusions about which was most effective.

8. Students' brochures might explain how antacids neutralize the acid that causes heartburn and indigestion. They also might include a data table or graph showing the results of their tests in order to show why their brand is most effective.

Extend Inquiry

Design an Experiment Students can compare a liquid antacid with a crushed chewable antacid tablet, using a procedure similar to the one in this lab. They will have to time the color changes to determine which form of antacid neutralizes acid faster. The expected outcome is for the liquid antacid to work faster.

Objectives

After this lesson, students will be able to
L.3.5.1 Explain why the body must digest food.
L.3.5.2 Describe how pH affects digestion.

Target Reading Skill 🔄

Sequencing Explain that organizing information from beginning to end helps students understand a step-by-step process.

Answers

Sample flowchart:
pH During Digestion
At a pH near 7, enzymes in the mouth start to break down carbohydrates.

At a pH near 2, stomach enzymes break down proteins.

At a pH near 8, enzymes in the small intestine complete the breakdown of carbohydrates, fats, and proteins.

All in One Teaching Resources

• Transparency L39

Preteach

Build Background Knowledge   L2

Stomach Acid

Ask: **What do you know about hydrochloric acid?** *(Students might say that it is one of the strongest acids.)* State that the stomach produces hydrochloric acid. Ask: **What role do you think hydrochloric acid plays in the stomach?** *(Students are likely to think that hydrochloric acid directly breaks down food in the stomach.)* Tell them that the role of hydrochloric acid is primarily to lower the stomach's pH. Say that, in this section, they will learn why the stomach must have low pH for digestion to occur and why pH is important throughout the digestive system.

Reading Preview

Key Concepts
• Why must your body digest food?
• How does pH affect digestion?

Key Terms
• digestion
• mechanical digestion
• chemical digestion

🔄 Target Reading Skill

Sequencing A sequence is the order in which a series of events occurs. As you read, make a flowchart that shows the sequence of changes in pH as food moves through the digestive system.

pH During Digestion

At a pH near 7, enzymes in the mouth start to break down carbohydrates.

↓

At a pH near 2, stomach enzymes break down proteins.

↓

Lab zone Discover **Activity**

Where Does Digestion Begin?

1. Obtain a bite-sized piece of crusty bread.
2. Chew the bread for about one minute. Do not swallow until after you notice a change in taste.

Think It Over
Inferring How did the bread taste before and after you chewed it? How can you explain the change in taste?

You may have seen commercials like the following: A man has a stomachache after eating spicy food. A voice announces that the problem is excess stomach acid. The remedy is an antacid tablet.

Ads like this one highlight the role of chemistry in digestion. You need to have acid in your stomach. But too much acid is a problem. Other parts of your digestive system need to be basic. What roles do acids and bases play in the digestion of food?

What Is Digestion?

Foods are made mostly of water and three groups of compounds: carbohydrates, proteins, and fats. Except for water, your body can't use foods in the form they are in when you eat them. **Foods must be broken down into simpler substances that your body can use for raw materials and energy.**

FIGURE 23
Digestion
This sandwich is about to begin a journey that includes changes in pH.

Lab zone Discover **Activity**

Skills Focus Inferring   L1

Materials piece of crusty bread

Time 5 minutes

Tips Do not use sweetened or fruit breads. You can substitute plain, salt-free crackers.

Expected Outcome After students have been chewing for about a minute, the bread will begin to taste sweet.

Think It Over The bread tasted sweeter after it had been chewed for a while. Students might explain the change in taste by saying saliva started to digest the bread.

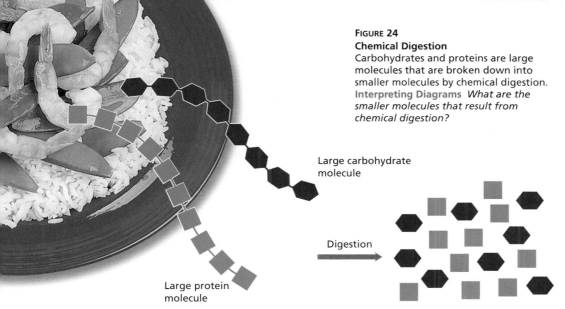

FIGURE 24
FIGURE 24
Chemical Digestion
Carbohydrates and proteins are large molecules that are broken down into smaller molecules by chemical digestion. **Interpreting Diagrams** *What are the smaller molecules that result from chemical digestion?*

Large carbohydrate molecule

Large protein molecule

Digestion

Small molecules of sugars and amino acids

The process of **digestion** breaks down the complex molecules of foods into smaller molecules. Digestion has two parts—mechanical and chemical.

Mechanical Digestion Mechanical digestion is a physical process in which large pieces of food are torn and ground into smaller pieces. The result is similar to what happens when a sugar cube is hit with a hammer. The size of the food is reduced, but the food isn't changed into other compounds.

Chemical Digestion Chemical digestion breaks large molecules into smaller ones. Look at Figure 24 to see what happens to large carbohydrate and protein molecules during chemical digestion. They are broken down into much smaller molecules. Some molecules are used by the body to get energy. Others become building blocks for muscle, bone, skin, and other organs.

Chemical digestion takes place with the help of enzymes. Recall from Chapter 15 that enzymes are catalysts that speed up reactions in living things. Enzymes require just the right conditions to work, including temperature and pH. **Some digestive enzymes work at a low pH. For others, the pH must be high or neutral.**

 Reading Checkpoint What happens to foods during chemical digestion?

pH in the Digestive System

Teach Key Concepts L2
pH and Enzymes in the Digestive System

Focus Use Figure 25 to show how pH changes during digestion, and help students infer why pH changes.

Teach Point out the pH values for the mouth, stomach, and small intestine shown in the table in Figure 25. Then, ask: **Which organ of the digestive system is neutral?** *(Mouth)* **Which is acidic?** *(Stomach)* **Which is basic?** *(Small intestine)* State that two digestive enzymes are amylase and pepsin. Add that amylase works best in a neutral environment, and pepsin works best in an acidic environment. Ask: **Where do you think amylase is found?** *(In the mouth)* **Where do you think pepsin is found?** *(In the stomach)*

Apply Tell students that a digestive fluid containing bicarbonate ions (HCO_3^-) creates a slightly basic solution. Ask: **Where do you think this digestive fluid is found?** *(In the small intestine)* **learning modality: verbal**

All in One Teaching Resources

• Transparency L40

Use Visuals: Figure 25 L2
Organs of the Digestive System

Focus Use Figure 25 to help students understand the roles of the different organs of the digestive system.

Teach Ask students to look at the digestive system pictured in the figure. Tell them to name the organs that foods or their byproducts pass through, starting with the mouth. *(Mouth, esophagus, stomach, small intestine, large intestine)* Ask: **In which organs of the digestive system does mechanical digestion take place?** *(Mouth and stomach)* **In which organs does chemical digestion take place?** *(Mouth, stomach, and small intestine)* Say that one role of the salivary glands is to make saliva, which contains a digestive enzyme.

Apply Ask: **What do you think is the role of the esophagus?** *(To carry food from the mouth to the stomach)* **learning modality: visual**

---

pH in the Digestive System

A bite of sandwich is about to take a journey through your digestive system. Figure 25 shows the main parts of the human digestive system. As you read, trace the food's pathway through the body. Keep track of the pH changes that affect the food molecules along the way.

Your Mouth The first stop in the journey is your mouth. Your teeth chew and mash the food. The food also is mixed with a watery fluid called saliva. Have you ever felt your mouth water at the smell of something delicious? The odor of food can trigger production of saliva.

What would you expect the usual pH of saliva to be? Remember that saliva tastes neither sour nor bitter. So you're correct if you think your mouth has a pH near 7, the neutral point.

Saliva contains amylase (AM uh lays), an enzyme that helps break down the carbohydrate starch into smaller sugar molecules. Amylase works best when the pH is near 7. You can sense the action of this enzyme if you chew a piece of bread. After about two minutes in your mouth, the starch is broken down into sugars. The sugars make the bread taste sweet.

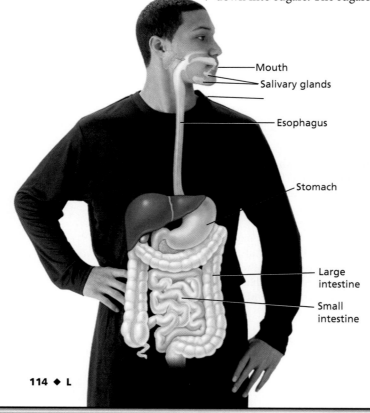

Mouth
Salivary glands
Esophagus
Stomach
Large intestine
Small intestine

114 ◆ L

FIGURE 25
Foods are exposed to several changes in pH as they move through the digestive system.
Relating Cause and Effect Why do certain digestive enzymes work only in certain parts of the digestive system?

pH Changes During Digestion	
Organ	**pH**
Mouth	7
Stomach	2
Small intestine	8

Your Stomach Next, the food is swallowed and arrives in your stomach, where mechanical digestion continues. Also, chemical digestion begins for foods that contain protein, such as meat, fish, and beans. Cells in the lining of your stomach release enzymes and hydrochloric acid. In contrast to the near-neutral pH of your mouth, the pH here drops to a very acidic level of about 2.

The low pH in your stomach helps digestion take place. Pepsin is one enzyme that works in your stomach. Pepsin helps break down proteins into small molecules called amino acids. Most enzymes work best in a solution that is nearly neutral. But pepsin is different. It works most effectively in acids.

Your Small Intestine Your stomach empties its contents into the small intestine. Here, digestive fluid containing bicarbonate ions (HCO_3^-) surrounds the food. This ion creates a slightly basic solution, with a pH of about 8. At this slightly basic pH, enzymes of the small intestine work best. These enzymes complete the breakdown of carbohydrates, fats, and proteins.

By now, the large food molecules from the sandwich have been split up into smaller ones. These smaller molecules pass through the walls of the small intestine into your bloodstream and are carried to the cells that will use them.

 Reading Checkpoint What acid do the cells in the lining of your stomach release?

Go Online
SCi*LINKS* NSTA

For: Links on digestion and pH
Visit: www.SciLinks.org
Web Code: scn-1235

Section 5 Assessment

 Target Reading Skill Sequencing Refer to your flowchart about the digestive system as you answer Question 2.

Reviewing Key Concepts

1. a. Reviewing What are the two parts of digestion?
  b. Comparing and Contrasting How do these two processes differ?
  c. Inferring People who have lost most of their teeth may have trouble chewing their food. How does this affect their digestive process?
2. a. Listing What is the pH in your mouth? Stomach? Small intestine?
  b. Sequencing Arrange the three body locations in part (a) from least acidic to most acidic.
  c. Applying Concepts Why are pH variations in different parts of the digestive system important to the process of digestion?

Writing in Science

News Report Suppose you are a news reporter who can shrink down in size and be protected from changes in the environment with a special suit. You are assigned to accompany a bite of food as it travels through the digestive system. Report your findings in a dramatic but accurate way. Include a catchy headline.

Chapter 3 L ◆ 115

Writing in Science

Writing Mode Description
Scoring Rubric
4 Exceeds criteria
3 Meets criteria
2 Includes a description with some details and a headline but contains some errors
1 Includes a general description only and/or contains serious errors

---

Go Online
SCi*LINKS* NSTA

For: Links on digestion and pH
Visit: www.SciLinks.org
Web Code: scn-1235

Download a worksheet that will guide students' review of Internet sources on digestion and pH.

Monitor Progress ⎯⎯⎯ L2

Answers
Figure 25 Because they require a specific pH in order to work, and pH varies in different parts of the digestive system

Reading Checkpoint Hydrochloric acid

Assess

Reviewing Key Concepts

1. a. Mechanical digestion and chemical digestion **b.** Mechanical digestion is a physical process in which large pieces of food are torn and ground into smaller pieces. Chemical digestion breaks large molecules into smaller ones. **c.** People who have trouble chewing their food are less able to digest their food mechanically.
2. a. The pH in your mouth is 7, in your stomach 2, and in your small intestine 8. **b.** The least acidic location is the small intestine, followed by the mouth, and then the stomach, which is most acidic. **c.** Some digestive enzymes work at a low pH. For others, the pH must be high or neutral.

Reteach L1
Use an overhead transparency of Figure 25 without the labels and pH values. Call on students to fill in the missing information.

Performance Assessment L2
Writing Ask students to write a paragraph explaining the role of pH in chemical digestion.

Students can keep their paragraphs in their portfolios. [Portfolio]

All in One Teaching Resources
• Section Summary: *Digestion and pH*
• Review and Reinforce: *Digestion and pH*
• Enrich: *Digestion and pH*

Interactive Textbook

- Complete student edition
- Section and chapter self-assessment
- Assessment reports for teachers

Help Students Read **L1**

Building Vocabulary

Words in Context Explain that when people generally use the word *salt*, they are referring to table salt, or sodium chloride (NaCl). However, in chemistry, salt refers to any ionic compound made from the neutralization of an acid with a base. Add that NaCl is just one of many different salts that can result from neutralization. Challenge students to use the word *salt* in two different sentences that show by the context which meaning of the word is intended.

Word Origins Tell students that almost half of the key terms in this chapter come from the Latin verb *solvere*, which means "to dissolve." Ask: **In addition to the key term *solution* and the other key terms that contain the word *solution*, which key terms come from this Latin word?** *(Solvent, solute, solubility)*

Connecting Concepts

Concept Maps Help students develop one way to show how the information in this chapter is related. Mixtures can be solutions, colloids, or suspensions, depending on the size of solute particles. Two important characteristics of solutions are concentration and solubility. Acids and bases are compounds with specific properties, such as pH, that are determined by the ions they produce in water. Enzymes involved in digestion require a specific pH in order to work. Have students brainstorm to identify the key concepts, key terms, details, and examples. Then, write each one on a self-sticking note, and attach it at random to chart paper or on the board.

Tell students that this concept map will be organized in hierarchical order, beginning at the top with the key concepts. Ask students

① Understanding Solutions

Key Concepts

- A solution has the same properties throughout. It contains solute particles that are too small to see.
- A colloid contains larger particles than a solution. The particles are still too small to be seen easily, but are large enough to scatter a light beam.
- Unlike a solution, a suspension does not have the same properties throughout. It contains visible particles that are larger than the particles in solutions or colloids.
- When a solution forms, particles of the solute leave each other and become surrounded by particles of the solvent.
- Solutes lower the freezing point and raise the boiling point of a solvent.

Key Terms

solution	solute	suspension
solvent	colloid	

② Concentration and Solubility

Key Concepts

- To measure concentration, you compare the amount of solute to the amount of solvent or to the total amount of solution.
- Solubility can be used to help identify a substance because it is a characteristic property of matter.
- Factors that affect the solubility of a substance include pressure, the type of solvent, and temperature.

Key Terms
dilute solution
concentrated solution
solubility
saturated solution
unsaturated solution
supersaturated solution

③ Describing Acids and Bases

Key Concepts

- An acid is a substance that tastes sour, reacts with metals and carbonates, and turns blue litmus paper red.
- A base is a substance that tastes bitter, feels slippery, and turns red litmus paper blue.
- Acids and bases have many uses around the home and in industry.

Key Terms

acid	indicator
corrosive	base

④ Acids and Bases in Solution

Key Concepts

- An acid is any substance that produces hydrogen ions (H^+) in water.
- A base is any substance that produces hydroxide ions (OH^-) in water.
- A low pH tells you that the concentration of hydrogen ions is high. In contrast, a high pH tells you that the concentration of hydrogen ions is low.
- In a neutralization reaction, an acid reacts with a base to produce a salt and water.

Key Terms

hydrogen ion (H^+)	neutralization
hydroxide ion (OH^-)	salt
pH scale	

⑤ Digestion and pH

Key Concepts

- Foods must be broken down into simpler substances that your body can use for raw materials and energy.
- Some digestive enzymes work at a low pH. For others, the pH must be high or neutral.

Key Terms

digestion	chemical digestion
mechanical digestion	

these questions to guide them in organizing the information on the self-sticking notes: **How do solutes affect solutions? How is concentration measured? What factors affect solubility? How do acids and bases differ? What is produced in a neutralization reaction? What happens during digestion?** Prompt students by using connecting words, such as "can be," "has properties of," "include," and "results in," to indicate the basis for the organization of the map. The

phrases should form a sentence between or among a set of concepts.

Answer Accept logical presentations by students.

All in One Teaching Resources

- Key Terms Review: *Acids, Bases, and Solutions*
- Connecting Concepts: *Acids, Bases, and Solutions*

Review and Assessment

Organizing Information

Concept Mapping Copy the concept map about solutions onto a sheet of paper. Then complete it and add a title. (For more on Concept Mapping, see the Skills Handbook.)

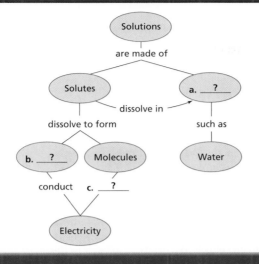

Solutions

are made of

Solutes → a. ____?____

dissolve in

dissolve to form / *such as*

b. ____?____   Molecules   Water

conduct   c. ____?____

Electricity

Reviewing Key Terms

Choose the letter of the best answer.

1. Sugar water is an example of a
   a. suspension.
   b. solution.
   c. solute.
   d. colloid.

2. A solution in which more solute may be dissolved is a(n)
   a. neutral solution.
   b. unsaturated solution.
   c. concentrated solution.
   d. saturated solution.

3. A compound that changes color when it contacts an acid or a base is called a(n)
   a. solute.
   b. solvent.
   c. indicator.
   d. salt.

4. A polyatomic ion made of hydrogen and oxygen is called a
   a. hydroxide ion.
   b. hydrogen ion.
   c. salt.
   d. base.

5. Ammonia is an example of a(n)
   a. acid.   b. salt.
   c. base.   d. antacid.

6. The physical part of digestion is called
   a. digestion.
   b. mechanical digestion.
   c. chemical digestion.
   d. solubility.

Writing in Science

Product Label Suppose you are a marketing executive for a maple syrup company. Write a description of the main ingredients of maple syrup that can be pasted on the syrup's container. Use what you've learned about concentration to explain how dilute tree sap becomes sweet, thick syrup.

Discovery CHANNEL SCHOOL

Acids, Bases, and Solutions
Video Preview
Video Field Trip
▶ Video Assessment

Review and Assessment

Organizing Information

a. Solvents
b. Ions
c. do not conduct

Reviewing Key Terms

1. b **2.** b **3.** c **4.** a **5.** c **6.** b

Writing in Science

Writing Mode Description

Scoring Rubric

4 Exceeds criteria; includes the correct list of ingredients and an accurate, detailed description

3 Meets criteria

2 Includes a list and description but contains some omissions and/or errors

1 Includes a vague description only and/or contains serious errors

Discovery CHANNEL SCHOOL
Video Assessment

Acids, Bases, and Solutions

Show the Video Assessment to review chapter content and as a prompt for the writing assignment. Discussion questions: **What substance in maple sap is concentrated to make maple syrup?** (*Sucrose*) **Why is heat necessary for the production of maple syrup?** (*Heating the sap causes water to evaporate, making the solution more concentrated. Heating also destroys bacteria in the syrup.*)

All in One Teaching Resources

- Transparency L41
- Chapter Test
- Performance Assessment Teacher Notes
- Performance Assessment Student Worksheet
- Performance Assessment Scoring Rubric

ExamView® Computer Test Bank CD-ROM

Checking Concepts

7. You could shine a flashlight though them. Light passes through a solution without scattering, but a colloid scatters the light.

8. A concentrated solution of sugar water contains more solute relative to the amount of solvent than a dilute solution. A concentrated solution also tastes sweeter and has a lower freezing point and higher boiling point.

9. Tomato juice would turn blue litmus paper red, and it would react with a base, such as baking soda.

10. An indicator is a different color in an acid than it is in a base.

11. A strong base might have a pH of 14, 13, or 12.

12. Hydrochloric acid (HCl) and sodium hydroxide (NaOH) combine to make the salt sodium chloride (NaCl).

Thinking Critically

13. As divers descend deeper under water, more nitrogen in the air dissolves in their blood because presure increases with depth. If divers return to the surface too quickly, nitrogen gas quickly comes out of solution, blocks blood flow, and causes severe pain called "the bends."

14. The solubility of a gas is lower at higher temperatures. Heating water reduces the solubility of dissolved gases in the water and causes some of the gas to come out of solution.

15. Based on the litmus paper changes, one liquid is an acid and the other is a base. When they react, they form a neutral solution of a salt in water. This reaction is called neutralization.

16. An acid forms hydrogen ions (H^+) in a water solution. A base forms hydroxide ions (OH^-) in a water solution.

17. KCl

18. Too much antacid could increase the pH in the stomach so that it is too high for the enzyme that digests protein (pepsin) to work well. Therefore, protein might not be digested as well in the person's stomach.

Math Practice

19. 100 g
20. 50 mL

Review and Assessment

Checking Concepts

7. Explain how you can tell the difference between a solution and a clear colloid.

8. Describe at least two differences between a dilute solution and a concentrated solution of sugar water.

9. Tomatoes are acidic. Predict two properties of tomato juice that you would be able to observe.

10. Explain how an indicator helps you distinguish between an acid and a base.

11. What might be a pH value of a strong base?

12. What combination of acid and base can be used to make the salt sodium chloride?

Thinking Critically

13. **Applying Concepts** A scuba diver can be endangered by "the bends." Explain how the effects of pressure on the solubility of gases is related to this condition.

14. **Relating Cause and Effect** When you heat tap water on the stove, you can see tiny bubbles of oxygen form. They rise to the surface long before the water begins to boil. Explain what causes these bubbles to appear.

15. **Drawing Conclusions** You have two clear liquids. One turns blue litmus paper red and one turns red litmus paper blue. If you mix them and retest with both litmus papers, no color changes occur. Describe the reaction that took place when the liquids were mixed.

16. **Comparing and Contrasting** Compare the types of particles formed in a water solution of an acid with those formed in a water solution of a base.

17. **Problem Solving** Fill in the missing salt product in the reaction below.

$$HCl + KOH \longrightarrow H_2O + \underline{\quad ? \quad}$$

18. **Predicting** Suppose a person took a dose of antacid greater than what is recommended. Predict how this action might affect the digestion of certain foods.

Math Practice

19. **Calculating a Concentration** If you have 1,000 grams of a 10 percent solution of sugar water, how much sugar is dissolved in the solution?

20. **Calculating a Concentration** The concentration of an alcohol and water solution is 25 percent alcohol by volume. What is the volume of alcohol in 200 mL of the solution?

Applying Skills

Use the diagram to answer Questions 21–24.

The diagram below shows the particles of an unknown acid in a water solution.

Water

Acid

21. **Interpreting Diagrams** How can you tell that the solution contains a weak acid?

22. **Inferring** Which shapes in the diagram represent ions?

23. **Making Models** Suppose another unknown acid is a strong acid. Make a diagram to show the particles of this acid dissolved in water.

24. **Drawing Conclusions** Explain how the pH of a strong acid compares with the pH of a weak acid of the same concentration.

 Chapter Project

Performance Assessment Demonstrate the indicators you prepared. For each indicator, list the substances you tested in order from most acidic to least acidic. Would you use the same materials as indicators if you did this project again? Explain.

Lab zone Chapter **Project**   L3

Performance Assessment In their presentations, students should identify the acid-base indicators they made and the substances they tested. They should also present and interpret their summarized test results. Suggest that students compare their results with the results of their classmates. They can try to determine which acid-base indicators produced results in closest agreement with pH test paper results.

Standardized Test Prep

Choose the letter of the best answer.

1. Which of the following pH values indicates a solution with the highest concentration of hydrogen ions?
   A pH = 1
   B pH = 2
   C pH = 7
   D pH = 14

2. A small beaker contains 50 milliliters of water at 20°C. If three sugar cubes are placed in the beaker, they will eventually dissolve. Which action would speed up the rate at which the sugar cubes dissolve?
   F Use less water initially.
   G Transfer the contents to a larger beaker.
   H Cool the water and sugar cubes to 5°C.
   J Heat and stir the contents of the beaker.

Use the graph below and your knowledge of science to answer Question 3.

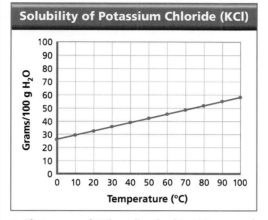

Solubility of Potassium Chloride (KCl)

3. If 30 grams of KCl are dissolved in 100 grams of water at 50°C, the solution can be best described as
   A saturated.
   B supersaturated.
   C unsaturated.
   D soluble.

4. Which safety procedures should be followed when using acids and bases in the laboratory?
   F Wear an apron and safety goggles.
   G Dispose of chemical wastes properly.
   H Wash your hands before leaving the lab.
   J all of the above

Constructed Response

5. Salt water is a solution of table salt (the solute) and water (the solvent). Describe a laboratory procedure that could be used to determine the concentration of salt in a sample of salt water. Indicate all measurements that must be made. (*Hint:* Remember that the concentration of a solution can be expressed as a ratio of the mass of the solute to the volume of the solution.)

Applying Skills

21. You can tell that the solution contains a weak acid because very few acid particles have broken up into hydrogen ions and negative ions.

22. The unpaired yellow cubes and the unpaired blue circles represent ions.

23. Students' diagrams should show that most of the particles of the strong acid have broken up into hydrogen ions and negative ions.

24. Hydrogen ion concentration is measured by pH. The higher the concentration, the lower the pH. A strong acid produces more hydrogen ions in solution, so it has a lower pH than a weak acid of the same concentration.

Standardized Test Prep

1. A   **2.** J   **3.** C   **4.** J
5. The mass of the salt water could be measured, and the water could be evaporated to recover the dissolved salt. Then, the mass of the salt could be measured and divided by the mass of the salt water to yield the concentration of the original saltwater solution.

Chapter at a Glance

PRENTICE HALL

TeacherEXPRESS™
Plan • Teach • Assess

Chapter Project *Check Out the Fine Print*

All in One Teaching Resources
- Chapter Project Teacher Notes, pp. 250–251
- Chapter Project Student Overview, pp. 252–253
- Chapter Project Student Worksheets, pp. 254–255
- Chapter Project Scoring Rubric, p. 256

Technology

Local Standards

Video Preview

Section 1

2 periods
1 block

Properties of Carbon

L.4.1.1 Describe how carbon is able to form a huge variety of compounds.

L.4.1.2 Identify four forms of pure carbon.

Section 2

5 periods
2 1/2 blocks

Carbon Compounds

L.4.2.1 List properties of organic compounds.

L.4.2.2 Identify properties of hydrocarbons.

L.4.2.3 Describe the kind of structures and bonding that hydrocarbons have.

L.4.2.4 Identify characteristics of substituted hydrocarbons, esters, and polymers.

Section 3

5–6 periods
2 1/2–3 blocks

Life With Carbon

L.4.3.1 List the four main classes of organic compounds in living things.

L.4.3.2 Explain how the organic compounds in living things differ from one another.

Video Field Trip

PHSchool.com

Review and Assessment

All in One Teaching Resources
- Key Terms Review, p. 284
- Transparency L54
- Performance Assessment Teacher Notes, p. 291
- Performance Assessment Scoring Rubric, p. 292
- Performance Assessment Student Worksheet, p. 293
- Chapter Test, pp. 294–297

Video Assessment

PHSchool.com

Test Preparation

Test Preparation
Blackline Masters

Lab zone | Chapter Activities Planner

Student Edition	Inquiry	Time	Materials	Skills	Resources
Chapter Project	Open-ended	Ongoing (2 weeks)	**All in One Teaching Resources** See p. 250	Interpreting data, classifying, drawing conclusions, communicating	**Lab zone Easy Planner** **All in One Teaching Resources** Support pp. 250–251
Section 1					
Discover Activity, p. 122	Guided	10 minutes	Paper, pencil	Observing	**Lab zone Easy Planner**
Section 2					
Discover Activity, p. 126	Guided	15 minutes	Paper cups, cotton balls or note cards, banana, pineapple, wintergreen candy, apple	Developing hypotheses	**Lab zone Easy Planner**
Try This Activity, p. 129	Directed	5 minutes	Petroleum jelly, water, cup, paper towel	Inferring	**Lab zone Easy Planner**
Skills Activity, p. 131	Directed	15 minutes		Classifying	**Lab zone Easy Planner**
At-Home Activity, p. 134	Guided	Home		Applying concepts, observing	**Lab zone Easy Planner**
Skills Lab, p. 135	Guided	Prep: 10 minutes Class: 40 minutes	Toothpicks, multicolored gumdrops	Designing a solution, evaluating the design	**Lab zone Easy Planner** **Lab Activity Video** **All in One Teaching Resources** Skills Lab: *How Many Molecules?*, pp. 271–272
Section 3					
Discover Activity, p. 136	Guided	15 minutes	60 mL milk, 2 plastic cups, 15 mL vinegar, 2 funnels, graduated cylinder, 2 pieces filter paper, 2 Erlenmeyer flasks	Observing	**Lab zone Easy Planner**
Try This Activity, p. 140	Guided	10 minutes		Making models	**Lab zone Easy Planner**
Try This Activity, p. 142	Directed	10 minutes, plus drying time	Brown paper, droppers, liquid samples such as vegetable oil, water, salad dressing, baby oil, fruit juice, milk, cream	Inferring	**Lab zone Easy Planner**
Consumer Lab, pp. 148–149	Directed	Prep: 20 minutes Class: 25 minutes	6 small cups, 6 plastic droppers, starch solution, iodine solution, vitamin C solution, samples of beverages to be tested (orange juice, apple juice, sports drink, fruit-flavored drink)	Controlling variables, interpreting data, inferring	**Lab zone Easy Planner** **Lab Activity Video** **All in One Teaching Resources** Consumer Lab: *Are You Getting Your Vitamins?*, pp. 281–283

Section 1 Properties of Carbon

ABILITY LEVELS
L1 Basic to Average
L2 For All Students
L3 Average to Advanced

 *2 periods, 1 block*

Objectives

L.4.1.1 Describe how carbon is able to form a huge variety of compounds.
L.4.1.2 Identify four forms of pure carbon.

Local Standards

Key Terms

• diamond • graphite • fullerene • nanotube

Preteach

Build Background Knowledge

Students explain why they think people value diamonds.

 **Discover Activity** *Why Do Pencils Write?* **L1**

Targeted Print and Technology Resources

All in One Teaching Resources

L2 Reading Strategy Transparency
L42: Using Prior Knowledge

⊙ **Presentation-Pro CD-ROM**

Instruct

Carbon Atoms and Bonding Use dot diagrams and structural diagrams to lead a discussion describing how carbon bonds to itself and to other elements.

Forms of Pure Carbon Ask questions to lead the class in completing a compare/contrast table of the forms of pure carbon.

Targeted Print and Technology Resources

All in One Teaching Resources

L2 Guided Reading, pp. 259–260
L2 Transparencies L43, L44

PHSchool.com Web Code: cgp-2041

⊙ **Student Edition on Audio CD**

Assess

Section Assessment Questions

Have students use their completed graphic organizers to answer the questions.

Reteach

Students diagram how carbon atoms form bonds with other elements.

Targeted Print and Technology Resources

All in One Teaching Resources

• Section Summary, p. 258
L1 Review and Reinforce, p. 261
L3 Enrich, p. 262

Section 2 Carbon Compounds

 5 periods, 2 1/2 blocks

Objectives

L.4.2.1 List properties of organic compounds.
L.4.2.2 Identify properties of hydrocarbons.
L.4.2.3 Describe the kind of structures and bonding that hydrocarbons have.
L.4.2.4 Identify characteristics of substituted hydrocarbons, esters, and polymers.

Local Standards

Key Terms

• organic compound • hydrocarbon • structural formula • isomer • saturated hydrocarbon • unsaturated hydrocarbon • substituted hydrocarbon • hydroxyl group • alcohol • organic acid • carboxyl group • ester • polymer • monomer

---

Preteach

Build Background Knowledge

Students describe properties of gasoline that they have observed.

 **Discover Activity** *What Do You Smell?* **L1**

Targeted Print and Technology Resources

All in One Teaching Resources
L2 Reading Strategy Transparency L45: Outlining

⊙ **Presentation-Pro CD-ROM**

Instruct

Organic Compounds Use the definition of *organic compound* in a discussion of their properties.

Hydrocarbons Lead a discussion about the properties of hydrocarbons.

Structure and Bonding in Hydrocarbons Use structural formulas of different hydrocarbons to discuss different ways that carbon can form bonds.

Substituted Hydrocarbons Use structural formulas of methanol and formic acid in a discussion about substituted hydrocarbons.

Esters Lead a discussion about the characteristics of esters.

Polymers Model monomers and polymers to illustrate what polymers are and how they form.

 **Skills Lab** *How Many Molecules?* **L2**

Targeted Print and Technology Resources

All in One Teaching Resources
L2 Guided Reading, pp. 265–268
L2 Transparencies L46, L47, L48, L49, L50
L2 Skills Lab: *How Many Molecules?*, pp. 271–272

📼 **Lab Activity Video/DVD**
Technology Lab: *Design and Build a Model of an Organic Compound*

www.SciLinks.org Web Code: scn-1242

⊙ **Student Edition on Audio CD**

Assess

Section Assessment Questions

Have students use their completed outlines to answer the questions.

Reteach

Students relate hydrocarbons, substituted hydrocarbons, esters, and polymers in a concept map.

Targeted Print and Technology Resources

All in One Teaching Resources
• Section Summary, p. 264
L1 Review and Reinforce, p. 269
L3 Enrich, p. 270

Section 3 **Life With Carbon**

 5–6 periods, 2 1/2–3 blocks

ABILITY LEVELS
L1 Basic to Average
L2 For All Students
L3 Average to Advanced

Objectives

L.4.3.1 List the four main classes of organic compounds in living things.

L.4.3.2 Explain how the organic compounds in living things differ from one another.

Local Standards

Key Terms

- carbohydrate • glucose • complex carbohydrate • starch • cellulose • protein
- amino acid • lipid • fatty acid • cholesterol • nucleic acid • DNA • RNA
- nucleotide

Preteach

Build Background Knowledge

Invite students to compare and contrast different foods.

 **Discover Activity** *What Is in Milk?* L1

Targeted Print and Technology Resources

 **Teaching Resources**

L2 Reading Strategy Transparency L51: Asking Questions

⊙ **Presentation-Pro CD-ROM**

Instruct

Carbohydrates Lead a discussion in which students compare and contrast simple and complex carbohydrates.

Proteins Use the structural formulas of alanine and serine to discuss protein structure.

Lipids Ask questions in a discussion about lipids contrasted with carbohydrates.

Nucleic Acids Lead a discussion about the structure of nucleic acids and their importance to living things.

Other Compounds in Foods Ask questions in a discussion about vitamins and minerals.

 Consumer Lab *Are You Getting Your Vitamins?* L2

Targeted Print and Technology Resources

 **Teaching Resources**

L2 Guided Reading, pp. 275–278
L2 Transparencies L52, L53
L2 Consumer Lab: *Are You Getting Your Vitamins?*, pp. 281–283

📼 **Lab Activity Video/DVD**
Consumer Lab: *Are You Getting Your Vitamins?*

www.SciLinks.org Web Code: scn-1243
PHSchool.com Web Code: cgh-2040

DISCOVERY
CHANNEL
SCHOOL
Video Field Trip

⊙ **Student Edition on Audio CD**

Assess

Section Assessment Questions

↻ Have students use their questions and answers to answer the questions.

Reteach

Students relate the key terms in a concept map.

Targeted Print and Technology Resources

Teaching Resources

- Section Summary, p. 274
L1 Review and Reinforce, p. 279
L3 Enrich, p. 280

Chapter 4 Content Refresher

Section 1 Properties of Carbon

Nanofoam Carbon nanofoam is a fifth form of carbon that was first made accidentally as a byproduct in experiments with nanotubes and fullerenes. Scientists now produce it by blasting graphite with a high powered laser in a chamber filled with argon gas. In this process, the graphite is heated to 10,000°C and evaporates into single carbon atoms. As the vapor cools, the carbon atoms condense in clusters of about 10,000 carbon atoms, about 6 to 9 nanometers in diameter. These clusters randomly connect to form a weblike foam—a structure that is something between the structures of diamond and graphite.

Nanofoam looks like soot and is extremely lightweight. Its most surprising property, however, is its strong attraction to magnets. At room temperature, the foam's magnetism begins to disappear in a few hours after synthesis. At lower temperatures, its magnetism may last for up to 12 months. Scientists think nanofoam's magnetic properties are caused by its structure. The carbon atoms in nanofoam form heptagonal structures that have an unpaired electron. The motion of this unpaired electron is the most likely cause of the foam's magnetism.

Section 2 Carbon Compounds

Sources of Hydrocarbons All hydrocarbons on Earth ultimately originated with photosynthetic organisms, such as plants and some microorganisms. In the process of photosynthesis, these organisms "fix" the carbon from carbon dioxide gas into hydrocarbons using energy from the sun. The chemical reactions of photosynthesis produce a 3-carbon sugar from which glucose and other carbon components are made.

$$6CO_2 + 6H_2O + \text{solar energy} \rightarrow C_6H_{12}O_6 + 6O_2$$

Photosynthetic organisms use glucose for energy to carry out cell processes and as building blocks for cell structures.

The hydrocarbons that we use today come from fossil fuels such as natural gas, petroleum, and coal. These fossil fuels are deposits of hydrocarbons formed millions of years ago from thick layers of decaying plants and marine organisms. Over time, these decaying organisms became buried by sediments and rock, which exerted intense pressure. Heat from Earth's interior, pressure from rock and sediments, and the action of bacteria slowly changed these decaying organisms into natural gas, petroleum, and coal.

Section 3 Life With Carbon

Cholesterol When people have their cholesterol levels checked, doctors are actually looking at the levels of lipoproteins in the blood. In the blood, cholesterol and other lipids are always associated with proteins in molecules called lipoproteins. Lipoproteins carry cholesterol and other lipids to and from cells. Doctors are most interested in the levels of two kinds of lipoproteins. Low-density lipoproteins, or LDLs, carry about 75 percent of the total cholesterol in the body. When too much LDL cholesterol is in the bloodstream, it can build up on artery walls. These deposits mix with other substances to form plaque, which can block arteries and cause heart attacks.

Address Misconceptions

Some students may think that any fat in their diets is not healthful. This misconception is addressed in Section 2, *Carbon Compounds.*

High-density lipoproteins, or HDLs, do not cause disease. Instead, scientists think HDLs carry cholesterol to the liver where it is excreted along with bile. Some scientists think that HDLs can remove excess cholesterol from plaque in the arteries.

Help Students Read

Active Comprehension
Reading With Specific Questions in Mind

Strategy Translate students' curiosity into a purpose for reading. When students look for the answers to their questions while reading, it helps them to stay engaged. Before students read, read aloud the second paragraph from *Properties of Carbon.*

Example
1. Ask: **What more would you like to know about the properties of carbon?** Make a list of student responses.
2. Tell students to read the rest of the section, keeping the questions in mind as they read.
3. After reading, discuss with students the extent to which each question was answered by the text. Invite students to comment on any new information they learned that may have been surprising.

Chapter 4

Carbon Chemistry

Chapter Preview

interactive Textbook

Butterflies, flowers, and all other living things contain carbon compounds.

Chapter Project L3

Objectives

Students will examine labels on food packages to identify carbon compounds found in different foods. After completing this Chapter Project, students will be able to
- interpret data collected from food labels
- classify foods based on their nutritional composition
- draw conclusions about how carbon compounds are related to the nutritional value of foods
- communicate their findings about carbon compounds in foods to the class

Skills Focus

Interpreting data, classifying, drawing conclusions, communicating

Project Time Line 2 weeks

All in One Teaching Resources
- Chapter Project Teacher Notes
- Chapter Project Worksheet 1
- Chapter Project Worksheet 2
- Chapter Project Scoring Rubric

Developing a Plan

During the first week, students should collect food labels, construct data tables, and record data from the food labels. During the second week, students will interpret this data and prepare displays in which they present their conclusions to the class.

Possible Materials

Encourage students to select labels from a wide variety of processed foods. Samples: breakfast cereals, instant soups, candy bars, potato chips, fruit drinks, canned soups, processed meats like bologna or salami, ice cream, and "natural" or "organic" foods such as juice, cereal, or energy bars.

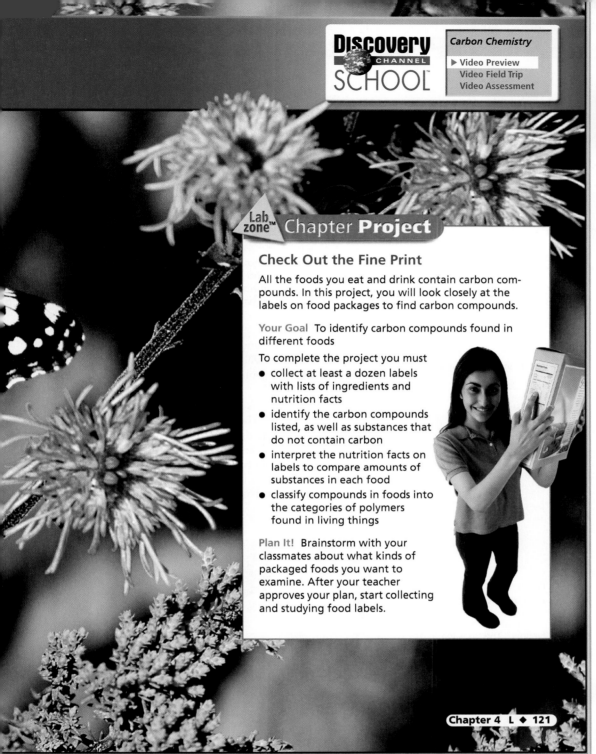

Chapter **Project**
Lab zone™

Check Out the Fine Print

All the foods you eat and drink contain carbon compounds. In this project, you will look closely at the labels on food packages to find carbon compounds.

Your Goal To identify carbon compounds found in different foods

To complete the project you must
- collect at least a dozen labels with lists of ingredients and nutrition facts
- identify the carbon compounds listed, as well as substances that do not contain carbon
- interpret the nutrition facts on labels to compare amounts of substances in each food
- classify compounds in foods into the categories of polymers found in living things

Plan It! Brainstorm with your classmates about what kinds of packaged foods you want to examine. After your teacher approves your plan, start collecting and studying food labels.

Chapter 4 L ◆ 121

Launching the Project
Obtain a label from a food product that students will be familiar with. List the ingredients on the board, and then challenge students to guess the identity of the food. This works best with foods that contain unfamiliar or strange-sounding ingredients. After the mystery food has been revealed, invite students to name processed foods that they commonly eat. Suggest that they collect labels from these foods.

Carbon Chemistry
Show the Video Preview to introduce the chapter and provide an overview of chapter content. Discussion question: **What elements are found in hydrocarbons?** *(Only hydrogen and carbon)*

Performance Assessment
The Chapter Project Scoring Rubric will help you evaluate how well students complete the Chapter Project. You may want to share the rubric with your students so they know what is expected. Students will be assessed on
- how well they identify all organic compounds in the food labels they collect
- the completeness and organization of their data tables, including their classifications of all carbon compounds
- their ability to compare different foods based on nutritional composition
- the thoroughness and clarity of their displays

Students can keep their data tables in their portfolios.

Portfolio

L ● 121

Objectives
After this lesson, students will be able to
L.4.1.1 Describe how carbon is able to form a huge variety of compounds.
L.4.1.2 Identify four forms of pure carbon.

Target Reading Skill

Using Prior Knowledge Explain that using prior knowledge helps students connect what they already know to what they are about to read.

Answer
Sample answer:

What You Know
1. Carbon atoms have 6 electrons.
2. Diamond is one form of carbon.

What You Learned
1. Carbon has four valence electrons and is able to form four bonds.
2. Diamond, graphite, fullerenes, and nanotubes are four forms of pure carbon.

All in One Teaching Resources
• Transparency L42

Preteach

Build Background Knowledge L2
Knowledge About Diamonds
Ask: **Why do you think people value diamonds?** (*Sample answer: Beauty, hardness, rarity*) Say that diamonds are made of pure carbon and that students will learn more about the forms of carbon in this section.

Reading Preview

Key Concepts
• How is carbon able to form such a huge variety of compounds?
• What are the four forms of pure carbon?

Key Terms
• diamond • graphite
• fullerene • nanotube

Target Reading Skill
Using Prior Knowledge Before you read, look at the section headings and visuals to see what this section is about. Then, write what you know about carbon in a graphic organizer like the one below. As you read, continue to write in what you learn.

What You Know
1. Carbon atoms have 6 electrons.
2.

What You Learned
1.
2.

Lab zone Discover Activity

Why Do Pencils Write?
1. Tear paper into two pieces about 5 cm by 5 cm. Rub the two pieces back and forth between your fingers.
2. Now rub pencil lead (graphite) on one side of each piece of paper. Try to get as much graphite as possible on the paper.
3. Rub together the two sides covered with graphite.
4. When you are finished, wash your hands.

Think It Over
Observing Did you notice a difference between what you observed in Step 3 and what you observed in Step 1? How could the property of graphite that you observed be useful for purposes other than writing?

Open your mouth and say "aah." Uh-oh, you have a small cavity. Do you know what happens next? Your tooth needs a filling. But first the dentist's drill clears away the decayed part of your tooth.

Why is a dentist's drill hard enough and sharp enough to cut through teeth? The answer has to do with the element carbon. The tip of the drill is covered with diamond chips. Diamond is a form of carbon and the hardest substance on Earth. Because the drill tip is made of diamonds, a dentist's drill stays sharp and useful. To understand why diamond is such a hard substance, you need to take a close look at the carbon atom and the bonds it forms.

FIGURE 1
Uses of Carbon
This colorized photo shows the tip of a dentist's drill (yellow). The tip is made of diamond and is strong enough to bore into a tooth (blue).

Lab zone Discover Activity

Skills Focus Observing

Materials paper, pencil

Time 10 minutes

Tips Students should try to cover the papers completely with a heavy coat of graphite. Use soft-leaded pencils.

L1 **Expected Outcome** The papers slide past each other more easily when covered in graphite.

Think It Over Yes. The papers slid more easily when covered in graphite. Sample answer: You could use graphite to lubricate, or reduce the friction between, moving parts.

FIGURE 2
Carbon Atoms and Bonding
Carbon atoms and the bonds between them can be modeled in several ways.

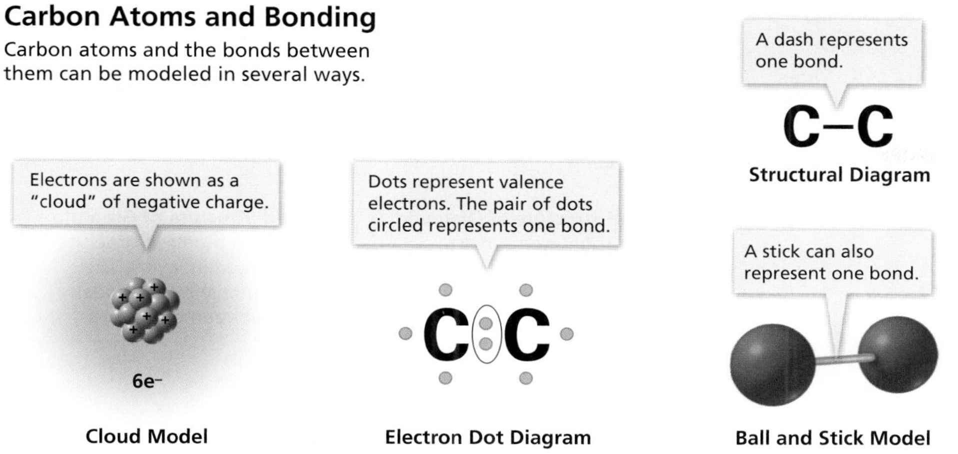

A dash represents one bond.

C–C

Structural Diagram

Electrons are shown as a "cloud" of negative charge.

6e⁻

Cloud Model

Dots represent valence electrons. The pair of dots circled represents one bond.

C∶C

Electron Dot Diagram

A stick can also represent one bond.

Ball and Stick Model

Carbon Atoms and Bonding

Recall that the atomic number of carbon is 6, which means that the nucleus of a carbon atom contains 6 protons. Surrounding the nucleus are 6 electrons. Of these electrons, four are valence electrons—the electrons available for bonding.

As you have learned, a chemical bond is the force that holds two atoms together. A bond between two atoms results from changes involving the atoms' valence electrons. Two atoms gain, lose, or share valence electrons in the way that makes the atoms most stable. The transfer or sharing of valence electrons creates chemical bonds. Figure 2 shows ways that bonds between atoms may be represented.

Atoms of most elements form chemical bonds. Carbon, however, is unique. **Few elements have the ability of carbon to bond with both itself and other elements in so many different ways. With four valence electrons, each carbon atom is able to form four bonds.** Therefore, it is possible to form molecules made of thousands of carbon atoms. By comparison, hydrogen, oxygen, and nitrogen can form only one, two, or three bonds, respectively, and cannot form such long chains.

As you can see in Figure 3, it is possible to arrange the same number of carbon atoms in different ways. Carbon atoms can form straight chains, branched chains, and rings. Sometimes, two or more carbon rings can even join together.

 Reading Checkpoint What makes up the chemical bond between two atoms?

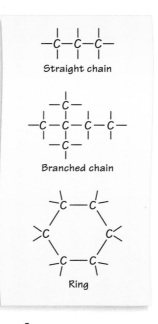

Straight chain

Branched chain

Ring

FIGURE 3
Arrangements of Carbon Atoms
Carbon chains and rings form the backbones for molecules that may contain other atoms.

Chapter 4 L ◆ 123

Differentiated Instruction

Special Needs L1
Modeling Carbon Arrangements Give students several paper clips and invite them to connect the paper clips together to make models of straight carbon chains, branched carbon chains, and carbon rings. Suggest

that they use Figure 3 as a guide. Ask: **What do the paper clips represent?** (Carbon atoms) **What is the largest number of carbon atoms that can bond to one carbon atom?** (Four) **learning modality: kinesthetic**

Instruct

Carbon Atoms and Bonding

Teach Key Concepts L2
Carbon Bonding

Focus Explain that carbon has four electrons available for bonding.

Teach Use the dot diagram in Figure 2 to show how carbon atoms share electrons to form chemical bonds. Ask: **What kind of a chemical bond does carbon form?** (*Covalent bond*) **How many bonds can each carbon atom form?** (*Four bonds*) Draw structural diagrams of carbon chains, branched chains, and rings.

Apply Point to the dashes on a structural diagram that has only one carbon. Ask: **What could bond with carbon here?** (*Sample answer: Carbon or the atoms of other elements, such as hydrogen, oxygen, and nitrogen*) **learning modality: visual**

All in One Teaching Resources
• Transparency L43

Independent Practice L2

All in One Teaching Resources
• Guided Reading and Study Worksheet: *Properties of Carbon*

⊙ Student Edition on Audio CD

Monitor Progress L2

Drawing Have students diagram three carbon atoms bonded together in a chain using a dot diagram.

Students can save their drawings in their portfolios.

Answer

 Reading Checkpoint Changes that occur when the atoms gain, lose, or share valence electrons

L ● 123

Forms of Pure Carbon

Teach Key Concepts L2

Comparing and Contrasting Forms of Carbon

Focus Say that because of the way that carbon forms bonds, pure carbon is found in several different forms.

Teach Ask: **What are four forms in which pure carbon can exist?** *(Diamond, graphite, fullerenes, and nanotubes)* Use a compare/contrast table to organize the similarities and differences among diamond, graphite, fullerenes, and nanotubes. Complete the table by asking: **How are the carbon atoms arranged in diamond?** *(In a crystal structure)* **How many carbon atoms are bonded to each carbon atom?** *(Four)* **What are some uses of diamond?** *(Jewelry and in cutting tools)* Repeat these questions for the other forms of carbon.

Apply Ask: **Which forms of carbon are natural?** *(Diamond and graphite)* **Which are synthesized?** *(Fullerenes and nanotubes)*

Extend The *active art* will show students different forms in which pure carbon can exist. **learning modality: visual**

 **Teaching Resources**

• Transparency L44

 Build Inquiry L3

Modeling Fullerenes

Materials short lengths of pipe cleaners, modeling clay, soccer ball

Time 15 minutes

Focus Tell students that in fullerenes, each carbon atom is bonded to three other carbon atoms to form a sphere.

Teach Challenge students to build a model of a fullerene. Suggest that they use the shape of a soccer ball as a guide.

Apply Ask: **What basic shapes make up your model?** *(Hexagons and pentagons)* **learning modality: kinesthetic**

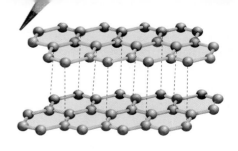

Crystal Structure of Diamond
The carbon atoms in a diamond are arranged in a crystal structure.

Layered Structure of Graphite
The carbon atoms in graphite are arranged in layers. The dashed lines show the weak bonds between the layers.

FIGURE 4
Forms of Pure Carbon

Pure carbon exists in the form of diamond, graphite, fullerenes, and nanotubes. The properties of each form result from the unique repeating pattern of its carbon atoms. Interpreting Diagrams *Which form of carbon has a crystal structure?*

Forms of Pure Carbon

Because of the ways that carbon forms bonds, the pure element can exist in different forms. **Diamond, graphite, fullerenes, and nanotubes are four forms of the element carbon.**

Diamond The hardest mineral, **diamond,** forms deep within Earth. At very high temperatures and pressures, carbon atoms form diamond crystals. Each carbon atom is bonded strongly to four other carbon atoms. The result is a solid that is extremely hard and nonreactive. The melting point of diamond is more than 3,500°C—as hot as the surface temperatures of some stars.

Diamonds are prized for their brilliance and clarity when cut as gems. Industrial chemists are able to make diamonds artificially, but these diamonds are not considered beautiful enough to use as gems. Both natural and artificial diamonds are used in industry. Diamonds work well in cutting tools, such as drills.

Graphite Every time you write with a pencil, you leave a layer of carbon on the paper. The "lead" in a lead pencil is actually mostly **graphite,** another form of the element carbon. In graphite, each carbon atom is bonded tightly to three other carbon atoms in flat layers. However, the bonds between atoms in different layers are very weak, so the layers slide past one another easily.

If you run your fingers over pencil marks, you can feel how slippery graphite is. Because it is so slippery, graphite makes an excellent lubricant in machines. Graphite reduces friction between the moving parts. In your home, you might use a graphite spray to help a key work better in a sticky lock.

✓ Reading Checkpoint **Why is a diamond such a hard and nonreactive substance?**

Spherical Structure of Fullerene
The carbon atoms in a fullerene form a sphere that resembles a geodesic dome.

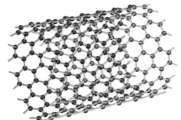

Cylindrical Structure of Nanotube
The carbon atoms in a nanotube are arranged in a cylinder.

Fullerenes and Nanotubes In 1985, scientists made a new form of carbon. It consists of carbon atoms arranged in the shape of a hollow sphere. This form of carbon was named **fullerene** (FUL ur een), for the architect Buckminster Fuller, who designed dome-shaped buildings called geodesic domes. One type of fullerene has been nicknamed "buckyballs."

In 1991, yet another form of carbon was made—the nanotube. In a **nanotube,** carbon atoms are arranged in the shape of a long, hollow cylinder, or tube. You can think of a nanotube as a sheet of graphite rolled into a cylinder. Only a few nanometers wide in diameter, nanotubes are tiny, light, flexible, and extremely strong. Nanotubes are also good conductors of electricity and heat.

Scientists are looking for ways to use the unique properties of fullerenes and nanotubes. For example, chemists are studying how fullerenes and nanotubes may be used to deliver medicine molecules into cells. Nanotubes may also be used as conductors in electronic devices and as super-strong cables.

Section 1 Assessment

Target Reading Skill Using Prior Knowledge Review your graphic organizer and revise it based on what you learned in this section.

Reviewing Key Concepts

1. a. **Identifying** How many bonds can a carbon atom form?
   b. **Explaining** What bonding properties of carbon allow it to form so many different compounds?
2. a. **Listing** List the four forms of pure carbon.

b. **Describing** Describe the carbon bonds in graphite.
c. **Relating Cause and Effect** How do the differences in carbon bonds explain why graphite and diamonds have different properties?

Writing in Science

Explanation Draw electron dot diagrams for a straight carbon chain and a branched chain. Then, write an explanation of what you did to show how the carbons are bonded.

Chapter 4 L ◆ 125

Assess

Reviewing Key Concepts

1. a. Four bonds **b.** Carbon atoms can bond with atoms of carbon and other elements in many different ways.
2. a. Diamond, graphite, fullerenes, and nanotubes **b.** In graphite, each carbon atom is bonded strongly with three other atoms in a flat layer, but weakly with atoms in other layers. **c.** In a diamond crystal, each carbon atom is bonded strongly with four other carbon atoms, making diamond hard. The carbon atoms in graphite are arranged in layers that can easily slide past one another, making graphite slippery.

Reteach L1

Students can draw diagrams showing how carbon forms bonds with other elements.

Performance Assessment L2
Oral Presentation Have students name one form of pure carbon and describe two of its characteristics.

Lab zone Chapter **Project**

Keep Students on Track Students should collect at least 12 different food labels. Help them read the labels. Point out that the ingredients on the labels are listed in order of decreasing amount. Explain that the nutritional values in the table of nutrition facts are based on a diet of 2,000 calories per day.

Writing in Science

Writing Mode Exposition/How-to
4 Exceeds criteria; includes accurate, complex electron dot diagrams and a highly detailed, step-by-step explanation of what they did
3 Meets criteria
2 Includes sketchy diagrams and/or brief explanations
1 Includes serious errors and/or omissions

Objectives

After this lesson, students will be able to

L.4.2.1 List properties of organic compounds.

L.4.2.2 Identify properties of hydrocarbons.

L.4.2.3 Describe the kind of structures and bonding that hydrocarbons have.

L.4.2.4 Identify characteristics of substituted hydrocarbons, esters, and polymers.

Target Reading Skill 🔄

Outlining Explain that using an outline format helps students organize information by main topic, subtopic, and details.

Answer

Sample outline:

Carbon Compounds

I. Organic compounds
II. Hydrocarbons
   A. Properties of hydrocarbons
   B. Chemical formulas of hydrocarbons
III. Structure and bonding in hydrocarbons
   A. Structural formulas
   B. Isomers
   C. Double bonds and triple bonds
   D. Saturated and unsaturated hydrocarbons
IV. Substituted hydrocarbons
   A. Compounds containing halogens
   B. Alcohols
   C. Organic acids
V. Esters
VI. Polymers

All in One Teaching Resources

• Transparency L45

Preteach

Build Background Knowledge   L2

Observations at the Gas Station

Have students think back to the last time they visited a gas station. Ask: **What are some properties of gasoline that you observed or that were described by warning signs?** *(Sample answer: Strong odor, liquid, highly flammable)*

Carbon Compounds

Reading Preview

Key Concepts

• What are some properties of organic compounds?
• What are some properties of hydrocarbons?
• What kind of structures and bonding do hydrocarbons have?
• What are some characteristics of substituted hydrocarbons, esters, and polymers?

Key Terms

• organic compound
• hydrocarbon
• structural formula • isomer
• saturated hydrocarbon
• unsaturated hydrocarbon
• substituted hydrocarbon
• hydroxyl group • alcohol
• organic acid • carboxyl group
• ester • polymer • monomer

🔄 Target Reading Skill

Outlining As you read, make an outline about carbon compounds. Use the red headings for the main ideas and the blue headings for supporting ideas.

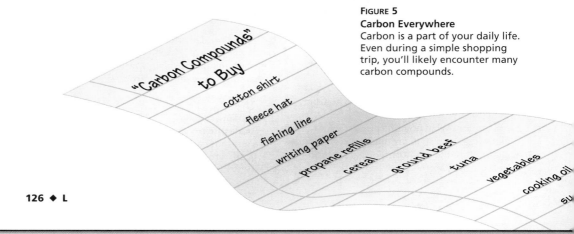

Lab zone Discover Activity

What Do You Smell?

1. Your teacher will provide you with some containers. Wave your hand toward your nose over the top of each container.
2. Try to identify each of the odors.
3. After you record what you think is in each container, compare your guesses to the actual substance.

Think It Over

Developing Hypotheses Develop a hypothesis to explain the differences between the smell of one substance and another.

Imagine that you are heading out for a day of shopping. Your first purchase is a cotton shirt. Then you go to the drug store, where you buy a bottle of shampoo and a pad of writing paper. Your next stop is a hardware store. There, you buy propane fuel for your camping stove. Your final stop is the grocery store, where you buy olive oil, cereal, meat, and vegetables.

What do all of these purchases have in common? They all are made of carbon compounds. Carbon atoms act as the backbone or skeleton for the molecules of these compounds. Carbon compounds include gases (such as propane), liquids (such as olive oil), and solids (such as cotton). Mixtures of carbon compounds are found in foods, paper, and shampoo. In fact, more than 90 percent of all known compounds contain carbon.

FIGURE 5
Carbon Everywhere
Carbon is a part of your daily life. Even during a simple shopping trip, you'll likely encounter many carbon compounds.

"Carbon Compounds" to Buy
cotton shirt
fleece hat
fishing line
writing paper
propane refills
cereal
ground beef
tuna
vegetables
cooking oil

Lab zone Discover Activity

Skills Focus Developing hypotheses   L1

Materials paper cups, cotton balls or note cards, banana, pineapple, wintergreen candy, apple

Time 15 minutes

Tips Mash each sample and place in separate cups. Cover with cotton or place note cards on top.

Expected Outcome Students will observe distinct odors in each cup.

Think It Over Sample hypothesis: Each sample has a different smell because it is made of a different compound or mixture of compounds.

Part of Living Things

Muscle
Blood
Seeds
Leaves
Feathers
Skin

From Living Things

Wool
Cotton
Wood
Silk
Paper
Natural gas

Produced Artificially

Gasoline
Fleece
Plastics
Shampoo
Detergent
Cosmetics

Organic Compounds

Carbon compounds are so numerous that they are given a specific name. With some exceptions, compounds that contain carbon are called **organic compounds.** This term is used because scientists once thought that organic compounds could be produced only by living things. (The word *organic* means "of living things.") Today, however, scientists know that organic compounds also can be found in products made from living things and in materials produced artificially in laboratories and factories. Organic compounds are part of the solid matter of every organism on Earth. They are part of products that are made from organisms, such as paper made from the wood of trees. Plastics, fuels, cleaning solutions, and many other such products are also organic compounds. The raw materials for most synthetic organic compounds come from petroleum, or crude oil.

Many organic compounds have similar properties in terms of melting points, boiling points, odor, electrical conductivity, and solubility. Many organic compounds have low melting points and low boiling points. As a result, they are liquids or gases at room temperature. Organic liquids generally have strong odors. They also do not conduct electricity. Many organic compounds do not dissolve well in water. You may have seen vegetable oil, which is a mixture of organic compounds, form a separate layer in a bottle of salad dressing.

Reading Checkpoint What is an organic compound?

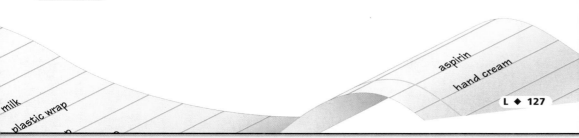

milk
plastic wrap
aspirin
hand cream

Hydrocarbons

Teach Key Concepts L2

Properties of Hydrocarbons

Focus Define *hydrocarbon*.

Teach Ask: **What elements do hydrocarbons contain?** (*Only hydrogen and carbon*) **What are two properties of hydrocarbons?** (*Mix poorly with water, burn easily*)

Apply Ask: **Why are hydrocarbons often used as fuels?** (*They release a lot of energy while burning.*) **learning modality: verbal**

Help Students Read

Active Comprehension Refer to the Content Refresher in this chapter, which provides guidelines for the Active Comprehension strategy.

Have students read the first two sentences of *Hydrocarbons*. Ask: **What would you like to learn about hydrocarbons?** (*Sample answer: What are some properties of hydrocarbons? How are hydrocarbons used?*) List their questions on the board. After students read, invite them to answer each question.

Modeling Hydrocarbons

Materials 12 toothpicks, 8 small foam balls, 3 large foam balls

Time 15 minutes

Focus Write the chemical formulas for methane, ethane, and propane on the board.

Teach Invite students to make models of methane, ethane, and propane. Ask: **What do the toothpicks represent?** (*Chemical bonds*)

Apply Challenge students to create even larger hydrocarbons and then write their chemical formulas. **learning modality: kinesthetic**

FIGURE 7
Hydrocarbons
Hydrocarbons contain only the elements carbon and hydrogen. From the fuel that heats the air in hot-air balloons (above) to multicolored oil slicks (below right), hydrocarbons are all around you.
Making Generalizations *What properties of hydrocarbons do the hot-air balloon and oil slick demonstrate?*

128 ◆ L

Hydrocarbons

Scientists classify organic compounds into different categories. The simplest organic compounds are the hydrocarbons. A **hydrocarbon** (HY droh KAHR bun) is a compound that contains only the elements carbon and hydrogen.

You might already recognize several common hydrocarbons. Methane, the main gas in natural gas, is used to heat homes. Propane is used in portable stoves and gas grills and to provide heat for hot-air balloons. Butane is the fuel in most lighters. Gasoline is a mixture of several different hydrocarbons.

Properties of Hydrocarbons Have you ever been at a gas station after a rainstorm? If so, you may have noticed a thin rainbow-colored film of gasoline or oil floating on a puddle, like the one in Figure 7. **Like many other organic compounds, hydrocarbons mix poorly with water. Also, all hydrocarbons are flammable.** Being flammable means that they burn easily. When hydrocarbons burn, they release a great deal of energy. For this reason, they are used as fuel for stoves, heaters, cars, buses, and airplanes.

Chemical Formulas of Hydrocarbons Hydrocarbon compounds differ in the number of carbon and hydrogen atoms in each molecule. You can write a chemical formula to show how many atoms there are of the elements that make up each molecule of a hydrocarbon. Recall from Chapter 1 that a chemical formula includes the chemical symbols of the elements in a compound. For molecular compounds, a chemical formula also shows the number of atoms of each element in a molecule.

The simplest hydrocarbon is methane. Its chemical formula is CH_4. The number 4 indicates the number of hydrogen atoms (H). Notice that the 4 is a subscript. Subscripts are written lower and smaller than the letter symbols of the elements. The symbol for carbon (C) in the formula is written without a subscript. This means that there is one carbon atom in the molecule.

A hydrocarbon with two carbon atoms is ethane. The formula for ethane is C_2H_6. The subscripts in this formula show that an ethane molecule is made of two carbon atoms and six hydrogen atoms.

A hydrocarbon with three carbon atoms is propane (C_3H_8). How many hydrogen atoms does the subscript indicate? If you answered eight, you are right.

 Reading Checkpoint What is a hydrocarbon?

Structure and Bonding in Hydrocarbons

The properties of hydrocarbon compounds are related to the compound's structure. **The carbon chains in a hydrocarbon may be straight, branched, or ring-shaped.** If a hydrocarbon has two or more carbon atoms, the atoms can form a single line, or a straight chain. In hydrocarbons with four or more carbon atoms, it is possible to have branched arrangements of the carbon atoms as well as a straight chain.

Structural Formulas To show how atoms are arranged in the molecules of a compound, chemists use a structural formula. A **structural formula** shows the kind, number, and arrangement of atoms in a molecule.

Figure 8 shows the structural formulas for molecules of methane, ethane, and propane. Each dash (—) represents a bond. In methane, each carbon atom is bonded to four hydrogen atoms. In ethane and propane, each carbon atom is bonded to at least one carbon atom as well as to hydrogen atoms. As you look at structural formulas, notice that every carbon atom forms four bonds. Every hydrogen atom forms one bond. There are never any dangling bonds. In other words, both ends of a dash are always connected to something.

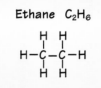

FIGURE 8
Structural Formulas
Each carbon atom in these structural formulas is surrounded by four dashes representing four bonds. **Interpreting Diagrams** *In propane, how many hydrogens is each carbon bonded to?*

Methane CH_4

Ethane C_2H_6

Propane C_3H_8

Teach Key Concepts L2
Structure of Hydrocarbons

Focus Explain that hydrocarbons have different structures based on how carbon bonds with other carbon atoms.

Teach Draw structural formulas of propane and isobutane. Ask: **Which is a straight chain?** *(Propane)* **Which is branched?** *(Isobutane)* Add structural formulas of ethene and ethyne. Ask: **Which have single bonds?** *(Propane and isobutane)* **Which has a double bond?** *(Ethene)* **Which has a triple bond?** *(Ethyne)*

Apply Ask: **How do saturated hydrocarbons differ from unsaturated hydrocarbons?** *(Unsaturated hydrocarbons have double or triple bonds and fewer hydrogen atoms per carbon atom.)* **learning modality: visual**

All in One **Teaching Resources**
• Transparency L46

Lab zone Try This Activity

Dry or Wet?
Petroleum jelly is manufactured from hydrocarbons.

1. Carefully coat one of your fingers in petroleum jelly.
2. Dip that finger in water. Also dip a finger on your other hand in water.
3. Inspect the two fingers, and note how they feel.
4. Use a paper towel to remove the petroleum jelly, and then wash your hands thoroughly.

Inferring Compare how your two fingers looked and felt in Steps 2 and 3. What property of hydrocarbons does this activity demonstrate?

Lab zone Try This Activity

Skills Focus Inferring L2

Materials petroleum jelly, water, cup, paper towel

Time 5 minutes

Tips Suggest that students coat their fingers by dipping a piece of paper towel into the petroleum jelly. This prevents them from covering the fingers of both hands.

Expected Outcome The finger covered with petroleum jelly is not as wet as the coated finger. This demonstrates that hydrocarbons do not mix well with water.

Extend Ask: **How does this property of petroleum jelly make it useful?** *(Sample answer: It forms a moisture-resistant barrier than can protect skin.)* **learning modality: kinesthetic**

Monitor Progress L2

Writing Have students list properties of hydrocarbons.

Answers
Figure 7 Hot-air balloon: flammable; oil slick: mix poorly with water
Figure 8 The center carbon is bonded to two hydrogens; both end carbons are bonded to three.

 Reading Checkpoint A compound that contains only carbon and hydrogen

Math Skill Making and interpreting graphs

Focus Explain that a bar graph is used to compare data in several different categories.

Teach Have students study the graph. Ask: **What is being compared?** *(Boiling points)* **What are the categories being compared?** *(Different hydrocarbons)*

Answers

1. Almost in the center of the y-axis
2. C_3H_8: about $-44°C$; C_5H_{12}: about $34°C$; C_6H_{14}: about $68°C$
3. About $78°C$
4. C_2H_6, C_3H_8, and C_4H_{10} are gases because all hydrocarbons with boiling points below room temperature (about $22°C$) are gases. C_5H_{12} and C_6H_{14} may be liquids or solids because hydrocarbons with boiling points higher than $23°C$ are liquids or solids at room temperature.

 **Teaching Resources**

• Transparencies L47, L48

Lab zone ▶ Build Inquiry
L2

Modeling Isomers

Materials 12 marshmallows, toothpicks

Time 15 minutes

Focus Tell students that isomers have the same chemical formula but have different structures.

Teach Explain that each marshmallow represents a carbon atom and each toothpick represents a chemical bond. Instruct students to connect six marshmallows with toothpicks to build a straight chain. Then, tell them to use the other six marshmallows to build a branched carbon chain. Have students add additional toothpicks to represent bonds to hydrogen atoms so that each carbon has four bonds. Ask: **What is the chemical formula for each chain?** *(Both are C_6H_{14}.)* **Do both chains have the same structural formula?** *(No. One is branched, the other is a straight chain.)*

Apply Ask: **Would you expect the isomers of C_6H_{14} to have the same physical properties?** *(No. Each has different physical properties because of their different structures.)* **learning modality: kinesthetic**

Math ▶ Analyzing Data

Boiling Points of Hydrocarbons

The graph shows the boiling points of several hydrocarbons. (*Note:* Some points on the y-axis are negative.)

Use the graph to answer the following questions.

1. **Reading Graphs** Where is $0°C$ on the graph?
2. **Interpreting Data** What is the approximate boiling point of C_3H_8? C_5H_{12}? C_6H_{14}?
3. **Calculating** What is the temperature difference between the boiling points of C_3H_8 and C_5H_{12}?
4. **Drawing Conclusions** At room temperature (about $22°C$), which of the hydrocarbons are solids? Liquids? Gases? How can you tell?

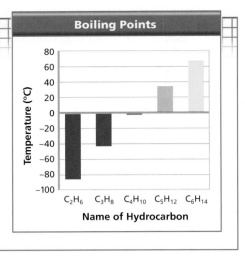

Boiling Points

Temperature (°C) vs. Name of Hydrocarbon: C_2H_6, C_3H_8, C_4H_{10}, C_5H_{12}, C_6H_{14}

Isomers Consider the chemical formula of butane—C_4H_{10}. This formula does not indicate how the atoms are arranged in the molecule. In fact, there are two different ways to arrange the carbon atoms in C_4H_{10}. These two arrangements are shown in Figure 9. Compounds that have the same chemical formula but different structures are called **isomers** (EYE soh murz). Each isomer is a different substance with its own characteristic properties.

Notice in Figure 9 that a molecule of one isomer, butane, is a straight chain. A molecule of the other isomer, isobutane, is a branched chain. Both molecules have 4 carbon atoms and 10 hydrogen atoms, but the atoms are arranged differently in the two molecules. And these two compounds have different properties. For example, butane and isobutane have different melting points and boiling points.

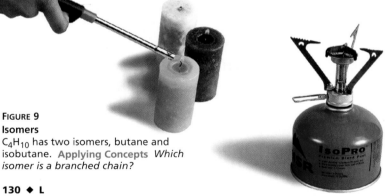

FIGURE 9
Isomers
C_4H_{10} has two isomers, butane and isobutane. **Applying Concepts** *Which isomer is a branched chain?*

Double Bonds and Triple Bonds So far in this section, structural formulas have shown only single bonds between any two carbon atoms (C—C). A single dash means a single bond. **In addition to forming a single bond, two carbon atoms can form a double bond or a triple bond.** A carbon atom can also form a single or double bond with an oxygen atom. Structural formulas represent a double bond with a double dash (C=C). A triple bond is indicated by a triple dash (C≡C).

Saturated and Unsaturated Hydrocarbons A hydrocarbon can be classified according to the types of bonds between its carbon atoms. If there are only single bonds, it has the maximum number of hydrogen atoms possible on its carbon chain. These hydrocarbons are called **saturated hydrocarbons.** You can think of each carbon atom as being "saturated," or filled up, with hydrogens. Hydrocarbons with double or triple bonds have fewer hydrogen atoms for each carbon atom than a saturated hydrocarbon does. They are called **unsaturated hydrocarbons.**

Notice that the names of methane, ethane, propane, and butane all end with the suffix -ane. In general, a chain hydrocarbon with a name ending in -ane is saturated, while a hydrocarbon ending with a name in -ene or -yne is unsaturated.

The simplest unsaturated hydrocarbon with one double bond is ethene (C_2H_4). Many fruits produce ethene gas. Ethene gas helps the fruit to ripen. The simplest hydrocarbon with one triple bond is ethyne (C_2H_2), which is commonly known as acetylene. Acetylene torches are used in welding.

Reading Checkpoint What is the difference between saturated and unsaturated hydrocarbons?

FIGURE 10
Unsaturated Hydrocarbons
Ethene gas (C_2H_4), which causes fruits such as apples to ripen, has one double bond. Acetylene (C_2H_2), the fuel in welding torches, has one triple bond.

Ethene C_2H_4

Acetylene (Ethyne)
C_2H_2

H—C≡C—H

L ◆ 131

L ● 131

Substituted Hydrocarbons

Teach Key Concepts L2

Characteristics of Substituted Hydrocarbons

Focus Tell students that carbon can form stable chemical bonds with oxygen, nitrogen, and sulfur, and with members of the halogen family.

Teach Draw structural formulas of methanol and formic acid. Ask: **What has been substituted for hydrogen in these compounds?** (*Methanol: a hydroxyl group; formic acid: oxygen and a hydroxyl group*)

Apply Ask: **How do these substitutions change the characteristics of the hydrocarbon?** (*Sample answer: Physical properties such as solubility and boiling points are different.*) **learning modality: visual**

 **Teaching Resources**

• Transparency L50

 Teacher Demo L1

Alcohol Solubility

Materials water, isopropyl alcohol, 2 (100-mL) graduated cylinders, food coloring, stirring stick

Time 10 minutes

Focus Tell students that unlike many carbon compounds, alcohols dissolve well in water.

Teach Pour 30 mL of water into a graduated cylinder. Show students 30 mL of isopropyl alcohol with a few drops of food coloring added in a second graduated cylinder. Mix together the alcohol and the water.

Apply Ask: **Did a solution form?** (*Yes. The mixture of water and alcohol is evenly colored.*) **learning modality: visual**

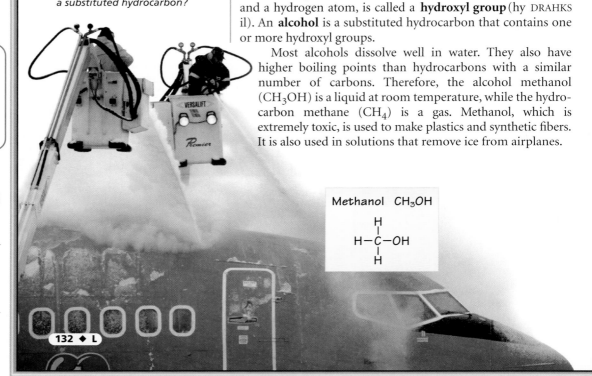

FIGURE 11
Alcohol
Methanol is used for de-icing an airplane in cold weather.
Classifying What makes methanol a substituted hydrocarbon?

Methanol CH_3OH

$$H-\overset{\displaystyle H}{\underset{\displaystyle H}{C}}-OH$$

Substituted Hydrocarbons

Hydrocarbons contain only carbon and hydrogen. But carbon can form stable bonds with several other elements, including oxygen, nitrogen, sulfur, and members of the halogen family. **If just one atom of another element is substituted for a hydrogen atom in a hydrocarbon, a different compound is created.** In a **substituted hydrocarbon,** atoms of other elements replace one or more hydrogen atoms in a hydrocarbon. Substituted hydrocarbons include halogen-containing compounds, alcohols, and acids.

Compounds Containing Halogens In some substituted hydrocarbons, one or more halogen atoms replace hydrogen atoms. Recall that the halogen family includes fluorine, chlorine, bromine, and iodine.

One compound, Freon (CCl_2F_2), was widely used as a cooling liquid in refrigerators and air conditioners. When Freon was found to damage the environment, its use was banned in the United States. However, a very hazardous compound that contains halogens, trichloroethane ($C_2H_3Cl_3$), is still used in dry-cleaning solutions. It can cause severe health problems.

Alcohols The group —OH can also substitute for hydrogen atoms in a hydrocarbon. Each —OH, made of an oxygen atom and a hydrogen atom, is called a **hydroxyl group** (hy DRAHKS il). An **alcohol** is a substituted hydrocarbon that contains one or more hydroxyl groups.

Most alcohols dissolve well in water. They also have higher boiling points than hydrocarbons with a similar number of carbons. Therefore, the alcohol methanol (CH_3OH) is a liquid at room temperature, while the hydrocarbon methane (CH_4) is a gas. Methanol, which is extremely toxic, is used to make plastics and synthetic fibers. It is also used in solutions that remove ice from airplanes.

Differentiated Instruction

Gifted and Talented L3
Testing for Organic Acids Challenge students to test a variety of fruits and vegetables for acidity. Provide students with universal acid-base indicator paper. Demonstrate how the paper works by dipping it in vinegar (acid) and ammonia (base). Students should design step-by-step testing procedures, including data tables, samples to test, and controls, and submit these for your approval. After students conduct their tests, invite them to share their results with the class. (*Organic acids are usually present in all samples that have a sour taste and turn indicator paper red, such as lemons, oranges, apples, and peaches.*) **learning modality: logical/ mathematical**

Formic acid   HCOOH

$$H-\overset{\displaystyle O}{\overset{\|}{C}}-OH$$

FIGURE 12
Organic Acid
Formic acid is the simplest organic acid. It is the acid produced by ants and is responsible for the pain caused by an ant bite.

When a hydroxyl group is substituted for one hydrogen atom in ethane, the resulting alcohol is ethanol (C_2H_5OH). Ethanol is produced naturally by the action of yeast or bacteria on the sugar stored in corn, wheat, and barley. Ethanol is a good solvent for many organic compounds that do not dissolve in water. It is also added to gasoline to make a fuel for car engines called "gasohol." Ethanol is used in medicines and is found in alcoholic beverages. The ethanol used for industrial purposes is unsafe to drink. Poisonous compounds such as methanol have been added. The resulting poisonous mixture is called denatured alcohol.

Organic Acids Lemons, oranges, and grapefruits taste a little tart or sour, don't they? The sour taste of many fruits comes from citric acid, an organic acid. An **organic acid** is a substituted hydrocarbon that contains one or more carboxyl groups. A **carboxyl group** (kahr BAHKS il) is written as —COOH.

You can find organic acids in many foods. Acetic acid (CH_3COOH) is the main ingredient of vinegar. Malic acid is found in apples. Butyric acid makes butter smell rancid when it goes bad. Stinging nettle plants make formic acid (HCOOH), a compound that causes the stinging feeling. The pain from ant bites also comes from formic acid.

Esters

If you have eaten wintergreen candy, then you are familiar with the smell of an ester. An **ester** is a compound made by chemically combining an alcohol and an organic acid. **Many esters have pleasant, fruity smells.** Esters are responsible for the smells of pineapples, bananas, strawberries, and apples. If you did the Discover activity, you smelled different esters. Other esters are ingredients in medications, including aspirin and the local anesthetic used by dentists.

FIGURE 13
Esters
Strawberries contain esters, which give them a pleasant aroma and flavor.

Chapter 4 L ◆ 133

Monitor Progress ——— L2

Answers

Figure 14 Polymers are made of chains of monomers.

Reading Checkpoint — A smaller molecule from which larger polymers can be made.

Assess

Reviewing Key Concepts

1. a. Sample answer: Strong odors, low melting and boiling points, poor conductors of electricity, do not dissolve well in water **b.** Sample answer: Test for electrical conductivity, melting point, and solubility in water

2. a. Hydrocarbons burn easily and mix poorly with water. **b.** All contain only the elements hydrogen and carbon. They differ in the number of carbon and hydrogen atoms.

3. a. Straight, branched, or ring-shaped **b.** Both have the same chemical formula, C_4H_{10}. Butane is a straight chain, while isobutane is a branched chain. **c.** The melting points and boiling points of butane and isobutane are quite different.

4. a. A hydrocarbon in which atoms of other elements replace one or more hydrogen atoms **b.** An alcohol and an organic acid **c.** Polymers

Reteach L1

Have students create a concept map to relate hydrocarbons, substituted hydrocarbons, esters, and polymers.

Performance Assessment L2

Drawing Have students draw diagrams to differentiate saturated, unsaturated, and substituted hydrocarbons.

All in One Teaching Resources

• Section Summary: *Carbon Compounds*
• Review and Reinforce: *Carbon Compounds*
• Enrich: *Carbon Compounds*

FIGURE 14
Monomers and Polymers
This chain of plastic beads is somewhat like a polymer molecule. The individual beads are like the monomers that link together to build a polymer.
Comparing and Contrasting *How do polymers differ from monomers?*

Polymers

A very large molecule made of a chain of many smaller molecules bonded together is called a **polymer** (PAHL ih mur). The smaller molecules are called **monomers** (MAHN uh murz). The prefix *poly-* means "many," and the prefix *mono-* means "one." **Organic compounds, such as alcohols, esters, and others, can be linked together to build polymers with thousands or even millions of atoms.**

Some polymers are made naturally by living things. For example, sheep make wool, cotton plants make cotton, and silkworms make silk. Other polymers, called synthetic polymers, are made in factories. If you are wearing clothing made from polyester or nylon, you are wearing a synthetic polymer right now! And any plastic item you use is most certainly made of synthetic polymers.

 Reading Checkpoint — What is a monomer?

Section 2 Assessment

⟳ **Target Reading Skill** Outlining Work with a partner to check the answers in your graphic organizer.

Reviewing Key Concepts

1. a. Listing List properties common to many organic compounds.
   b. Applying Concepts You are given two solid materials, one that is organic and one that is not organic. Describe three tests you could perform to help you decide which is which.
2. a. Identifying What are some properties of hydrocarbons?
   b. Comparing and Contrasting How are hydrocarbons similar? How are they different?
3. a. Reviewing What are three kinds of carbon chains found in hydrocarbons?
   b. Describing Compare the structure and bonding of butane and isobutane.

c. Relating Cause and Effect Relate the properties of butane and isobutane to their structure and bonding.
4. a. Defining What is a substituted hydrocarbon?
   b. Classifying What kind of substituted hydrocarbons react to form an ester?
   c. Drawing Conclusions What results from combining many hydrocarbons together?

Lab zone At-Home **Activity**

Mix It Up You can make a simple salad dressing to demonstrate one property of organic compounds. In a transparent container, thoroughly mix equal amounts of a vegetable oil and a fruit juice. Stop mixing, and observe the oil and juice mixture for several minutes. Explain your observations to your family.

134 ◆ L

Lab zone At-Home **Activity**

Mix It Up L2

The oil and fruit juice separate into two layers with the oil on top. Students should explain that oil is a hydrocarbon and that hydrocarbons do not dissolve in water or water solutions such fruit juice.

How Many Molecules?

Problem

In this lab you will use gumdrops to represent atoms and toothpicks to represent bonds. How many different ways can you put the same number of carbon atoms together?

Skills Focus

making models

Materials

• toothpicks   • multicolored gumdrops
• other materials supplied by your teacher

Procedure

1. You will need gumdrops of one color to represent carbon atoms and gumdrops of another color to represent hydrogen atoms. When building your models, always follow these rules:
   • Each carbon atom forms four bonds.
   • Each hydrogen atom forms one bond.
   CAUTION: *Do not eat any of the food substances in this experiment.*

2. Make a model of CH_4 (methane).

3. Now make a model of C_2H_6 (ethane).

4. Make a model of C_3H_8 (propane). Is there more than one way to arrange the atoms in propane? (*Hint:* Are there any branches in the carbon chain or are all the carbon atoms in one line?)

5. Now make a model of C_4H_{10} (butane) in which all the carbon atoms are in one line.

6. Make a second model of butane with a branched chain.

7. Compare the branched-chain model with the straight-chain model of butane. Are there other ways to arrange the atoms?

8. Predict how many different structures can be formed from C_5H_{12} (pentane).

9. Test your prediction by building as many different models of pentane as you can.

Analyze and Conclude

1. **Making Models** Did any of your models have a hydrogen atom between two carbon atoms? Why or why not?

2. **Observing** How does a branched chain differ from a straight chain?

3. **Drawing Conclusions** How many different structures have the formula C_3H_8? C_4H_{10}? C_5H_{12}? Use diagrams to explain your answers.

4. **Predicting** If you bend a straight chain of carbons, do you make a different structure? Why or why not?

5. **Communicating** Compare the information you can get from models to the information you can get from formulas like C_6H_{14}. How does using models help you understand the structure of a molecule?

More to Explore

Use a third color of gumdrops to model an oxygen atom. An oxygen atom forms two bonds. Use the rules in this lab to model as many different structures for the formula $C_4H_{10}O$ as possible.

Chapter 4 L ◆ 135

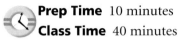

How Many Molecules? [L2]

Prepare for Inquiry

Key Concept
Models of organic compounds show their similarities and differences.

Skills Objectives
After this lab, students will be able to
• make models to explore the relationship between the number of carbon atoms in a formula and the number of differently structured molecules that can be formed

Prep Time 10 minutes
Class Time 40 minutes

Advance Planning
Obtain enough gumdrops for each group to have 15 of one color and 36 of another. Additional gumdrops of a third color are required for the More to Explore. Each group needs 48 toothpicks.

Alternative Materials
Substitute raisins, grapes, or clay for gumdrops.

All in One Teaching Resources
• Lab Worksheet: *How Many Molecules?*

Guide Inquiry

Invitation
Show students a set of blocks of four different colors. Challenge volunteers to create as many different four-block combinations as possible.

Introduce the Procedure
Make sure students understand that carbon forms four bonds and hydrogen forms only one bond.

Extend Inquiry

More to Explore
Be sure students show the correct number of bonds for each atom. Models can include structures with 4-carbon chains or 3-carbon chains with one branched carbon; the hydroxyl group can be at the end or in the middle of a chain. Some students may see that they can also place the oxygen atom within the chain.

Analyze and Conclude

1. No. If they did, a hydrogen atom would have two bonds, which is not possible.

2. In a branched chain, a carbon atom can be bonded to more than two other carbon atoms. In a straight chain, a carbon atom can be bonded to one or two other carbon atoms.

3. C_3H_8: one; C_4H_{10}: two; C_5H_{12}: three. Diagrams should support students' answers.

4. No; the atoms are still connected the same way. To make a different structure, branching must occur.

5. Using a model helps to visualize the different structures. C_6H_{14} tells how many carbon and hydrogen atoms are in the molecule, but not how they are connected.

Objectives

After this lesson, students will be able to

L.4.3.1 List the four main classes of organic compounds in living things.

L.4.3.2 Explain how the organic compounds in living things differ from one another.

Target Reading Skill

Asking Questions Explain that changing a head into a question helps students anticipate the ideas, facts, and events they are about to read.

Answer

Sample questions and answers:

What is a carbohydrate? (*A carbohydrate is an energy-rich organic compound made of the elements carbon, hydrogen, and oxygen.*)

What are proteins? (*Proteins are polymers formed from amino acid monomers.*)

What are lipids? (*Lipids are energy-rich compounds made of carbon, oxygen, and hydrogen.*)

What are nucleic acids? (*Nucleic acids are very large organic molecules made up of carbon, oxygen, hydrogen, nitrogen, and phosphorus.*)

What are other compounds in foods? (*Other compounds in foods include vitamins, minerals, and water.*)

All in One Teaching Resources

• Transparency L51

Preteach

Build Background Knowledge · L2

Carbon in Foods

Show students a piece of beef jerky, a carrot, and a candy bar. Ask: **What do these things have in common?** (*Sample answer: All are foods. All have carbon polymers.*) **What makes them different?** (*Sample answer: Taste, texture, chemical makeup*)

Reading Preview

Key Concepts

• What are the four main classes of organic compounds in living things?

• How are the organic compounds in living things different from one another?

Key Terms

• carbohydrate • glucose
• complex carbohydrate
• starch • cellulose • protein
• amino acid • lipid
• fatty acid • cholesterol
• nucleic acid • DNA • RNA
• nucleotide

Target Reading Skill

Asking Questions Before you read, preview the red headings. In a graphic organizer like the one below, ask a *what* question for each heading. As you read, write the answers to your questions.

Life With Carbon

Question	Answer
What is a carbohydrate?	A carbohydrate is . . .

Lab zone · Discover Activity

What Is in Milk?

1. Pour 30 mL of milk into a plastic cup.
2. Pour another 30 mL of milk into a second plastic cup. Rinse the graduated cylinder. Measure 15 mL of vinegar and add it to the second cup. Swirl the two liquids together and let the mixture sit for a minute.
3. Set up two funnels with filter paper, each supported in a narrow plastic cup.
4. Filter the milk through the first funnel. Filter the milk and vinegar through the second funnel.
5. What is left in each filter paper? Examine the liquid that passed through each filter paper.

Think It Over

Observing Where did you see evidence of solids? What do you think was the source of these solids?

Have you ever been told to eat all the organic compounds on your plate? Have you heard how eating a variety of polymers and monomers contributes to good health? What? No one has ever said those things to you? Well, maybe what you really heard was something about eating all the vegetables on your plate, or eating a variety of foods to give you a healthy balance of carbohydrates, proteins, fats, and other nutrients. All these nutrients are organic compounds, which are the building blocks of all living things.

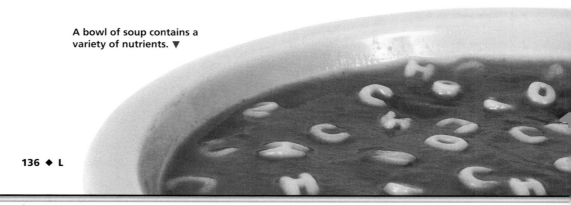

A bowl of soup contains a variety of nutrients. ▼

Lab zone · Discover Activity

Skills Focus Observing · L1

Materials 60 mL milk, 2 plastic cups, 15 mL vinegar, 2 funnels, graduated cylinder, 2 pieces filter paper, 2 Erlenmeyer flasks

Time 15 minutes

Tips Paper coffee filters can be used in place of filter paper.

Expected Outcome The plain milk will pass through the filter unchanged. The milk with vinegar will leave protein solids (curds) in the filter.

Think It Over The solids were in the mixture of milk and vinegar. Sample answer: The solids came from the milk after reacting with the vinegar.

Foods provide organic compounds, which the cells of living things use, change, or store. **The four classes of organic compounds required by living things are carbohydrates, proteins, lipids, and nucleic acids.** Carbohydrates, proteins, and lipids are nutrients. Nutrients (NOO tree unts) are substances that provide the energy and raw materials the body needs to grow, repair worn parts, and function properly.

Carbohydrates

A **carbohydrate** (kahr boh HY drayt) is an energy-rich organic compound made of the elements carbon, hydrogen, and oxygen. The word *carbohydrate* is made of two parts: *carbo-* and *-hydrate*. *Carbo-* means "carbon" and *-hydrate* means "combined with water." If you remember that water is made up of the elements hydrogen and oxygen, then you should be able to remember the three elements in carbohydrates.

Simple Carbohydrates The simplest carbohydrates are sugars. You may be surprised to learn that there are many different kinds of sugars. The sugar listed in baking recipes, which you can buy in bags or boxes at the grocery store, is only one kind. Other sugars are found naturally in fruits, milk, and some vegetables.

One of the most important sugars in your body is the monomer **glucose.** Its chemical formula is $C_6H_{12}O_6$. Glucose is sometimes called "blood sugar" because the body circulates glucose to all body parts through blood. The structural formula for a glucose molecule is shown in Figure 15.

The white sugar that sweetens cookies, candies, and many soft drinks is called sucrose. Sucrose is a more complex molecule than glucose and has a chemical formula of $C_{12}H_{22}O_{11}$.

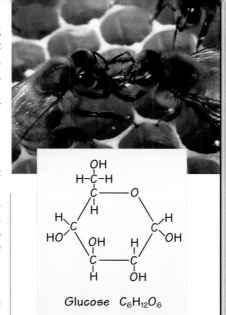

Glucose $C_6H_{12}O_6$

FIGURE 15
Carbohydrates
The honey made by honeybees contains glucose, a simple carbohydrate. **Applying Concepts** *What are some other examples of foods that contain carbohydrates?*

Chapter 4 L ◆ 137

Instruct

Carbohydrates

Teach Key Concepts L2
Comparing and Contrasting Carbohydrates

Focus Tell students that carbohydrates are organic compounds found in foods.

Teach Ask: **What do all carbohydrates have in common?** *(All are energy-rich and made of carbon, hydrogen, and oxygen.)* **What are the two basic types of carbohydrates?** *(Simple and complex)* **How do simple and complex carbohydrates differ?** *(Complex carbohydrates are polymers built from simple carbohydrate monomers.)*

Apply Ask: **What is an example of a simple carbohydrate?** *(Sample answer: Glucose)* **A complex carbohydrate?** *(Sample answer: Starch, cellulose)* **learning modality: verbal**

Independent Practice L2

 **Teaching Resources**

• Guided Reading and Study Worksheet: *Life With Carbon*

⊙ Student Edition on Audio CD

Differentiated Instruction

Less Proficient Readers L1
Organizing Information After students read *Carbohydrates*, have them make a table with two columns labeled Simple Carbohydrates and Complex Carbohydrates. Then instruct students to read *Carbohydrates* again. This time, students should look for information about the structure, the function, and examples of each type of carbohydrate to complete the table. Consider having students repeat this activity for proteins, lipids, and nucleic acids. **learning modality: verbal**

Monitor Progress L2

Oral Presentation Have students name the four classes of organic compounds in living things.

Answer
Figure 15 Sample answer: Fruits, milk, vegetables, cookies, candies, soft drinks

Carbon Chemistry

Show the Video Field Trip to let students understand carbon chemistry and the forms that pure carbon can take. Discussion question: **What are three forms of pure carbon?** *(Diamond, graphite, and nanotubes)*

• Tech & Design in History •

Focus Tell students that aspirin was developed just over 100 years ago in a period of rapid industrialization and beginning social awareness. Henry Ford had just invented the automobile, and the first large-scale electrical power plant had been opened at Niagara Falls.

Teach After students have studied the timeline, say that advances in the development of any product are usually in response to a need. Ask: **What need would each of the advances on the timeline satisfy?** *(Sample answer: Urea—advances in chemical procedures; aspirin—pain relief; artificial diamond—inexpensive alternative for industrial use; DNA—advances in research; skin—better way to treat burns; fat substitute—reduce calories and fat in foods; cancer drug—treat cancer with less damage to healthy body cells)*

Writing in Science

Writing Mode Research
4 Exceeds criteria; includes a concise, descriptive paragraph that tells how the discovery happened and how it changed people's lives
3 Meets criteria
2 Includes brief but accurate information
1 Includes serious errors and/or omissions

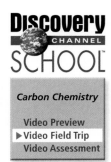

Complex Carbohydrates When you eat plants or food products made from plants, you are often eating complex carbohydrates. Each molecule of a simple carbohydrate, or sugar, is relatively small compared to a molecule of a complex carbohydrate. A **complex carbohydrate** is a polymer—a large, chainlike molecule made of smaller molecules linked together. In this case, the smaller molecules are simple carbohydrates bonded to one another. As a result, just one molecule of a complex carbohydrate may have hundreds of carbon atoms.

Two of the complex carbohydrates assembled from glucose molecules are starch and cellulose. **Starch and cellulose are both polymers built from glucose, but the glucose molecules are arranged differently in each case.** Having different arrangements means that starch and cellulose are different compounds. They serve different functions in the plants that make them. Your body also uses starch very differently from the way it uses cellulose.

• Tech & Design in History •

Advances in Organic Chemistry
Since the first organic compound was synthesized, biologists and chemists have synthesized many useful compounds, both biological and non-biological.

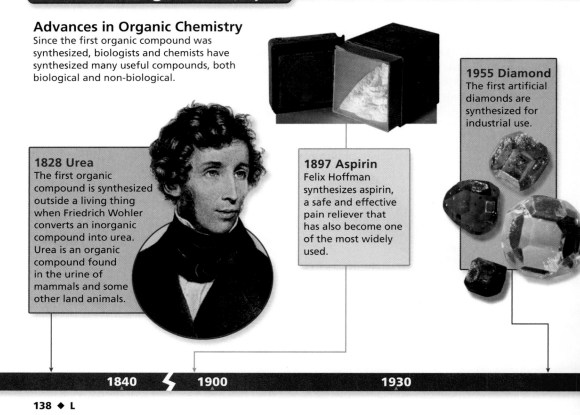

1828 Urea
The first organic compound is synthesized outside a living thing when Friedrich Wohler converts an inorganic compound into urea. Urea is an organic compound found in the urine of mammals and some other land animals.

1897 Aspirin
Felix Hoffman synthesizes aspirin, a safe and effective pain reliever that has also become one of the most widely used.

1955 Diamond
The first artificial diamonds are synthesized for industrial use.

1840   1900   1930

Background

History of Science Felix Hoffman, a chemist with the Bayer Company in Germany, has been credited with the invention of aspirin, but he was not the first to discover it. Hippocrates, an ancient Greek physician, discovered that chewing willow bark would relieve pain and fever. Scientists in the 19th century found that the active agent in willow bark is salicylic acid, which is hard on the stomach. In 1853, a French chemist, Charles Gerhardt, developed a way to make salicylic acid less irritating. But he lost interest in his discovery and abandoned his research. Felix Hoffman rediscovered Gerhardt's work while searching for a way to relieve his father's arthritic pain. He made improvements to the taste and irritability of the compound, which the Bayer Company named aspirin.

Starch Plants store energy in the form of the complex carbohydrate **starch.** You can find starches in food products made from wheat grains, such as bread, cereal, and pasta. Starches are also found in rice, potatoes, and other vegetables.

The process of breaking large molecules, such as starch, into smaller ones involves chemical reactions that occur during digestion. The body digests the large starch molecules from these foods into individual glucose molecules. The body then breaks apart the glucose molecules, releasing energy in the process. This energy allows the body to carry out its life functions.

 Reading Checkpoint What happens to starch molecules during digestion?

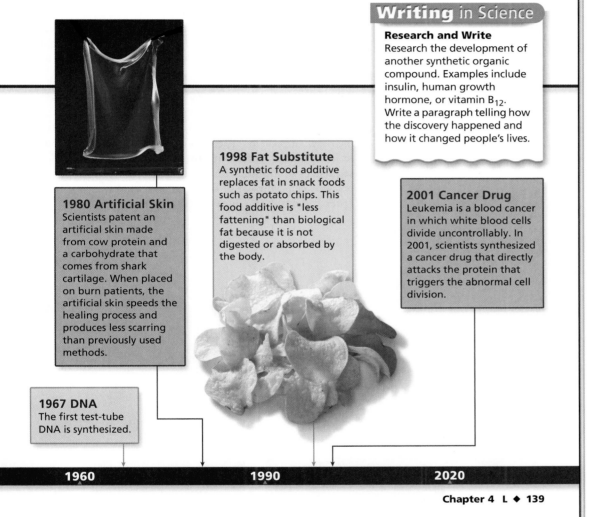

1980 Artificial Skin
Scientists patent an artificial skin made from cow protein and a carbohydrate that comes from shark cartilage. When placed on burn patients, the artificial skin speeds the healing process and produces less scarring than previously used methods.

1998 Fat Substitute
A synthetic food additive replaces fat in snack foods such as potato chips. This food additive is "less fattening" than biological fat because it is not digested or absorbed by the body.

2001 Cancer Drug
Leukemia is a blood cancer in which white blood cells divide uncontrollably. In 2001, scientists synthesized a cancer drug that directly attacks the protein that triggers the abnormal cell division.

1967 DNA
The first test-tube DNA is synthesized.

1960   1990   2020

Writing in Science

Research and Write
Research the development of another synthetic organic compound. Examples include insulin, human growth hormone, or vitamin B_{12}. Write a paragraph telling how the discovery happened and how it changed people's lives.

Identify Starchy Foods

Materials dilute iodine solution, dropper, 7 plastic cups, potato slice, cooked rice or pasta, bread, breakfast cereal, lettuce leaf, celery stalk, beef jerky

Time 15 minutes

Focus Explain that iodine is an indicator for the presence of starch.

Teach Consider having students predict which of the food samples contain starch. Place each food sample in a plastic cup and add several drops of the iodine solution. Ask: **How can you tell which foods contain starch?** *(Foods that cause iodine to change color contain starch.)*

Apply Ask: **What kinds of foods contain starch?** *(Foods made from grains and potatoes; some vegetables have small amounts of starch.)* **learning modality: visual**

Monitor Progress   L2

Writing Have students write a statement in which they describe the relationship between complex carbohydrates and simple carbohydrates, using starch and cellulose as examples.

Answer

 Reading Checkpoint They are broken down into individual glucose molecules.

L ● 139

Proteins

Teach Key Concepts   L2

Protein Structure

Focus Tell students that proteins are polymers that make up many body structures.

Teach Ask: **What monomers make up proteins?** *(Amino acids)* Use the structural formulas of alanine and serine to show that all amino acids have a carboxyl group and an amine group. Say that there are 20 different amino acids. Ask: **How are different proteins made?** *(Different sequences of amino acids are linked into long chains.)*

Apply Ask: **How are proteins similar to and different from complex carbohydrates?** *(Both are polymers. Complex carbohydrate monomers are simple sugars. Protein monomers are amino acids. Simple sugars consist only of carbon, hydrogen, and oxygen. Amino acids also have nitrogen.)* **learning modality: visual**

 **Teaching Resources**

• Transparency L52

Proteins in Foods

Materials plastic dropper, Biuret reagent, plastic cups, apple, butter, egg white, tuna, cooked dried beans, wheat cereal, vegetable oil

Time 10 minutes

Focus Tell students that Biuret reagent is used to test for the presence of proteins.

Teach Place a sample of each food in a small plastic cup. Invite students to predict which foods contain protein and which do not. Consider tallying predictions on the board. Add 10 drops of Biuret reagent to each food sample. Ask: **How do you know which food samples have protein?** *(The reagent turned pink.)*

Apply Ask: **What foods are good sources of protein?** *(Sample answer: Meat, fish, milk products, beans, eggs)* **learning modality: visual**

Lab zone Try This Activity

Alphabet Soup

Here's how you can model the rearrangement of amino acids in your body.

1. Rearrange the letters of the word *proteins* to make a new word or words. (Don't worry if the new words don't make sense together.)

2. Choose three other words with ten or more letters. Repeat the activity.

Making Models What words did you make from *proteins*? What new words did you make from the words you chose? How does this activity model the way your body uses proteins in food to make new proteins?

FIGURE 16
Cellulose and Proteins
Cellulose, found in celery and other vegetables, is a carbohydrate your body needs. Your body also needs proteins, which are available in fish and meat.

Cellulose Plants build strong stems and roots with the complex carbohydrate **cellulose** and other polymers. If you imagine yourself crunching on a stick of celery, you will be able to imagine what cellulose is like. Most fruits and vegetables are high in cellulose. So are foods made from whole grains. Even though the body can break down starch, it cannot break down cellulose into individual glucose molecules. Therefore the body cannot use cellulose as an energy source. In fact, when you eat foods with cellulose, the molecules pass through you undigested. However, this undigested cellulose helps keep your digestive tract active and healthy. Cellulose is sometimes called fiber.

Proteins

If the proteins in your body suddenly disappeared, you would not have much of a body left! Your muscles, hair, skin, and fingernails are all made of proteins. A bird's feathers, a spider's web, a fish's scales, and the horns of a rhinoceros are also made of proteins.

Chains of Amino Acids What are proteins made of? **Proteins** are polymers formed from smaller molecules called amino acids. An **amino acid,** then, is a monomer and a building block of proteins. There are 20 kinds of amino acids found in living things. **Different proteins are made when different sequences of amino acids are linked into long chains.** Since proteins can be made of combinations of amino acids in any order and number, a huge variety of proteins is possible.

Lab zone Try This Activity

Skills Focus Making models   L1

Materials none

Time 10 minutes

Tips Suggest that students try the activity with other words from this section such as *carbohydrates, cholesterol,* or *nucleic acids.*

Expected Outcome Sample rearrangements of *proteins* are *pins* and *rote.* Rearrangements of these are *spin* and *tore.* This activity models the rearrangement of proteins in the body as proteins are digested to amino acids, which are reassembled into other proteins used by cells.

Extend Challenge students to model the rearrangement of amino acids with materials such as colored beads or colored interlocking blocks. **learning modality: verbal**

The structure of an amino acid is shown in Figure 17. Each amino acid molecule has a carboxyl group (—COOH). The *acid* in the term *amino acid* comes from this part of the molecule. An amino group, with the structure —NH$_2$, is the source of the *amino* half of the name. The remaining part of the molecule differs for each kind of amino acid.

Food Proteins Become Your Proteins Some of the best sources of protein include meat, fish, eggs, and milk or milk products. If you did the Discover activity, you used vinegar to separate proteins from milk. Some plant products, such as beans, are good sources of protein as well.

The body uses proteins from food to build and repair body parts and to regulate cell activities. But first the proteins must be digested. Just as starch is broken down into glucose molecules, proteins are broken down into amino acids. Then the body reassembles those amino acids into thousands of different proteins that can be used by cells.

 Reading Checkpoint What are good sources of dietary protein?

Lipids

The third class of organic compounds in living things is lipids. Like carbohydrates, **lipids** are energy-rich compounds made of carbon, oxygen, and hydrogen. Lipids include fats, oils, waxes, and cholesterol. **Gram for gram, lipids release twice as much energy in your body as do carbohydrates.** Lipids behave somewhat like hydrocarbons, the compounds of carbon and hydrogen you read about in Section 2. They mix poorly with water.

FIGURE 18
Fats and Oils
Foods that contain fats and oils include peanut butter, butter, cheese, corn, and olives. **Classifying** *Which class of organic compounds do fats and oils belong to?*

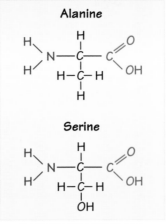

Alanine

Serine

Key

N   Amino group

C   Carboxyl group

Chapter 4   L ◆ 141

Lipids

Teach Key Concepts L2
Contrasting Lipids and Carbohydrates

Focus Explain that lipids are made up of carbon, hydrogen, and oxygen.

Teach Ask: **How are lipids similar to carbohydrates?** *(Both are energy-rich compounds made of carbon, oxygen, and hydrogen.)* **How are lipids different?** *(Lipids releases twice as much energy and mix poorly with water.)*

Apply Ask: **How do unsaturated fatty acids differ from saturated fatty acids?** *(Unsaturated fatty acids are found in oils and have one or more double bonds. Saturated fatty acids have no double bonds between carbon atoms and have higher melting points.)* **learning modality: verbal**

Help Students Read L1
Active Comprehension Refer to the Content Refresher in this chapter, which provides guidelines for the Active Comprehension strategy.

Divide the class into groups, and invite volunteers to take a turn reading one of the first three sentences of *Lipids*. Then groups should list what they would like to know about lipids. Students can finish reading *Lipids* to themselves. Remind them to keep their questions in mind as they read. After reading, reassemble the class and discuss how well the text answered their questions. Invite students to share any information they found especially interesting or surprising.

Monitor Progress _____ L2

Skills Check Have students compare and contrast the way their bodies use carbohydrates and proteins.

Answers
Figure 18 Lipids

 Reading Checkpoint Meat, fish, eggs, and milk are good sources of protein.

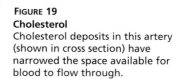
Finding Lipids in Foods

Materials potato chips, peanuts, butter, vegetable oil, beef jerky, lettuce leaf, apple, cooked dried beans, cheese, brown paper

Time 15 minutes

Focus Tell students that fats and oils in foods will leave an oily spot that is easily visible on brown paper.

Teach Before students test the food samples, invite them to predict which foods contain lipids. Invite students to place a small sample of each food on the brown paper. Students should label the paper with the location of each sample. After five minutes, instruct students to remove the food sample and observe the presence of oily spots. A watery sample will leave a spot, which will evaporate. Challenge students to discern the difference.

Apply Ask: **What foods contain lipids?** (*Sample answer: Meats, cheese, nuts, butter, and foods cooked in oils such as potato chips*) **learning modality: visual**

Address Misconceptions L1
Low-Fat Diets

Focus Some students may think that any fat in their diets is not healthful.

Teach Explain that if a person's fat intake is too low, he or she could become deficient in essential fatty acids. The body uses essential fatty acids as building blocks for molecules that help regulate blood pressure, blood clotting, and the immune response. Other fats help absorb some vitamins.

Apply Explain that some low-carb diets promote eating fewer carbohydrates, but more proteins and fats. Ask: **Would this be a sensible diet plan?** (*No. The body may get more fat and cholesterol than it needs, which can contribute to heart disease.*) Emphasize that the best diet is a balance of complex carbohydrates, proteins, and fats. **learning modality: verbal**

Lab zone **Try This Activity**

Like Oil or Water?
Oils mix poorly with water. They also do not evaporate very quickly when exposed to air.

1. Obtain a piece of brown paper and some samples of liquids provided by your teacher.
2. Using a dropper, place one drop of liquid from each sample on the paper.
3. Wait 5 minutes.
4. Note which of the liquids leaves a spot.

Inferring Which of the liquids is a fat or oil? How can you tell?

Fats and Oils Have you ever gotten grease on your clothes from foods that contain fats or oils? Fats are found in foods such as meat, butter, and cheese. Oils are found in foods such as corn, sunflower seeds, peanuts, and olives.

Fats and oils have the same basic structure. Each fat or oil is made from three **fatty acids** and one alcohol named glycerol. There is one main difference between fats and oils, however. Fats are usually solid at room temperature, whereas oils are liquid. The temperature at which a fat or an oil becomes a liquid depends on the chemical structure of its fatty acid molecules.

You may hear fats and oils described as "saturated" or "unsaturated." Like saturated hydrocarbons, the fatty acids of saturated fats have no double bonds between carbon atoms. Unsaturated fatty acids are found in oils. Monounsaturated oils have fatty acids with one double bond. Polyunsaturated oils have fatty acids with many double bonds. (Remember that *mono* means "one" and *poly* means "many.") Saturated fats tend to have higher melting points than unsaturated oils have.

Cholesterol Another important lipid is **cholesterol** (kuh LES tuh rawl), a waxy substance found in all animal cells. The body needs cholesterol to build cell structures and to form compounds that serve as chemical messengers. Unlike other lipids, cholesterol is not a source of energy. The body produces the cholesterol it needs from other nutrients. Foods that come from animals—cheese, eggs, and meat—also provide cholesterol. Because plants do not produce cholesterol, foods from plant sources, such as vegetable oils, never contain cholesterol.

Although cholesterol is often found in the same foods as saturated fats, they are different compounds. An excess level of cholesterol in the blood can contribute to heart disease. So can saturated fats. And saturated fats can affect the level of cholesterol in the blood. For this reason it is wise to limit your intake of both nutrients.

 Reading Checkpoint **What are sources of cholesterol in the diet?**

FIGURE 19
Cholesterol
Cholesterol deposits in this artery (shown in cross section) have narrowed the space available for blood to flow through.

142 ◆ L

Lab zone **Try This Activity**

Skills Focus Inferring L2

Materials brown paper, droppers, liquid samples such as vegetable oil, water, salad dressing, baby oil, fruit juice, milk, cream

Time 10 minutes, plus drying time

Tips If five minutes is not enough drying time, make sure each sample is well marked and check them before the end of class. If you leave them overnight, some of the oils will evaporate and the marks will be harder to see.

Expected Outcome All of the oil-based liquids will leave a wet mark on the brown paper

Extend Students can mix each liquid sample with water in a small plastic cup to observe if the sample will dissolve. **learning modality: visual**

FIGURE 20
The Molecules of Life

Complex carbohydrates, proteins, lipids, and nucleic acids are all large organic molecules. They are built of smaller molecules linked in different patterns. *Applying Concepts* *What are the building blocks of proteins?*

Proteins
The building blocks of proteins are amino acids. Although protein chains are never branched, each chain can twist and bend, forming complex three-dimensional shapes.

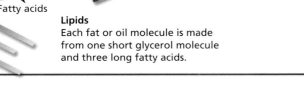

Amino acids

Starch

Cellulose

Glucose

Complex Carbohydrates
Complex carbohydrates are polymers of simple carbohydrates. Starch and cellulose, both made of glucose, differ in how their molecules are arranged.

Nucleic Acids
DNA is made from four different kinds of nucleotides. In each DNA molecule, two strands are twisted in a spiral ladder shape.

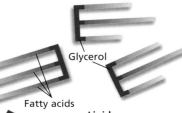

Glycerol

Fatty acids

Lipids
Each fat or oil molecule is made from one short glycerol molecule and three long fatty acids.

Nucleotides

Nucleic Acids

The fourth class of organic compounds in living things is nucleic acids. **Nucleic acids** (noo KLEE ik) are very large organic molecules made up of carbon, oxygen, hydrogen, nitrogen, and phosphorus. You have probably heard of one type of nucleic acid—**DNA,** deoxyribonucleic acid (dee ahk see ry boh noo KLEE ik). The other type of nucleic acid, ribonucleic acid (ry boh noo KLEE ik), is called **RNA.**

Use Visuals: Figure 20 L2
Molecules of Life

Focus Invite students to examine Figure 20.

Teach Ask: **What smaller molecules make up each large organic molecule?** *(Carbohydrates—glucose; lipids—three fatty acids and glycerol; proteins—amino acids; nucleic acids—nucleotides)* **How do combinations of smaller molecules result in different large molecules?** *(Carbohydrates—starch and cellulose are made of different arrangements of glucose; lipids—glycerol and different combinations of fatty acids; proteins—different sequences of amino acids; nucleic acids—different sequences of nucleotides)*

Apply Ask: **Which of the large organic molecules do you think can form the most patterns?** *(Sample answer: Proteins or nucleic acids because they have more monomers that are different.)* **learning modality: visual**

All in One Teaching Resources
• Transparency L53

Nucleic Acids

Teach Key Concepts L2
Importance of Nucleic Acids

Focus Tell students that nucleic acids are not nutrients found in food.

Teach Ask: **What are two types of nucleic acids?** *(DNA and RNA)* **What are the building blocks of nucleic acids?** *(Nucleotides)* **What is the importance of the order of nucleotides in DNA?** *(The differences among living things depend on the order of nucleotides in DNA.)*

Apply Ask: **What is the relationship between nucleic acids and proteins?** *(The order of nucleotides in DNA determines the sequence of amino acids in proteins made by a cell.)* **learning modality: verbal**

Monitor Progress _____ L2

Oral Presentation Have students describe how fats and oils are similar and different.

Answers
Figure 20 Amino acids

 Reading Checkpoint Foods that come from animals such as cheese, eggs, and meat

Building Nucleotide Chains

Materials 4 colors of self-stick notes, 4 paper slips, small bag or box

Time 15 minutes

Focus Ask: **How many different nucleotides are found in DNA?** *(Four)*

Teach Small groups can build random chains of nucleotides. Have students write the name of each color of self-stick note on separate slips of paper, fold the slips, and put them in the box. Then, instruct group members to take turns drawing a slip of paper, adding that color of self-stick note to the growing nucleic acid, and returning the folded slip to the box. When the chain is ten nucleotides long, invite groups to compare their chains. Ask: **What do you observe about the order of colors in each chain?** *(Sample answer: The order is different for each.)*

Apply Ask: **What does the order of nucleotides determine?** *(The proteins in a cell, which ultimately determine the characteristics of an organism)* **learning modality: kinesthetic**

Other Compounds in Foods

Teach Key Concepts L2
Vitamins and Minerals

Focus Say that vitamins and minerals do not provide the body with energy or raw materials.

Teach Ask: **What is the role of vitamins in the body?** *(As helper molecules in a variety of chemical reactions)* **What are minerals?** *(Elements needed by the body)* **Compared to carbohydrates, lipids, and proteins, how much of these compounds do you need?** *(Only small amounts)*

Apply Ask: **What are two classes of compounds needed by the body that are not organic compounds?** *(Minerals and water)* **learning modality: verbal**

FIGURE 21
Vitamins and Minerals
Sources of vitamins and minerals include fruits, vegetables, nuts, meats, and dairy products.
Observing *Which of these foods can you identify in the painting?*

144 ◆ L

Nucleotides DNA and RNA are made of different kinds of small molecules connected in a pattern. The building blocks of nucleic acids are called **nucleotides** (NOO klee oh tydz). In even the simplest living things, the DNA contains billions of nucleotides! There are only four kinds of nucleotides in DNA. RNA is also built of only four kinds of nucleotides, but the nucleotides in RNA differ from those in DNA.

DNA and Proteins **The differences among living things depend on the order of nucleotides in their DNA.** The order of DNA nucleotides determines a related order in RNA. The order of RNA nucleotides, in turn, determines the sequence of amino acids in proteins made by a living cell.

Remember that proteins regulate cell activities. Since the DNA of one living thing differs from the DNA of other living things, living things differ from each other. The cells in a hummingbird grow and function differently from the cells in a flower or in you. When living things reproduce, they pass DNA and the information it carries to the next generation.

 Reading Checkpoint What are the building blocks of nucleic acids?

Other Compounds in Foods

Carbohydrates, proteins, and lipids are not the only compounds your body needs. Your body also needs vitamins, minerals, water, and salts. **Unlike the nutrients discussed so far, vitamins and minerals are needed only in small amounts.** They do not directly provide you with energy or raw materials.

Vitamins Vitamins are organic compounds that serve as helper molecules in a variety of chemical reactions in your body. For example, vitamin C, or ascorbic acid, is important for keeping your skin and gums healthy. Vitamin D helps your bones and teeth develop and keeps them strong.

Minerals Minerals are elements in the form of ions needed by your body. Unlike the other nutrients discussed in this chapter, minerals are not organic compounds. Minerals include calcium, iron, iodine, sodium, and potassium. They are important in many body processes.

If you eat a variety of foods, you will probably get the vitamins and minerals you need. Food manufacturers add some vitamins and minerals to packaged foods to replace vitamins and minerals that are lost in food processing. Such foods say "enriched" on their labels.

Sometimes manufacturers add extra vitamins and minerals to foods to "fortify," or strengthen, the nutritional value of the food. For example, milk is usually fortified with vitamin A and vitamin D.

Water Although water, H_2O, is not an organic compound, it is a compound that your body needs to survive. In fact, you would be able to survive only a few days without fresh water. Water makes up most of your body's fluids, including about 90 percent of the liquid part of your blood.

Nutrients and other important substances are dissolved in the watery part of the blood and carried throughout the body. Many chemical reactions, such as the breakdown of nutrients, take place in water. Wastes from cells dissolve in the blood and are carried away.

Reading Checkpoint **What is a vitamin?**

Go Online SciLinks NSTA

For: Links on organic compounds
Visit: www.SciLinks.org
Web Code: scn-1243

Section 3 Assessment

Target Reading Skill **Asking Questions** Review your graphic organizer and revise it based on what you just learned in the section.

Reviewing Key Concepts

1. a. **Naming** What are the four main classes of organic compounds required by living things?
   b. **Classifying** To what class of organic compounds does each of the following belong: glucose, RNA, cholesterol, cellulose, and oil?
   c. **Making Generalizations** How is each class of organic compounds used by the body?
2. a. **Identifying** What are the building blocks of complex carbohydrates?
   b. **Comparing and Contrasting** Compare the building blocks found in complex carbohydrates with those found in proteins.
   c. **Making Judgments** Would it matter if you ate foods that provided only carbohydrates but not proteins? Explain your reasoning.

Writing in Science

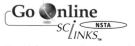

Advertisement Collect several food advertisements from magazines and watch some TV commercials. What do the ads say about nutrients? What do they emphasize? What do they downplay? Choose one ad and rewrite it to reflect the nutritional value of the product.

Go Online SciLinks NSTA

For: Links on organic compounds
Visit: www.SciLinks.org
Web Code: scn-1243

Download a worksheet that will guide students' review of Internet sources on organic compounds.

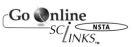

Monitor Progress L2

Answers

Figure 21 Sample answer: Squashes, onions, grapes, pears, and peas

Reading Checkpoint Nucleotides

Reading Checkpoint An organic compound that serves as a helper molecule in a chemical reaction in the body

Assess

Reviewing Key Concepts

1. a. Carbohydrates, proteins, lipids, nucleic acids **b.** Glucose and cellulose are carbohydrates; RNA is a nucleic acid; cholesterol and oil are lipids.
c. Carbohydrates provide the body with energy and keep the digestive system healthy. Proteins are used to build and repair body parts. Lipids provide energy, build cell structures, and form compounds that serve as chemical messengers. Nucleic acids determine the differences among living things.
2. a. Simple carbohydrates, or sugars
b. Complex carbohydrates are built from simple carbohydrates; proteins are built from amino acids. **c.** While your body needs carbohydrates for energy, it uses proteins primarily for growth and repair. Without enough protein, your body would not grow or heal properly.

Reteach L1

Have students construct a concept map to show the relationship among all the key terms.

Performance Assessment L2

Writing Have students choose one organic molecule and describe its structure and function in the human body.

All in One Teaching Resources

- Section Summary: *Life With Carbon*
- Review and Reinforce: *Life With Carbon*
- Enrich: *Life With Carbon*

Lab zone Chapter Project

Keep Students on Track In their data tables, students should classify the ingredients on their food labels as organic and not organic. Organic compounds can be further classified as carbohydrates, proteins, lipids, and vitamins. Minerals are not organic. Suggest that students list the ingredients that they cannot identify. They might need help deciphering the complex names for various food additives.

Writing in Science

Writing Mode Persuasion

Scoring Rubric

4 Exceeds criteria; includes a highly persuasive, concise advertisement that accurately describes the nutritional value of a food product
3 Meets criteria
2 Includes an unpersuasive advertisement with a few errors
1 Includes a brief advertisement with serious errors

Science and Society

A Sweet Dilemma

Key Concept
Artificial sweeteners have fewer calories, but have been associated with health risks.

Build Background Knowledge
Recalling Carbohydrates
Ask: **To which class of organic compounds in living things does sugar belong?** *(Carbohydrates)* **How does the body use carbohydrates?** *(For the energy needed to carry out life functions)* **What happens if you eat more carbohydrates than your body can use?** *(Some students may know that the excess carbohydrates are stored in the body as fat.)*

Introduce the Debate
Ask: **Why do people choose artificial sweeteners?** *(Sample answer: To lose weight, to enjoy sweet foods without raising blood sugar)* Point out that the decision to use artificial sweeteners over sugar is an individual one. Each person must weigh the health risks of both sugar and artificial sweeteners before choosing either.

Facilitate the Debate
- Invite students to participate in a mock planning meeting for a school event. Assign students to play the roles of people at the meeting. Two students can be committee members who are planning refreshments for the function. Two can be students who are concerned about the health risks of artificial sweeteners. Four students can be people who have health risks associated with consuming sugar. Concerned students will explain the risks of artificial sweeteners. People with health risks should explain how sugar adversely affects their health. Committee members will ask questions and listen to both groups, and then decide about what kinds of refreshments to provide at the school function.
- Remind students to present arguments based on research, not on emotional responses.
- After the debate, lead a class discussion about the issues and possible solutions raised by each group.

A Sweet Dilemma

Do you have a sweet tooth? Many people do. But there is a price to be paid for sweetness. Excess energy from sugars is easily stored by the body in the form of fat. The bacteria that cause tooth decay use sugars in the mouth as food. And for people who have the disease diabetes, sugary foods can raise blood sugar to a life-threatening level.

▲ **Foods made with natural sugar**

Food scientists have developed three organic compounds that taste sweet but provide few calories per serving—saccharin, cyclamate, and aspartame. Aspartame, for example, is 200 times as sweet as the sugar sucrose. Unfortunately, saccharin, cyclamate, and aspartame all have health risks associated with their use.

The Issues

Why Use Artificial Sweeteners?
Artificial sweeteners allow people with diabetes to enjoy sweet foods and beverages safely without raising their blood sugar level. But most people consume artificial sweeteners to lose weight. Advertising has glamorized being thin. In addition, being overweight can lead to serious health conditions, such as heart disease and high blood pressure.

What Are Possible Dangers?
Studies of saccharin and cyclamate have shown that large doses can lead to cancer and birth defects in lab animals. The U.S. Food and Drug Administration (FDA) has banned cyclamate, but many products still contain saccharin. The FDA, therefore, requires all products containing saccharin to have labels warning of possible health risks.

Early tests on aspartame showed it to be safe. For about 1 in every 10,000 people, however, the use of aspartame can be very dangerous. If a person has the genetic disorder called phenylketonuria (PKU), then one of the amino acids in aspartame can interfere with normal development. These people must avoid aspartame, especially as infants.

Background

Facts and Figures Some researchers have found what they think to be a connection between heavy aspartame consumption and an increased incidence of brain tumors. These researchers also report symptoms such as aggression, suicidal depression, aberrant behavior, sleep disorders, and extreme mood swings.

However, the U.S. Food and Drug Administration has conducted its own studies and stands by its original approval of the substance. The FDA claims there is no evidence of a connection between an increase in the occurrence of brain tumors and the consumption of aspartame. It says that the data are coincidental and that the level of brain tumor onset has actually leveled off since the late 1980s, although aspartame consumption has increased.

▲ **Foods made with sugar substitutes**

How Much Is Too Much?

Different people have different health concerns. Thus, the question of how much sugar or artificial sweetener is too much depends on the individual. For some people, no artificial sweetener is the answer. For others, moderate amounts, such as one or two servings a day, may be safe. But more scientific evidence must be collected to answer how much is too much.

You Decide

1. Identify the Problem
In your own words, explain the issues about the use of artificial sweeteners.

2. Analyze the Options
List the pros and cons for using artificial sweeteners as well as the pros and cons for using sugar.

3. Find a Solution
You are planning refreshments for a school event. Should you provide artificially sweetened soft drinks? Write a brief statement supporting your opinion.

For: More on natural and artificial sweeteners
Visit: PHSchool.com
Web Code: cgh-2040

You Decide

1. Sample answer: Artificial sweeteners enable people with diabetes and people on diets to have sweet foods and beverages. Artificial sweeteners have been associated with health risks.

2. Sample answer: Artificial sweeteners have fewer calories per serving, but are associated with health risks. Sugar is high in calories and can be dangerous to diabetics, but it is a natural sweetener that does not cause cancer or birth defects.

3. Sample answer: I would provide beverages with artificial sweeteners and beverages sweetened with sugar so that individuals could make their own choices based on their health concerns.

For: More on natural and artificial sweeteners
Visit: PHSchool.com
Web Code: cgh-2040

Students can research this issue online.

Extend

Challenge students to find alternative beverages that are low in sugar and not sweetened with artificial sweeteners. Have students explain why these beverages may be a more healthful alternative.

L ● 147

Are You Getting Your Vitamins?

Are You Getting Your Vitamins?

Prepare for Inquiry

Key Concept
Some beverages contain more vitamin C than others.

Skills Objective
After this lab, students will be able to
- control variables to test for the presence of vitamin C in different beverages
- interpret data about the amount of vitamin C in different beverages
- infer the action of iodine in the procedure

🕐 **Prep Time** 20 minutes
Class Time 25 minutes

Advance Planning
- **Starch Solution** While stirring rapidly with a stirring rod, direct a stream of spray starch into 75–100 mL of water in a beaker. A mixture at the correct strength shows an opalescent blue tinge. You can also dilute liquid starch. Use 20 parts water to 1 part starch.
- **Iodine Solution** Tincture of iodine, sold as a skin antiseptic, works well. Use a brand with a plastic dropper, or fill pipettes or droppers.
- **Vitamin C Solution** Crush a 1,000-mg vitamin C tablet, mix with 1,000 mL of warm water. Allow insoluble parts to settle. Pour off the clear top layer or pour through filter paper.

All in One Teaching Resources
- Lab Worksheet: *Are You Getting Your Vitamins?*

Guide Inquiry

Invitation
Solicit from students a list of foods that are good sources of vitamin C. (*Sample answer: Citrus fruits, tomatoes, leafy green vegetables*) Explain that vitamin C maintains blood vessel strength, protects against infection, and keeps skin and gums healthy.

Problem
Fruit juices contain vitamin C, an important nutrient. Which juice should you drink to obtain the most vitamin C?

Skills Focus
controlling variables, interpreting data, inferring

Materials
- 6 small cups • 6 plastic droppers • starch solution • iodine solution • vitamin C solution • samples of beverages to be tested (orange juice, apple juice, sports drink, fruit-flavored drink)

Procedure ▨ 🛡 🔟

PART 1 Vitamin C Test

1. Using a plastic dropper, place 25 drops of tap water into one of the small cups. Add 2 drops of starch solution.

2. Add 1 drop of iodine solution to the cup. **CAUTION:** *Iodine solution can stain skin or clothing.* Observe the color of the mixture. Save this cup to use for comparison in Step 4.

3. Using a fresh dropper, place 25 drops of vitamin C solution into another cup. Add 2 drops of starch solution.

4. Add 1 drop of iodine solution to the cup and swirl. Continue adding iodine a drop at a time, swirling after each drop, until you get a dark blue color similar to the color obtained in Step 2. Record the number of iodine drops.

5. Save the cup from Step 4 and use it for comparison during Part 2.

PART 2 Comparison Test

6. Make a data table in your notebook similar to the one on the next page.

7. Which beverage sample do you think has the most vitamin C? Which do you think has the least? Rank your beverage samples according to your predictions.

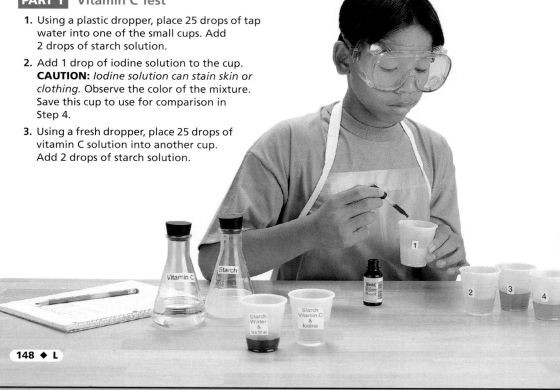

Introduce the Procedure
Explain that when vitamin C reacts with iodine, iodine loses its red color. If vitamin C and starch are both available, iodine reacts first with vitamin C. When the vitamin C is gone, the iodine will react with the starch to give a blue color. Ask: **What is the relationship between the amount of vitamin C and the number of drops of iodine needed to give a color change?** (*The more drops of iodine, the more vitamin C present*)

Demonstrate how to add one drop of iodine at a time and how to gently swirl the cup.

Data Table

Test Sample	Drops of Iodine	Predicted Rank	Actual Rank
Vitamin C			
Orange juice			
Apple juice			
Sports drink			
Fruit-flavored drink			

8. Adapt the procedure from Part 1 so you can compare the amount of vitamin C in your beverage samples to the vitamin C solution.

9. Carry out your procedure after your teacher approves.

Analyze and Conclude

1. **Controlling Variables** What was the purpose for the test of the mixture of starch and water in Step 2?

2. **Controlling Variables** What was the purpose for the test of the starch, water, and vitamin C in Step 4?

3. **Drawing Conclusions** What do you think caused differences between your data from Step 2 and Step 4?

4. **Controlling Variables** Why did you have to add the same amount of starch to each of the beverages?

5. **Predicting** What would happen if someone forgot to add the starch to the beverage before they began adding iodine?

6. **Measuring** Of the four drinks you tested, which took the most drops of iodine before changing color? Which took the fewest?

7. **Interpreting Data** Which beverage had the most vitamin C? Which had the least? How do you know?

8. **Inferring** When you tested orange juice, the color of the first few drops of the iodine faded away. What do you think happened to the iodine?

9. **Communicating** If a beverage scored low in your test for vitamin C, does that mean it isn't good for you? Write a paragraph in which you explain what other factors might make a beverage nutritious or take away from its nutrient value.

Design an Experiment

Foods are often labeled with expiration dates. Labels often also say to "refrigerate after opening." Design an experiment to find out if the vitamin C content of orange juice changes over time at different temperatures. *Obtain your teacher's permission before carrying out your investigation.*

Expected Outcome

The amount of vitamin C in orange juice varies. There is none in most sports drinks. Fruit drinks that are highly fortified with vitamins and minerals will either match or exceed the values obtained for orange juice.

Analyze and Conclude

1. This test was used as a control to show the reaction between iodine and starch alone.

2. To show that the reaction between iodine and starch will occur in the presence of vitamin C, but only after more drops of iodine are added.

3. The presence of vitamin C.

4. It is important to keep all factors constant except the one you are changing (the amount of vitamin C).

5. They would not see a color change when the vitamin C was gone.

6. Sample answer: The fruit-flavored drink required the most drops of iodine, and the sports drink the fewest.

7. The fruit-flavored drink had the most vitamin C. The sports drink had the least. The number of drops of iodine required to show a color change is directly related to the amount of vitamin C in the beverage tested.

8. The iodine was reacting with the vitamin C in the juice.

9. No. It may have other vitamins or valuable nutrients such as minerals and proteins. Too much sugar, fat, or caffeine might take away from the nutritional value of a beverage.

Extend Inquiry

Design an Experiment Sample procedure: Pour half a container of orange juice into a separate empty container; keep one container in the refrigerator and the other at room temperature. Test samples of both every day until tests on consecutive days show a decrease in the level of vitamin C.

Troubleshooting the Experiment

Students may forget to add starch. If students tell you that a beverage is not changing, ask them which beverage they are testing and how many drops of iodine they have added. If it is near the amount needed, suggest they add another drop or two of starch. If the color does not change, students can continue with iodine.

nteractive Textbook

- Complete student edition
- Section and chapter self-assessments
- Assessment reports for teachers

Help Students Read L1

Building Vocabulary

Word/Part Analysis Have students look up the meaning of the prefix *iso-* and the suffix *-mer* from the word *isomer*. Then have students write a definition for *isomer* based on the meanings of its word parts. (Iso- *comes from the Greek word* isos, *which means "equal." The suffix* -mer *comes from the Greek word* meros, *meaning "part." Sample definition: Isomers are two molecules with equal parts, but different properties.*)

Word Origins Tell students that *saturated* means "thoroughly filled, unable to hold more." Ask: **How does this meaning relate to the meaning of *saturated hydrocarbon*?** (*A saturated hydrocarbon is thoroughly filled with hydrogen atoms. It is unable to hold any more.*)

Connecting Concepts

Concept Maps Help students develop one way to show how the information in this chapter is related. A carbon atom can form four bonds and has the ability to bond with itself and many other elements. Carbon acts as the backbone of many different organic compounds, including the building blocks for all living things. Have students brainstorm to identify the key concepts, key terms, details, and examples. Then write each item on a self-stick note and attach it at random to chart paper or to the board.

Tell students that this concept map will be organized in hierarchical order and to begin at the top with the key concepts. Ask students these questions to guide them to categorize the information on the self-stick notes: **How does carbon form bonds? What are physical and chemical properties of carbon compounds? What carbon compounds are essential for life?**

1 Chemical Bonding, Carbon Style

Key Concepts

- Few elements have the ability of carbon to bond with both itself and other elements in so many different ways. With four valence electrons, each carbon atom is able to form four bonds.
- Diamond, graphite, fullerenes, and nanotubes are four forms of the element carbon.

Key Terms

diamond   fullerene
graphite   nanotube

2 Carbon Compounds

Key Concepts

- Many organic compounds have similar properties, in terms of melting points, boiling points, odor, electrical conductivity, and solubility.
- Hydrocarbons mix poorly with water. Also, all hydrocarbons are flammable.
- The carbon chains in a hydrocarbon may be straight, branched, or ring-shaped. In addition to forming a single bond, two carbon atoms can form a double bond or a triple bond.
- If just one atom of another element is substituted for a hydrogen atom in a hydrocarbon, a different compound is created.
- Many esters have pleasant fruity smells.
- Organic compounds, such as alcohols, esters, and others, can be linked together to build polymers with thousands or even millions of atoms.

Key Terms

organic compound   hydroxyl group
hydrocarbon   alcohol
structural formula   organic acid
isomer   carboxyl group
saturated   ester
  hydrocarbon   polymer
unsaturated   monomer
  hydrocarbon
substituted
  hydrocarbon

3 Life With Carbon

Key Concepts

- The four classes of organic compounds required by living things are carbohydrates, proteins, lipids, and nucleic acids.
- Starch and cellulose are both polymers built from glucose, but the glucose molecules are arranged differently in each case.
- Different proteins are made when different sequences of amino acids are linked into long chains.
- Gram for gram, lipids release twice as much energy in your body as do carbohydrates.
- Vitamins and minerals are needed only in small amounts.
- The differences among living things depend on the order of nucleotides in their DNA.

Key Terms

carbohydrate   lipid
glucose   fatty acid
complex carbohydrate   cholesterol
starch   nucleic acid
cellulose   DNA
protein   RNA
amino acid   nucleotide

Prompt students by using connecting words or phrases, such as "include," "are made by," and "are used for," to indicate the basis for the organization of the map. The phrases should form a sentence between or among a set of concepts.

Answer
Accept logical presentations by students.

All in One Teaching Resources
- Key Terms Review: *Carbon Chemistry*
- Connecting Concepts: *Carbon Chemistry*

Go Online
PHSchool.com

For: Self-Assessment
Visit: PHSchool.com
Web Code: cga-2040

Organizing Information

Comparing and Contrasting Copy the Venn Diagram comparing proteins and nucleic acids onto a separate sheet of paper. Then complete it and add a title. (For more on Comparing and Contrasting, See the Skills Handbook.)

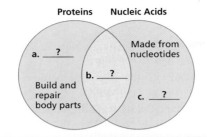

Proteins   Nucleic Acids

a. ___?___

Made from nucleotides

b. ___?___

Build and repair body parts

c. ___?___

Reviewing Key Terms

Choose the letter of the best answer.

1. A form of carbon in which the carbon bonds are arranged in a repeating pattern similar to a geodesic dome is
   a. a fullerene.
   b. graphite.
   c. diamond.
   d. a nanotube.

2. A compound that contains only hydrogen and carbon is defined as
   a. a monomer.
   b. an isomer.
   c. a hydrocarbon.
   d. a polymer.

3. The group –COOH is characteristic of
   a. an organic acid.
   b. an alcohol.
   c. a hydroxyl group.
   d. a hydrocarbon.

4. The smaller molecules from which cellulose is made are
   a. glucose.
   b. amino acids.
   c. nucleotides.
   d. fatty acids.

5. Cholesterol is a type of
   a. nucleic acid.
   b. carbohydrate.
   c. lipid.
   d. cellulose.

If the statement is true, write *true*. If it is false, change the underlined word or words to make the statement true.

6. Because the bonds between layers of carbon atoms are weak, layers of <u>fullerenes</u> slide easily past one another.

7. Hydrocarbons that contain only single bonds are said to be <u>unsaturated hydrocarbons.</u>

8. An <u>organic acid</u> is characterized by one or more hydroxy groups.

9. <u>Polymers</u> are compounds that have the same chemical formula but different structures.

10. Proteins are made up of long chains of <u>amino acids.</u>

Writing in Science

Web Site You are writing a feature article on carbon for a chemistry Web site. In your article, describe four forms of the element carbon. Include in your descriptions how the carbon atoms are arranged and how the bonds between the carbon atoms affect the properties of the substance. Include any helpful illustration.

Discovery CHANNEL SCHOOL

Carbon Chemistry

Video Preview
Video Field Trip
▶ Video Assessment

Chapter 4 L ◆ 151

Organizing Information

Sample title: Comparing and Contrasting Proteins and Nucleic Acids
a. Sample answer: Made from amino acids
b. Sample answer: Organic molecules
c. Sample answer: Determines the sequence of amino acids in proteins

Reviewing Key Terms

1. a 2. c 3. a 4. a 5. c
6. graphite
7. saturated hydrocarbons
8. alcohol
9. Isomers
10. true

Writing in Science

Writing Mode Description
Scoring Rubric
4 Exceeds criteria; includes an accurate and highly descriptive article about the forms of carbon, complete with detailed illustrations
3 Meets criteria
2 Includes a brief description and/or a few errors
1 Includes serious errors and/or omissions

Discovery CHANNEL SCHOOL Video Assessment

Carbon Chemistry

Show the Video Assessment to review chapter content and as a prompt for the writing assignment. Discussion questions: **What two forms of carbon have the most similar carbon bonding?** *(Graphite and nanotubes)* **Why would engineers want to use nanotubes in the building of the Mega-City Pyramid?** *(Nanotubes are lightweight and super strong.)*

**Go Online**
PHSchool.com

For: Self-Assessment
Visit: PHSchool.com
Web Code: cga-2040

Students can take a practice test online that is automatically scored.

 **Teaching Resources**

- Transparency L54
- Chapter Test
- Performance Assessment Teacher Notes
- Performance Assessment Student Worksheet
- Performance Assessment Scoring Rubric

ExamView® Computer Test Bank CD-ROM

Checking Concepts

11. One valence electron from each carbon atom is shared with the other atom.

12. Diamonds, graphite, fullerenes, and nanotubes are all forms of carbon.

13. By smell; many esters have pleasant, fruity smells.

14. The body breaks starch into glucose for energy. The body cannot break down cellulose. It passes through the body undigested. However, cellulose keeps the digestive tract active and healthy.

15. Fats that are solid at room temperature contain fatty acids that are saturated. Liquid fats contain unsaturated fatty acids.

16. The order of nucleotides in DNA determines the amino acid sequences of proteins, which regulate cell activities and are used to build and repair body parts. Differences among living things depend on the order of these nucleotides.

Thinking Critically

17. Carbon atoms are able to form four bonds with other carbon atoms and with other elements. Carbon atoms can also form straight chains, branched chains, and rings.

18. Diagram B represents a saturated hydrocarbon because it has only single bonds and has the maximum number of hydrogen atoms. Diagram A represents an unsaturated hydrocarbon because it has a double bond and fewer hydrogen atoms for each carbon atom.

19. $C_{12}H_{25}COOH$—organic acid; C_7H_{16}—hydrocarbon; C_2H_5Cl—halogen-containing compound; C_4H_9OH—alcohol

20. Do they have different structural formulas?

Review and Assessment

Checking Concepts

11. What happens to the electrons when one carbon atom forms a single bond with another carbon atom?

12. What do diamonds, graphite, fullerenes, and nanotubes have in common?

13. How would you notice the presence of esters in a fruit such as a pineapple?

14. Starches and cellulose are both complex carbohydrates. How does your body handle these compounds differently?

15. Compare and contrast the fatty acids in fats that are solid at room temperature with fatty acids in oils that are liquids.

16. Why is the order of nucleotides in DNA important?

Thinking Critically

17. **Relating Cause and Effect** What features of the element carbon allow it to form the "backbone" of such a varied array of different compounds?

18. **Applying Concepts** Which of the diagrams below represents a saturated hydrocarbon? Which represents an unsaturated hydrocarbon? Explain your answer.

19. **Classifying** Classify each of the following compounds as a hydrocarbon, an alcohol, an organic acid, or a halogen-containing compound:

$C_{12}H_{25}COOH$ C_2H_5Cl
C_7H_{16} C_4H_9OH

20. **Posing Questions** Glucose and fructose are both simple carbohydrates with the formula $C_6H_{12}O_6$. What else do you need to know about glucose and fructose to decide if they should be considered different compounds?

Applying Skills

Use the following structural formulas to answer Questions 21–25.

21. **Classifying** Which type of substituted hydrocarbons are compounds A and B? What information in the structural formulas did you use to decide your answer?

22. **Observing** What is the correct subscript for the carbon atoms (C) in the chemical formula that corresponds to each structural formula?

23. **Inferring** Are compounds A and B isomers? How can you tell?

24. **Predicting** Would you expect these two compounds to have identical properties or different properties? Explain.

25. **Problem Solving** What kind of compound would result if an organic acid were chemically combined with compound A? What properties would you expect the new compound to have?

Lab zone Chapter **Project**

Performance Assessment Display your data table classifying compounds in foods, along with the labels from which you collected your data. Point out the nutrients that are found in almost all foods and the nutrients found in only a few.

Lab zone Chapter **Project**   L3

Performance Assessment
Students' displays should categorize their foods based on nutrient content. As students present their displays to the class, encourage classmates to ask questions about each food, its ingredients, and how particular compounds were identified. Presenters should compare the ingredients of foods and show why one is better than another.

Choose the letter of the best answer.

1. The formula $C_5H_{11}OH$ represents an
   A amino acid.
   B organic acid.
   C alcohol.
   D ester.

2. Material X is an organic compound with these physical characteristics: no odor; mixes poorly with water; highly flammable. Of the following choices, material X is most likely a(n)
   F carbohydrate.
   G ester.
   H lipid.
   J hydrocarbon.

Use the structural diagrams below and your knowledge of science to answer Questions 3–5.

3. Isomers are organic compounds having the same chemical formula, but different structures. Which pair of compounds are isomers?
   A 1 and 2   **B** 1 and 3
   C 2 and 3   **D** 2 and 4

4. Which structural diagram represents an unsaturated hydrocarbon?
   F 1   **G** 2
   H 3   **J** 4

5. What is the ratio of carbon atoms to hydrogen atoms in the compound represented by 1?
   A 1 to 9
   B 9 to1
   C 3 to 6
   D 6 to 3

Constructed Response

6. Explain why carbohydrates, lipids, and proteins are important parts of a well-balanced diet.

Applying Skills

21. A and B are alcohols because both compounds contain hydroxyl (−OH) groups.

22. Each structural formula contains three carbon atoms; the subscript for carbon is three.

23. Yes. They are isomers because they have the same chemical formula but different structural formulas.

24. They would have different properties. Isomers differ in properties, such as boiling point and melting point, because the atoms in their molecules are arranged differently.

25. Combining compound A, an alcohol, with an organic acid would produce an ester. An ester typically has a pleasant, fruity smell.

Standardized Test Prep

1. C   **2.** J   **3.** D   **4.** F   **5.** C
6. Carbohydrates, proteins, and lipids are nutrients. They provide the energy and raw materials the body needs to grow, repair worn parts, and function properly.

Interdisciplinary Exploration

Soap—The Dirt Chaser

This interdisciplinary feature presents the central theme of soap by connecting four different disciplines: science, social studies, language arts, and mathematics. The four explorations are designed to capture students' interest and help them see how the content they are studying in science relates to other school subjects and to real-world events. Share with others for a team-teaching experience.

All in One Teaching Resources

- Interdisciplinary Exploration: *Science*
- Interdisciplinary Exploration: *Social Studies*
- Interdisciplinary Exploration: *Language Arts*
- Interdisciplinary Exploration: *Mathematics*

Build Background Knowledge
Carbon Chemistry
Help students recall what they learned in the chapter *Carbon Chemistry*. Ask: **What is a hydrocarbon?** *(A compound that contains only carbon and hydrogen)* **What is an ester?** *(An organic compound made from an alcohol and an organic acid)* **What organic molecule in living things contains glycerol?** *(Lipids)* Explain that because soaps are made with fats, glycerol is one of the ingredients.

Introduce the Exploration
Ask: **What happens if you try to wash a greasy pot using only water?** *(The grease does not wash away.)* **Why not?** *(Oil and water do not mix.)* Reinforce these ideas by reviewing what students learned about polar and nonpolar molecules in the chapter *Atoms and Bonding*. Ask **What type of molecule is water?** *(Polar)* **What type of molecules make up many kinds of dirt and grease?** *(Nonpolar)* **Why do oil and water not mix well?** *(The polar molecules of water are more attracted to one another than to the nonpolar molecules in greasy dirt.)* **What happens when you add soap?** *(Soap can mix with both water and the substances in grease, so the grease disperses in the water and is washed away.)* Explain that students will explore how soap works, what soap is made of, and how it is made.

Interdisciplinary Exploration

Soap—The Dirt Chaser

What slippery substance
- **makes things cleaner, fresher, brighter?**
- **can you put on your head and on your floors?**
- **rids your hands of germs?**

It's soap, which is a cleaner made from materials that are found in nature. People figured out how to make soap by heating natural fats or oils, alkali (a chemical they got from wood ashes), and water. Detergent is also a cleaner. It's similar to soap, but made from manufactured materials.

In a year, the average American uses about 11 kilograms of soap just to keep clean! Some of that soap is used for baths and showers. Soap is also used by medical experts to clean wounds and prevent infection.

In your home you use soaps and detergents to clean dishes, laundry, windows, floors, and much more. Even factories use soaps in the process of making products such as rubber, jewelry, aluminum, antifreeze, leather, and glossy paper.

So, if you lived without soap, you and your surroundings would be a lot dirtier! You would look and feel quite different. You may just owe your way of life to soap!

Car Wash
Young workers apply soap to this windshield.

154 ◆ L

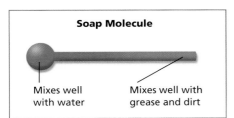

Soap Molecule

Mixes well with water

Mixes well with grease and dirt

Soap Molecules
These molecules help loosen dirt. Water washes away the dirt.

How Soap Works

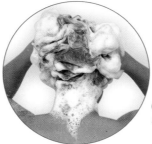

❶ You rub shampoo and water into your hair.

❷ Soap molecules in shampoo loosen the grease and dirt on your hair.

❸ Soap molecules break the dirt into tiny pieces.

❹ Water carries away the dirt surrounded by soap molecules.

Wash the Dirt Away

Soap manufacturers claim that their products can wash away the dirt from the dirtiest clothes. How does that work? First, you need to wet the clothes with water that contains soap. The soap then spreads out and soaks into the material.

Each molecule of soap is shaped like a tiny tadpole. The tail-like end is similar to a hydrocarbon molecule. It mixes poorly with water, but it mixes well with dirt and grease. The large end, on the other hand, mixes well with water. When you wash, the soap molecules surround the dirt and break it up into tiny pieces that water can wash away.

Some dirt is difficult to dissolve. It takes longer for the soap molecules to loosen it. In these cases, rubbing, scrubbing, and squeezing may help to lift the dirt.

Some water, called hard water, has minerals dissolved in it—calcium, magnesium, and iron. In hard water, soap forms deposits, called scum. Scum doesn't dissolve and is difficult to wash away. It keeps clean hair from being shiny and leaves a "bathtub ring."

The invention of detergents helped solve the problem of scum and stubborn stains. For many cleaning tasks, detergent is more effective than soap. Detergent also dissolves in cold water more easily than soap.

L ◆ 155

Explore Science Concepts

Discuss After students read *Wash the Dirt Away*, discuss the article by asking such questions as: **Why won't soap alone clean dirty objects?** (*Water is needed to dissolve and wash away the soap and dirt mixture.*) **How does rubbing, scrubbing, and squeezing help lift the dirt?** (*The actions break up the dirt into smaller pieces so the soap molecules can surround them.*) **What are some advantages to using detergent over soap?** (*Sample answer: You can wash in cold water instead of hot, which saves energy.*)

Use Visuals Have students study the diagrams showing how soap works. Ask: **Which part of the soap molecule mixes with dirt and grease?** (*The tail-like end*) **Which part mixes with water?** (*The large end*) **How does the structure of a soap molecule affect its function?** (*The tail-like end binds to dirt and grease particles, leaving the water-soluble big end of the soap molecule sticking out. This makes the dirt and grease soluble so that it will mix with water and wash away.*)

Demonstrate Show students the action of detergent and water on stained scraps of fabric. Prepare fabric scraps stained separately with dirt, oil, grass, or food. First rub laundry detergent on the stains. Students will observe that the stains are still there. Rinse the fabric in warm water, while rubbing the stain to help remove it. In some cases, the fabric may have a residual stain. Ask: **How could you remove the stain completely?** (*Sample answer: Rewash the fabric in detergent and water. Wash the fabric longer.*)

Background

Facts and Figures Homes with hard water typically install water softeners because hard water not only forms soap scum that is difficult to clean but also deposits minerals such as calcium and iron in pipes, water heaters, and other appliances that use water.

Hard water is commonly softened using ion exchange water softeners. In a water softener, the water is pumped through a tank that contains resin beads. The beads are saturated with sodium. As the hard water is forced through the beads, calcium and magnesium ions in the water switch places with the sodium ions on the resin beads. The sodium ions become dissolved in the water.

Eventually, the resin beads are no longer saturated with sodium and need to be "recharged." Salty water is pumped through the beads to replenish the sodium.

Explore Science Concepts

Use Visuals Invite volunteers to read aloud the captions in the illustration while other students follow along in the diagram. Suggest that students use their fingers to trace the process of soapmaking. Then ask: **What is saponification?** (*The chemical reaction that occurs when the fatty acids combine with alkali*) **What results from saponification?** (*Neat soap and glycerol, or glycerin*) **What is a mold?** (*An empty container you pour the liquid soap into so the soap will harden into a specific shape*) **What is a mill?** (*A machine that grinds substances into smaller particles*) **Have you ever tried to wash with unmilled soap? How does it feel different from milled soap?** (*Unmilled soap is hard and rough. Sometimes it feels as if it has hard pieces, like pieces of sand, embedded in it.*)

Review Remind students of what they learned about acids and bases in the chapter, *Acids, Bases, and Solutions.* Ask: **What is an acid?** (*A substance that tastes sour, reacts with metals and carbonates, and turns blue litmus paper red*) **What ingredients in soapmaking are acids?** (*Fatty acids from fats and oils*) **What is a base?** (*A substance that tastes bitter, feels slippery, and turns red litmus paper blue*) **What ingredient in soapmaking is a base?** (*The alkali solution*)

Chemistry of Soap

How is soap made? It's the product of heating two types of compounds—an acid and a base. Acids and bases are compounds that have physical and chemical properties opposite to each other. An acid tastes sour. Grapefruits, pickles, and vinegar have acids in them. A base has properties that make it taste bitter and feel slippery. Bases and acids combine to neutralize each other.

Natural fats and oils are the source of the acids in soapmaking. Fats and oils are polymers, made of three fatty acid monomers and an alcohol called glycerol.

In soapmaking, the fatty acids combine with an alkali solution (made of bases). The mixture is processed using water and heat. The resulting chemical reaction is called *saponification.* Saponification produces the main material of soaps, called "neat" soap. The glycerol left over, also called glycerin, is pumped away.

The difference between solid and liquid soaps depends on the alkali that's added. In a solid soap, the alkali solution is the base sodium hydroxide. In liquid soaps, the alkali solution is the base potassium hydroxide.

Making Soap Using the Continuous Process

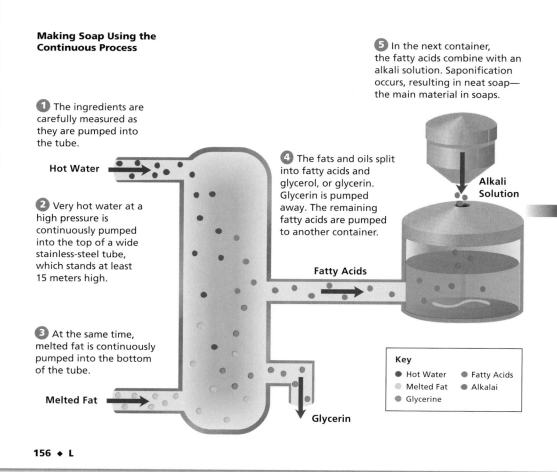

5 In the next container, the fatty acids combine with an alkali solution. Saponification occurs, resulting in neat soap—the main material in soaps.

1 The ingredients are carefully measured as they are pumped into the tube.

Hot Water

2 Very hot water at a high pressure is continuously pumped into the top of a wide stainless-steel tube, which stands at least 15 meters high.

3 At the same time, melted fat is continuously pumped into the bottom of the tube.

Melted Fat

4 The fats and oils split into fatty acids and glycerol, or glycerin. Glycerin is pumped away. The remaining fatty acids are pumped to another container.

Alkali Solution

Fatty Acids

Glycerin

Key
- ● Hot Water
- ● Melted Fat
- ● Glycerine
- ● Fatty Acids
- ● Alkalai

Background

History of Science In the early years of soapmaking, fat from goats and other animals was combined with lye, which was obtained from wood ashes. In later processes, developed perhaps in the 1200s, olive oil was used in place of animal fat.

In 1783, a Swedish chemist named Carl Scheele accidentally performed saponification and produced glycerin. A French chemist investigated Scheele's discovery and concluded that fats first split chemically into fatty acids and glycerol to form soap.

Soapmaking

After saponification occurs, neat soap is poured into molds. Other ingredients are sometimes added at this stage. Then the bars are stamped with a brand name or design and wrapped for shipment.

To make cosmetic soaps, an additional process called milling is needed. The neat soap is poured into large slabs instead of into molds. When the slab cools, several sets of rollers press and crush it. This process makes finer, gentler soaps that people can use on their face and hands.

At this stage, a variety of other ingredients can be added, such as scents, colors, or germicides (to kill bacteria). Air can be whipped into soap to make it float. Soapmakers compete to find the combination of ingredients that will be most attractive and smell pleasant to customers.

6 Neat soap is poured into molds and allowed to harden. Before neat soap is made into bars, flakes, or powdered soap, other optional ingredients such as abrasives (scrubbing agents) can be added.

7 Cosmetic soaps require an additional process. After the neat soap cools, it goes through the milling process. The soap is fed through rollers that crush it. Perfumes and other ingredients can be added at this stage.

Science Activity

 Make your own soap, using lard, baking soda, water, and salt.

- Prepare a solution of baking soda by dissolving 5 grams in 10 milliliters of water.
- Mix the baking soda solution with 20 grams of lard in a 400-milliliter glass beaker.
- Boil gently on a hot plate for 20 minutes. Stir continuously while the mixture is boiling.
- Let the mixture cool. Transfer to a plastic beaker. Place in an ice water bath for 5–10 minutes. Stir.
- Make a saturated salt solution by dissolving 20 grams in 25 milliliters of water. Add to the mixture. Stir.
- Remove soap curdles by pouring through cheesecloth. Drain any liquid. Put soap into a dish to dry and harden.
- Put a portion of soap into warm water and stir. Observe the bubbles.
- Test with litmus paper to see if it is acid or base. (Blue litmus paper turns red in an acid. Red litmus paper turns blue in a base.)

8 The finished soap is pressed, cut, stamped, and wrapped for shipment.

L ◆ 157

Science Activity

Materials lard, baking soda, water, salt, balance, graduated cylinder, glass beaker, hot plate, plastic beaker, ice water bath, cheesecloth, dish, red and blue litmus paper

Focus Ask: **What is the fatty acid ingredient in this soap recipe?** *(Lard)* **What is the alkali ingredient?** *(Baking soda)*

Teach Have students work in pairs. Suggest that they take turns reading the instructions aloud and performing the measurements. You may need to demonstrate what "boil gently" means. Emphasize the importance of stirring constantly while the mixture is boiling on the hot plate. Ask: **Why must you keep stirring?** *(So that the substances will thoroughly mix and saponification will occur)* You may substitute vegetable shortening for lard if you have students who follow Jewish kosher or Muslim halal laws.

Expected Outcome Students' final soap should have a fairly consistent appearance and form bubbles in water. Soap made with vegetable shortening will be softer than soap made with lard. Litmus tests should indicate that the soap is a base.

Background

Facts and Figures Once the chemistry of detergents was understood in the 1940s, other soap products quickly followed. Here is a timeline of soap products.
- 1950s: automatic dishwasher powders; liquid soap, all-purpose cleaners; fabric softeners; detergents with bleach
- 1960s: prewash stain removers, laundry powders containing enzymes
- 1970s: liquid hand soaps, laundry detergents with built-in fabric softener
- 1980s: detergents for cold-water washing, concentrated laundry powder
- 1990s: antibacterial agents added to hand soaps, superconcentrated detergents
- 2000s: cleaning products in disposable sheets

Explore Social Studies Concepts

Include Community Resources

Contact your local historical society to find out if any sites in your area reenact colonial soapmaking. If so, make arrangements for the class to observe the soapmaking process. Or invite an interpreter from the historical society to describe the process to the class. Suggest that students prepare one question to ask about the use of soap, the soapmaking process, or ingredients used to make soap.

Extend Explain that soap makers often made candles as well. Invite students to investigate how candles were made during colonial times in the United States. Have them find out the ingredients used to make candles and the process by which candles were made. Then students can make comparisons between candle making and soapmaking.

Social Studies Activity

Focus Tell students that time lines help place the development of a product within the context of historical events and lifestyles.

Teach Divide the class into small groups. Have each group make notes and collect materials to create a bulletin board display of the time line in the classroom. You may wish to assign each group to a different part of the time line. Allow students to use the information from this explore in their time lines. When students present their time lines, ask: **What do you think people in earlier times used as a cleaner before the development of soap?** (Sample answer: Water)

Scoring Rubric

4 Exceeds criteria; time line has many detailed, well-researched events with photos or illustrations that are balanced across the time period
3 Meets criteria
2 Includes one event, with or without illustrations, for each assigned event
1 Includes no illustrations and/or events are omitted

The Development of Soap

People have made soap for at least 2,300 years. The ancient Babylonians, Arabs, Greeks, Romans, and Celts made soap and sometimes traded it. The English word comes from "saipo," the Celts' name for soap. But these early cultures used soap primarily as a hair dye or a medicine, not as a cleaner! Only in the period from A.D. 100–199 did soap become known as a cleaning agent.

Soapmaking in Western Europe began about A.D. 100. First France was a leading producer, then Italy by 700, and Spain by 800. England didn't begin making soap until about 1200. But even then, most people didn't use soap for bathing.

Around 1790, Nicolas Leblanc, a French scientist, discovered that alkali could be made from common table salt and water. After that, soap could be made more easily and sold for profit.

Cutting Soap
This illustration shows that cutting soap required strength and precision.

In North America beginning around 1650, colonists made their own soap. Families would make up to a year's supply for their own use. Then around 1800, some people started collecting waste fats and ashes from their neighbors and making soap in large quantities. Soon bars of soap were sold from door to door.

In 1806, William Colgate, a soap and candle maker, started a business called Colgate and Company. His company produced soap and another cleaner, toothpaste. Today, nearly all soap is made in factories using large machinery.

The first detergent was produced in Germany around 1916, during World War I. Because fats were in short supply, detergent was meant to be a substitute for fat-based soap. However, people found that detergent was a better cleaner than soap for many purposes. The first household detergents appeared in the United States in 1933.

Soap Ad
This Lenox Soap advertisement is from 1898.

LENOX SOAP
LATHERS FREELY
IN HARD WATER
PROCTER & GAMBLE
LENOX SOAP
CINCINNATI
"JUST FITS THE HAND"

Social Studies Activity

Create a time line of important events in the history of soapmaking. Find photos or make illustrations for the time line. Include the following events:

- early uses and users of soap
- beginning of the soapmaking industry
- early North American soapmaking
- first detergent

Before they discovered soap, what do you think people in earlier times used as a cleaner?

Background

Facts and Figures Like soap, candles were once been made from animal fat. Candles have also been made from beeswax, paraffin, and solid vegetable oils.

The earliest candles were made using a fiber wick made of flax or cotton. The wick was dipped in a vat of warm molten wax. Then the wick and the wax that stuck to it were left to cool and dry. After the wax was dry, the candle was dipped again. Layer by layer, the candle was formed from repeated dippings.

Some candles today are still made using this method. However, most mass-produced candles are made by machine, using molds.

Colonial Soapmaking

Making soap in North America in the 1600s was an exhausting, unpleasant process. For months, colonists saved barrels of ashes from their wood fires. Then they poured hot water over the ashes. An alkali solution, called lye, dripped out of a spigot in the bottom of the barrel.

In a large kettle over a roaring outdoor fire, they boiled the alkali solution with fat, such as greases, which they had also saved. They had to keep the fire high and hot and stir the mixture for hours. When it was thick, they ladled the liquid soap into shallow boxes. Families made soap in the spring and sometimes again in the fall.

The following passage is from the novel *The Iron Peacock* by Mary Stetson Clarke. The story takes place in 1650 in Massachusetts Bay Colony. In the passage, two large supports hold a crossbar where the pot is hung over the fire. The women stir the pot with a homemade tool.

Colonial Soapmaking
Soapmaking was an all-day process done at home.

The next morning was fair, the air washed sparkling clear. Duncan built a fire under the framework. Maura measured the grease, adding a quantity of lye. Ross and Duncan placed the crossbar under the handle of the pot and raised it until it rested on the supports. Maura took up a long wooden bar with a shorter one set at right angles to it, and began stirring the contents of the pot.

"We'll be back at noon to lend you a hand," said Duncan.

Maura and Joanna took turns stirring the soap. When Maura judged it to be of the right consistency, they let the fire die down.

After the men had lifted the pot off the fire, Joanna and Maura ladled the thick brown liquid into boxes lined with old pieces of cloth.

It cooled quickly into thick cream-colored slabs. Maura would cut it into cakes in a few days, when it was solid enough to handle. Then she would stack the bars in a dry place where the air could circulate around them until the soap had seasoned enough for use.

Language Arts Activity

Reread the passage and list the steps for making soap. Think of a process or activity that you know well. It can be packing for a trip or preparing for a party. Jot down the steps and number them. Then, write a description of the process. Include steps and details so that a reader unfamiliar with your activity would know how to do it.

Background

Facts and Figures Legend describes how soap was accidentally discovered at a place called Mount Sapo, from which soap got its name. On Mount Sapo was an altar on which animals were sacrificed. Ashes from fires mixed with animal fats and dripped into a nearby stream. Washerwomen noticed that washing in this stream produced better results than washing elsewhere.

Although soap has been used for thousands of years, its actual origins are unknown. Many reference books give different suggestions for when and how soap might have been discovered. It may have been independently discovered by different people at different times and in different places.

Explore Language Arts Concepts

Oral Presentation Invite students to take turns reading the passage. As they read, other students can list on the board the steps in making soap. After reading, ask: **Where did the colonists get fat or grease?** *(From the animals they used for food)* **What do you think the boxes were made of?** *(Wood)* **Why do you think they lined the boxes with cloth?** *(Sample answer: So the soap would not stick to the boxes, to make it easier to remove the soap later, so the liquid soap didn't leak from the box)* Point out that a cake of soap is the same as a bar of soap. Then, compare colonial soapmaking with modern soapmaking described in science exploration. List the steps in modern soapmaking next to the steps of colonial soapmaking. Ask: **What are the similarities in the processes?** *(Sample answer: Heat, alkali, and lipids are used as ingredients.)* **What are differences?** *(Sample answer: The equipment and the actual ingredients)*

Use Visuals Have students look at the illustration for this exploration. Ask: **Why do you think making soap in the 1600s was an exhausting, unpleasant experience?** *(Sample answer: Lots of stirring over a hot, smoky fire; bad odor from cooking soap)* **Why do you think soap was made in the fall or spring?** *(Sample answer: Temperature was cool, but above freezing.)*

Language Arts Activity

Focus Tell students that organizing the steps of a process from beginning to end helps them to better understand it.

Teach Remind students to list the steps in the process or activity first. It is easier to fill in detailed instructions afterwards. Tell students to assume that someone who is completely unfamiliar with the task should be able to perform it using their procedure. Also suggest that students follow the steps of their completed process to check it for clarity and completeness.

Scoring Rubric
4 Exceeds criteria; highly detailed, step-by-step procedure for an activity or process
3 Meets criteria
2 Includes all the steps in the procedure, but with little detail
1 Some steps are out of order and/or omitted

Explore Mathematics Concepts

Use Math Skills Tell students that a ratio compares two numbers by division. As an example of a ratio, express the number of boys to girls in the class. Show that the ratio can be written in several ways: 8 boys to 10 girls; 8 : 10; or $\frac{8}{10}$, which can be reduced to $\frac{4}{5}$. Then explain that a proportion is a mathematical sentence saying that two ratios are equivalent. You can set up a proportion to estimate an unknown quantity. As an example, say you want to know how many girls are in the class for each boy. Write the proportion:

$$\frac{8 \text{ boys}}{10 \text{ girls}} = \frac{1 \text{ boy}}{x \text{ girls}}$$

$8x = 10$
$x = 1.25$
The ratio of boys to girls is 1 to 1.25.

Math Activity

Focus Tell students to break word problems into parts, identify the mathematical operation required, and identify the relevant values and labels.

Teach Remind students always to check the labels of the quantities given. They may have to convert grams to kilograms. Ask: **How many grams are in one kilogram?** *(1000 g)* To find the ratio of alkali to oil, point out that students must first total the mass of oils in the soap. Remind students how to use proportions to calculate unknown quantities in a ratio. Tell students that the final ratio of alkali to oil should be equal to 1 : x. Finally, point out that the problem says that the recipe makes one bar of soap with a mass of 141.75 g. However, if they add the mass of the ingredients, they get the sum of 182.8 g. Explain that the extra mass is lost as waste during the process of soapmaking.

Answers
- The ratio of alkali to oil is 1 : 7.18.
- The batch makes 12 bars of soap.
- To make this batch, you would need 201.6 g alkali, 544.8 g water, 506.4 g olive oil, 434.4 g coconut oil, and 506.4 g palm oil.
- Two batches of soap would be needed for one year.
- The family uses 12 + 6 + 18 = 36 bars of soap in a year, or 3 batches.

A Year's Supply of Soap

What would you do if you had to make a year's supply of your own soap, using modern ingredients? You probably buy the soap you use from a store. But it is still possible to make soap yourself by using the right ingredients and following specific instructions.

Soap recipes are as varied and numerous as food recipes. You can make soap using the oil from avocados, hazelnuts, or sunflower seeds. To add natural scents, you might include rose, cinnamon, cloves, lavender, lemon, mint, grapefruit, pine, rose, vanilla, or something else.

Colors might come from beetroot, cocoa, goldenrod, licorice, paprika, or even seaweed. You can even include "scrubbers" such as cornmeal, oatmeal, or poppy seeds!

Math Activity

Here is the ingredient list for one bar of soap with a mass of 141.8 grams.

List of Ingredients

16.8 grams alkali

45.4 grams water

42.2 grams olive oil

36.2 grams coconut oil

42.2 grams palm oil

Use the list to find the answers to these questions:

- What is the ratio of alkali to oil in this recipe? Round to the nearest tenth.

- If you made a large batch with a total mass of 1.7 kg, about how many bars of soap would you get in that batch?

- How much of each ingredient would you need to make this batch?

- If your family used two bars of soap per month, how many batches of soap would you make to provide one year's supply?

- How many batches would you make if your family used four bars of soap per month through the summer (June, July, and August), two bars per month through the winter (December, January, and February), and three bars per month during the rest of the year?

Soap Study

Organize a class project to survey and test soaps and soap products that are on the market today. Work in small groups. Choose one kind of cleaner to study, such as bar soaps, dishwashing detergents, laundry detergents, or another cleaner.

As your group investigates one kind of product, answer these questions:

- Look at the labels. What kinds of oils and other ingredients are listed?

- What do the makers claim these ingredients do? What language do they use to make these claims?

- How many kinds of surfaces can you clean with this product?

Next, collect several brands. Design an experiment to help you decide which brand works best.

- Decide what you will test for, such as how well the brand cleans grease.

- Develop a grading scale for rating the products.

- Before you begin, predict what your results will be.

- Keep all variables the same except for the brand.

- Perform the tests, collect data, and take careful notes.

Decide how to present your results to the class. You might include photographs of the test results, create a graph, or write a report describing and summarizing the results.

Soap Study

Time 6 days (3 days to plan and collect cleaners, study the labels, and design the tests; 3 days to perform the tests and prepare the presentation)

Tips You may choose to assign small groups the kind of cleaner to study. If possible, find a copy of a consumer testing magazine with an article about cleaners. Students can learn how the magazine tested the products and presented its findings.

- Review all testing procedures before students perform the tests.

- For some cleaners, students should wear rubber gloves and safety goggles.

- Stress that chemicals used in common cleaners can be dangerous. Make sure students read the safety warnings on all containers and take those warnings seriously.

- Do not permit students to test products that may interact dangerously, such as ammonia and bleach. Explain the possible consequences of mishandling these products.

Extend Invite students to combine their findings to make a display for the school hallway.

Think Like a Scientist

The Skills Handbook is designed as a reference for students to use whenever they need to review inquiry, reading, or math skills. You can use the activities in this part of the Skills Handbook to teach or reinforce inquiry skills.

Observing

Focus Remind students that an observation is what they can see, hear, smell, taste, or feel.

Teach Invite students to make observations of the classroom. List these observations on the board. Challenge students to identify the senses they used to make each observation. Then, ask: **Which senses will you use to make observations from the photograph on this page?** (*Sight is the only sense that can be used to make observations from the photograph.*)

Activity

Some observations that students might make include that the boy is skateboarding, wearing a white helmet, and flying in the air. Make sure that students' observations are confined to only things that they can actually see in the photograph.

Inferring

Focus Choose one or two of the classroom observations listed on the board, and challenge students to interpret them. Guide students by asking why something appears as it does.

Teach Encourage students to describe their thought processes in making their inferences. Point out where they used their knowledge and experience to interpret the observations. Then invite students to suggest other possible interpretations for the observations. Ask: **How can you find out whether an inference is correct?** (*By further investigation*)

Activity

One possible inference is that the boy just skated off a ramp at a skate park. Invite students to share their experiences that helped them make the inference.

Predicting

Focus Discuss the weather forecast for the next day. Point out that this prediction is an inference about what will happen in the

Think Like a Scientist

Scientists have a particular way of looking at the world, or scientific habits of mind. Whenever you ask a question and explore possible answers, you use many of the same skills that scientists do. Some of these skills are described on this page.

Observing

When you use one or more of your five senses to gather information about the world, you are **observing.** Hearing a dog bark, counting twelve green seeds, and smelling smoke are all observations. To increase the power of their senses, scientists sometimes use microscopes, telescopes, or other instruments that help them make more detailed observations.

An observation must be an accurate report of what your senses detect. It is important to keep careful records of your observations in science class by writing or drawing in a notebook. The information collected through observations is called evidence, or data.

Inferring

When you interpret an observation, you are **inferring,** or making an inference. For example, if you hear your dog barking, you may infer that someone is at your front door. To make this inference, you combine the evidence—the barking dog—and your experience or knowledge—you know that your dog barks when strangers approach—to reach a logical conclusion.

Notice that an inference is not a fact; it is only one of many possible interpretations for an observation. For example, your dog may be barking because it wants to go for a walk. An inference may turn out to be incorrect even if it is based on accurate observations and logical reasoning. The only way to find out if an inference is correct is to investigate further.

Predicting

When you listen to the weather forecast, you hear many predictions about the next day's weather—what the temperature will be, whether it will rain, and how windy it will be. Weather forecasters use observations and knowledge of weather patterns to predict the weather. The skill of **predicting** involves making an inference about a future event based on current evidence or past experience.

Because a prediction is an inference, it may prove to be false. In science class, you can test some of your predictions by doing experiments. For example, suppose you predict that larger paper airplanes can fly farther than smaller airplanes. How could you test your prediction?

Activity

Use the photograph to answer the questions below.

Observing Look closely at the photograph. List at least three observations.

Inferring Use your observations to make an inference about what has happened. What experience or knowledge did you use to make the inference?

Predicting Predict what will happen next. On what evidence or experience do you base your prediction?

future based on observations and experience.

Teach Help students differentiate between a prediction and an inference. You might organize the similarities and differences in a Venn diagram on the board. Both are interpretations of observations using experience and knowledge, and both can be incorrect. Inferences describe current or past events. Predictions describe future events.

Activity

Students might predict that the boy will land and skate to the other side. Others might predict that the boy will fall. Students should also describe the evidence or experience on which they based their predictions.

Classifying

Could you imagine searching for a book in the library if the books were shelved in no particular order? Your trip to the library would be an all-day event! Luckily, librarians group together books on similar topics or by the same author. Grouping together items that are alike in some way is called **classifying.** You can classify items in many ways: by size, by shape, by use, and by other important characteristics.

Like librarians, scientists use the skill of classifying to organize information and objects. When things are sorted into groups, the relationships among them become easier to understand.

Activity

Classify the objects in the photograph into two groups based on any characteristic you choose. Then use another characteristic to classify the objects into three groups.

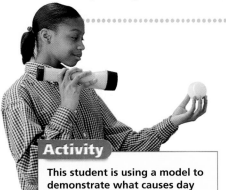

Activity

This student is using a model to demonstrate what causes day and night on Earth. What do the flashlight and the tennis ball in the model represent?

Making Models

Have you ever drawn a picture to help someone understand what you were saying? Such a drawing is one type of model. A model is a picture, diagram, computer image, or other representation of a complex object or process. **Making models** helps people understand things that they cannot observe directly.

Scientists often use models to represent things that are either very large or very small, such as the planets in the solar system, or the parts of a cell. Such models are physical models—drawings or three-dimensional structures that look like the real thing. Other models are mental models—mathematical equations or words that describe how something works.

Communicating

Whenever you talk on the phone, write a report, or listen to your teacher at school, you are communicating. **Communicating** is the process of sharing ideas and information with other people. Communicating effectively requires many skills, including writing, reading, speaking, listening, and making models.

Scientists communicate to share results, information, and opinions. Scientists often communicate about their work in journals, over the telephone, in letters, and on the Internet.

They also attend scientific meetings where they share their ideas with one another in person.

Activity

On a sheet of paper, write out clear, detailed directions for tying your shoe. Then exchange directions with a partner. Follow your partner's directions exactly. How successful were you at tying your shoe? How could your partner have communicated more clearly?

Skills Handbook ◆ 163

Classifying

Focus Encourage students to think of common things that are classified.

Teach Ask: **What things at home are classified?** (*Clothing might be classified in order to place it in the appropriate dresser drawer; glasses, plates, and silverware are grouped in different parts of the kitchen; screws, nuts, bolts, washers, and nails might be separated into small containers.*) **What are some things that scientists classify?** (*Scientists classify many things they study, including organisms, geological features and processes, and kinds of machines.*)

Activity

Some characteristics students might use include color, pattern of color, use of balls, and size. Students' criteria for classification should clearly divide the balls into two, and then three, distinct groups.

Making Models

Focus Ask: **What are some models you have used to study science?** (*Students might have used human anatomical models, solar system models, maps, or stream tables.*) **How have these models helped you?** (*Models can help you learn about things that are difficult to study because they are very large, very small, or highly complex.*)

Teach Be sure students understand that a model does not have to be three-dimensional. For example, a map is a model, as is a mathematical equation. Have students look at the photograph of the student modeling the causes of day and night on Earth. Ask: **What quality of each item makes this a good model?** (*The flashlight gives off light, and the ball is round and can be rotated by the student.*)

Activity

The flashlight represents the sun and the ball represents Earth.

Communicating

Focus Have students identify the methods of communication they have used today.

Teach Ask: **How is the way you communicate with a friend similar to and different from the way scientists communicate about their work to other scientists?** (*Both may communicate using various methods, but scientists must be very detailed and precise, whereas communication between friends may be less detailed and*

precise.) Encourage students to communicate like a scientist as they carry out the activity.

Activity

Students' answers will vary but should identify a step-by-step process for tying a shoe. Help students identify communication errors such as leaving out a step, putting steps in the wrong order, or disregarding the person's handedness.

Making Measurements

Students can refer to this part of the Skills Handbook whenever they need to review how to make measurements with SI units. You can use the activities here to teach or reinforce SI units.

Measuring in SI

Focus Review SI units with students. Begin by providing metric rulers, graduated cylinders, balances, and Celsius thermometers. Use these tools to reinforce that the meter is the unit of length, the liter is the unit of volume, the gram is the unit of mass, and the degree Celsius is the unit of temperature.

Teach Ask: **If you want to measure the length and the width of the classroom, which SI unit would you use?** *(Meter)* **Which unit would you use to measure the amount of mass in your textbook?** *(Gram)* **Which would you use to measure how much water a drinking glass holds?** *(Liter)* **When would you use the Celsius scale?** *(To measure the temperature of something)* Then use the measuring equipment to review SI prefixes. For example, ask: **What are the smallest units on the metric ruler?** *(Millimeters)* **How many millimeters are there in one centimeter?** *(10 millimeters)* **How many in 10 centimeters?** *(100 millimeters)* **How many centimeters are there in one meter?** *(100 centimeters)* **What does 1,000 meters equal?** *(One kilometer)*

Activity

Length The length of the shell is 7.8 centimeters, or 78 millimeters. If students need more practice measuring length, have them use meter sticks and metric rulers to measure various objects in the classroom.

Activity

Liquid Volume The volume of water in the graduated cylinder is 62 milliliters. If students need more practice, have them use a graduated cylinder to measure different volumes of water.

Making Measurements

By measuring, scientists can express their observations more precisely and communicate more information about what they observe.

Measuring in SI

The standard system of measurement used by scientists around the world is known as the International System of Units, which is abbreviated as SI (**Système International d'Unités,** in French). SI units are easy to use because they are based on multiples of 10. Each unit is ten times larger than the next smallest unit and one tenth the size of the next largest unit. The table lists the prefixes used to name the most common SI units.

Common SI Prefixes		
Prefix	**Symbol**	**Meaning**
kilo-	k	1,000
hecto-	h	100
deka-	da	10
deci-	d	0.1 (one tenth)
centi-	c	0.01 (one hundredth)
milli-	m	0.001 (one thousandth)

Length To measure length, or the distance between two points, the unit of measure is the **meter (m).** The distance from the floor to a doorknob is approximately one meter. Long distances, such as the distance between two cities, are measured in kilometers (km). Small lengths are measured in centimeters (cm) or millimeters (mm). Scientists use metric rulers and meter sticks to measure length.

Common Conversions	
1 km	= 1,000 m
1 m	= 100 cm
1 m	= 1,000 mm
1 cm	= 10 mm

Activity

The larger lines on the metric ruler in the picture show centimeter divisions, while the smaller, unnumbered lines show millimeter divisions. How many centimeters long is the shell? How many millimeters long is it?

Liquid Volume To measure the volume of a liquid, or the amount of space it takes up, you will use a unit of measure known as the **liter (L).** One liter is the approximate volume of a medium-size carton of milk. Smaller volumes are measured in milliliters (mL). Scientists use graduated cylinders to measure liquid volume.

Activity

The graduated cylinder in the picture is marked in milliliter divisions. Notice that the water in the cylinder has a curved surface. This curved surface is called the *meniscus*. To measure the volume, you must read the level at the lowest point of the meniscus. What is the volume of water in this graduated cylinder?

Common Conversion
1 L = 1,000 mL

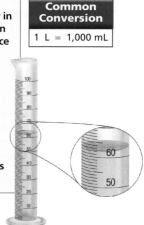

Mass To measure mass, or the amount of matter in an object, you will use a unit of measure known as the **gram (g).** One gram is approximately the mass of a paper clip. Larger masses are measured in kilograms (kg). Scientists use a balance to find the mass of an object.

Common Conversion

1 kg = 1,000 g

Activity

The mass of the potato in the picture is measured in kilograms. What is the mass of the potato? Suppose a recipe for potato salad called for one kilogram of potatoes. About how many potatoes would you need?

0.25 KG

Temperature To measure the temperature of a substance, you will use the **Celsius scale.** Temperature is measured in degrees Celsius (°C) using a Celsius thermometer. Water freezes at 0°C and boils at 100°C.

Time The unit scientists use to measure time is the **second (s).**

Activity

What is the temperature of the liquid in degrees Celsius?

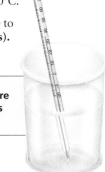

Converting SI Units

To use the SI system, you must know how to convert between units. Converting from one unit to another involves the skill of **calculating,** or using mathematical operations. Converting between SI units is similar to converting between dollars and dimes because both systems are based on multiples of ten.

Suppose you want to convert a length of 80 centimeters to meters. Follow these steps to convert between units.

1. Begin by writing down the measurement you want to convert—in this example, 80 centimeters.

2. Write a conversion factor that represents the relationship between the two units you are converting. In this example, the relationship is 1 meter = 100 centimeters. Write this conversion factor as a fraction, making sure to place the units you are converting from (centimeters, in this example) in the denominator.

3. Multiply the measurement you want to convert by the fraction. When you do this, the units in the first measurement will cancel out with the units in the denominator. Your answer will be in the units you are converting to (meters, in this example).

Example

80 centimeters = ▦ meters

$$80 \text{ centimeters} \times \frac{1 \text{ meter}}{100 \text{ centimeters}} = \frac{80 \text{ meters}}{100}$$

$$= 0.8 \text{ meters}$$

Activity

Convert between the following units.
1. 600 millimeters = ▦ meters
2. 0.35 liters = ▦ milliliters
3. 1,050 grams = ▦ kilograms

Activity

Mass The mass of the potato is 0.25 kilograms. You would need 4 potatoes to make one kilogram. If students need more practice, give them various objects, such as coins, paper clips, and books, to measure mass.

Activity

Temperature The temperature of the liquid is 35°C. Students who need more practice can measure the temperatures of various water samples.

Converting SI Units

Focus Review the steps for converting SI units, and work through the example with students.

Teach Ask: **How many millimeters are in 80 centimeters?** *(With the relationship 10 millimeters = 1 centimeter, students should follow the steps to calculate that 80 centimeters is equal to 800 millimeters.)* Have students do the conversion problems in the activity.

Activity

1. *600 millimeters = 0.6 meters*
2. *0.35 liters = 350 milliliters*
3. *1,050 grams = 1.05 kilograms*
If students need more practice converting SI units, have them make up conversion problems to trade with partners.

Conducting a Scientific Investigation

Students can refer to this part of the Skills Handbook whenever they need to review the steps of a scientific investigation. You can use the activities here to teach or reinforce these steps.

Posing Questions

Focus Ask: **What do you do when you want to learn about something?** (*Answers might include asking questions about it or looking for information in books or on the Internet.*) Explain that scientists go through the same process to learn about something.

Teach Tell students that the questions scientists ask may have no answers or many different answers. To answer their questions, scientists often conduct experiments. Ask: **Why is a scientific question important to a scientific investigation?** (*It helps the scientist decide if an experiment is necessary; the answer might already be known. It also helps focus the idea so that the scientist can form a hypothesis.*) **What is the scientific question in the activity on the next page?** (*Is a ball's bounce affected by the height from which it is dropped?*)

Developing a Hypothesis

Focus Emphasize that a hypothesis is one possible explanation for a set of observations. It is *not* a guess. It is often based on an inference.

Teach Ask: **On what information do scientists base their hypotheses?** (*Their observations and previous knowledge or experience*) Point out that a hypothesis does not always turn out to be correct. Ask: **When a hypothesis turns out to be incorrect, do you think the scientist wasted his or her time? Explain.** (*No. The scientist learned from the investigation and will develop another hypothesis that could prove to be correct.*)

Designing an Experiment

Focus Have a volunteer read the Experimental Procedure in the box. Invite students to identify the manipulated variable (*amount of salt*), the variables kept constant (*amount and temperature of water, location of containers*), the control (*Container 3*), and the responding variable (*time required for the water to freeze*).

Conducting a Scientific Investigation

In some ways, scientists are like detectives, piecing together clues to learn about a process or event. One way that scientists gather clues is by carrying out experiments. An experiment tests an idea in a careful, orderly manner. Although experiments do not all follow the same steps in the same order, many follow a pattern similar to the one described here.

Posing Questions

Experiments begin by asking a scientific question. A scientific question is one that can be answered by gathering evidence. For example, the question "Which freezes faster—fresh water or salt water?" is a scientific question because you can carry out an investigation and gather information to answer the question.

Developing a Hypothesis

The next step is to form a hypothesis. A **hypothesis** is a possible explanation for a set of observations or answer to a scientific question. In science, a hypothesis must be something that can be tested. A hypothesis can be worded as an *If . . . then . . .* statement. For example, a hypothesis might be *"If I add salt to fresh water, then the water will take longer to freeze."* A hypothesis worded this way serves as a rough outline of the experiment you should perform.

Teach Ask: **How might the experiment be affected if Container 1 had only 100 milliliters of water?** (*It wouldn't be an accurate comparison with the containers that have more water.*) Also make sure that students understand the importance of the control. Then, ask: **What operational definition is used in this experiment?** (*"Frozen" means the time at which a wooden stick can no longer move in a container.*)

Designing an Experiment

Next you need to plan a way to test your hypothesis. Your plan should be written out as a step-by-step procedure and should describe the observations or measurements you will make.

Two important steps involved in designing an experiment are controlling variables and forming operational definitions.

Controlling Variables In a well-designed experiment, you need to keep all variables the same except for one. A **variable** is any factor that can change in an experiment. The factor that you change is called the **manipulated variable**. In this experiment, the manipulated variable is the amount of salt added to the water. Other factors, such as the amount of water or the starting temperature, are kept constant.

The factor that changes as a result of the manipulated variable is called the **responding variable.** The responding variable is what you measure or observe to obtain your results. In this experiment, the responding variable is how long the water takes to freeze.

An experiment in which all factors except one are kept constant is called a **controlled experiment.** Most controlled experiments include a test called the control. In this experiment, Container 3 is the control. Because no salt is added to Container 3, you can compare the results from the other containers to it. Any difference in results must be due to the addition of salt alone.

Forming Operational Definitions Another important aspect of a well-designed experiment is having clear operational definitions. An **operational definition** is a statement that describes how a particular variable is to be measured or how a term is to be defined. For example, in this experiment, how will you determine if the water has frozen? You might decide to insert a stick in each container at the start of the experiment. Your operational definition of "frozen" would be the time at which the stick can no longer move.

Experimental Procedure
1. Fill 3 containers with 300 milliliters of cold tap water.
2. Add 10 grams of salt to Container 1; stir. Add 20 grams of salt to Container 2; stir. Add no salt to Container 3.
3. Place the 3 containers in a freezer.
4. Check the containers every 15 minutes. Record your observations.

Interpreting Data

The observations and measurements you make in an experiment are called **data.** At the end of an experiment, you need to analyze the data to look for any patterns or trends. Patterns often become clear if you organize your data in a data table or graph. Then think through what the data reveal. Do they support your hypothesis? Do they point out a flaw in your experiment? Do you need to collect more data?

. . . .

Drawing Conclusions

A **conclusion** is a statement that sums up what you have learned from an experiment. When you draw a conclusion, you need to decide whether the data you collected support your hypothesis or not. You may need to repeat an experiment several times before you can draw any conclusions from it. Conclusions often lead you to pose new questions and plan new experiments to answer them.

Activity

Is a ball's bounce affected by the height from which it is dropped? Using the steps just described, plan a controlled experiment to investigate this problem.

Interpreting Data

Focus Ask: **What kind of data would you collect from the experiment with freezing salt water?** *(Time and state of the water)*

Teach Ask: **What if you forgot to record some data during an investigation?** *(You wouldn't be able to draw valid conclusions because some data are missing.)* Then, ask: **Why are data tables and graphs a good way to organize data?** *(They make it easier to record data accurately, as well as compare and analyze data.)* **What kind of data table and graph might you use for this experiment?** *(A table would have columns for each container with a row for each time interval in which the state of water is recorded. A bar graph would show the time elapsed until water froze for each container.)*

Drawing Conclusions

Focus Help students understand that a conclusion is not necessarily the end of a scientific investigation. A conclusion about one experiment may lead right into another experiment.

Teach Point out that in scientific investigations, a conclusion is a summary and explanation of the results of an experiment. For the Experimental Procedure described on this page, tell students to suppose that they obtained the following results: Container 1 froze in 45 minutes, Container 2 in 80 minutes, and Container 3 in 25 minutes. Ask: **What conclusions can you draw from this experiment?** *(Students might conclude that water takes longer to freeze as more salt is added to it. The hypothesis is supported, and the question of which freezes faster is answered—fresh water.)*

Activity

You might wish to have students work in pairs to plan the controlled experiment. Students should develop a hypothesis, such as, "If I increase the height from which a ball is dropped, then the height of its bounce will increase." They can test the hypothesis by dropping a ball from varying heights (the manipulated variable). All trials should be done with the same kind of ball and on the same surface (constants). For each trial, they should measure the height of the bounce (responding variable). After students have designed the experiment, provide rubber balls, and invite them to carry out the experiment so they can collect and interpret data and draw conclusions.

Technology Design Skills

Students can refer to this part of the Skills Handbook whenever they need to review the process of designing new technologies. You can use the activities here to teach or reinforce the steps in this process.

Identify a Need

Focus Solicit from students any situations in which they have thought that a tool, machine, or other object would be really helpful to them or others. Explain that this is the first step in the design of new products.

Teach Point out that identifying specific needs is very important to the design process. Ask: **If it was specified that the toy boat be wind-powered, how might that affect the design?** (*The boat would likely be designed with sails.*)

Research the Problem

Focus Explain that research focuses the problem so that the design is more specific.

Teach Ask: **What might happen if you didn't research the problem before designing the solution?** (*Answers include developing a design that has already been found to fail, using materials that aren't the best, or designing a solution that already exists.*) **What would you research before designing your toy boat?** (*Students might research designs and materials.*)

Design a Solution

Focus Emphasize the importance of a design team. Ask: **Why are brainstorming sessions important in product design?** (*A group will propose more new ideas than one person.*)

Teach Divide the class into teams to design the toy boat. Instruct them to brainstorm design ideas. Then, ask: **Why do you think engineers evaluate constraints after brainstorming?** (*Evaluating constraints while brainstorming often stops the flow of new ideas.*) **What design constraints do you have for your toy boat?** (*Materials must be readily available and teacher-approved. The boat must be 15 centimeters or less in length and must travel 2 meters in a straight line carrying a load of 20 pennies*)

Technology Design Skills

Engineers are people who use scientific and technological knowledge to solve practical problems. To design new products, engineers usually follow the process described here, even though they may not follow these steps in the exact order. As you read the steps, think about how you might apply them in technology labs.

Identify a Need

Before engineers begin designing a new product, they must first identify the need they are trying to meet. For example, suppose you are a member of a design team in a company that makes toys. Your team has identified a need: a toy boat that is inexpensive and easy to assemble.

Research the Problem

Engineers often begin by gathering information that will help them with their new design. This research may include finding articles in books, magazines, or on the Internet. It may also include talking to other engineers who have solved similar problems. Engineers often perform experiments related to the product they want to design.

For your toy boat, you could look at toys that are similar to the one you want to design. You might do research on the Internet. You could also test some materials to see whether they will work well in a toy boat.

Drawing for a boat design ▼

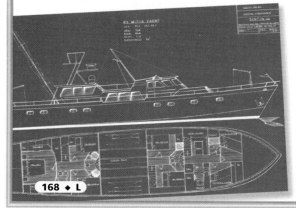

Design a Solution

Research gives engineers information that helps them design a product. When engineers design new products, they usually work in teams.

Generating Ideas Often design teams hold brainstorming meetings in which any team member can contribute ideas. **Brainstorming** is a creative process in which one team member's suggestions often spark ideas in other group members. Brainstorming can lead to new approaches to solving a design problem.

Evaluating Constraints During brainstorming, a design team will often come up with several possible designs. The team must then evaluate each one.

As part of their evaluation, engineers consider constraints. **Constraints** are factors that limit or restrict a product design. Physical characteristics, such as the properties of materials used to make your toy boat, are constraints. Money and time are also constraints. If the materials in a product cost a lot, or if the product takes a long time to make, the design may be impractical.

Making Trade-offs Design teams usually need to make trade-offs. In a **trade-off,** engineers give up one benefit of a proposed design in order to obtain another. In designing your toy boat, you will have to make trade-offs. For example, suppose one material is sturdy but not fully waterproof. Another material is more waterproof, but breakable. You may decide to give up the benefit of sturdiness in order to obtain the benefit of waterproofing.

Build and Evaluate a Prototype

Once the team has chosen a design plan, the engineers build a prototype of the product. A **prototype** is a working model used to test a design. Engineers evaluate the prototype to see whether it works well, is easy to operate, is safe to use, and holds up to repeated use.

Think of your toy boat. What would the prototype be like? Of what materials would it be made? How would you test it?

Troubleshoot and Redesign

Few prototypes work perfectly, which is why they need to be tested. Once a design team has tested a prototype, the members analyze the results and identify any problems. The team then tries to **troubleshoot,** or fix the design problems. For example, if your toy boat leaks or wobbles, the boat should be redesigned to eliminate those problems.

Communicate the Solution

A team needs to communicate the final design to the people who will manufacture and use the product. To do this, teams may use sketches, detailed drawings, computer simulations, and word descriptions.

Activity

You can use the technology design process to design and build a toy boat.

Research and Investigate

1. Visit the library or go online to research toy boats.

2. Investigate how a toy boat can be powered, including wind, rubber bands, or baking soda and vinegar.

3. Brainstorm materials, shapes, and steering for your boat.

Design and Build

4. Based on your research, design a toy boat that
   • is made of readily available materials
   • is no larger than 15 cm long and 10 cm wide

   • includes a power system, a rudder, and an area for cargo
   • travels 2 meters in a straight line carrying a load of 20 pennies

5. Sketch your design and write a step-by-step plan for building your boat. After your teacher approves your plan, build your boat.

Evaluate and Redesign

6. Test your boat, evaluate the results, and troubleshoot any problems.

7. Based on your evaluation, redesign your toy boat so it performs better.

Skills Handbook ◆ 169

Activity

The design possibilities are endless. Students might use small plastic containers, wood, foil, or plastic drinking cups for the boat. Materials may also include toothpicks, straws, or small wooden dowels. Brainstorm with students the different ways in which a toy boat can be propelled. The boats may be any shape, but must be no longer than 15 centimeters.

As student groups follow the steps in the design process, have them record their sources, brainstorming ideas, and prototype design in a logbook. Also give them time to troubleshoot and redesign their boats. When students turn in their boats, they should include assembly directions with a diagram, as well as instructions for use.

Build and Evaluate a Prototype

Focus Explain that building a prototype enables engineers to test design ideas.

Teach Relate building and testing a prototype to conducting an experiment. Explain that engineers set up controlled experiments to test the prototype. Ask: **Why do you think engineers set up controlled experiments?** (*From the data, they can determine which component of the design is working and which is failing.*) **How would you test your prototype of the toy boat**? (*Answers will vary depending on the toy boat's propulsion system.*)

Troubleshoot and Redesign

Focus Make sure students know what it means to troubleshoot. If necessary, give an example. One example is a stapler that isn't working. In that case, you would check to see if it is out of staples or if the staples are jammed. Then you would fix the problem and try stapling again. If it still didn't work, you might check the position of staples and try again.

Teach Explain that engineers often are not surprised if the prototype doesn't work. Ask: **Why isn't it a failure if the prototype doesn't work?** (*Engineers learn from the problems and make changes to address the problems. This process makes the design better.*) Emphasize that prototypes are completely tested before the product is made in the factory.

Communicate the Solution

Focus Inquire whether students have ever read the instruction manual that comes with a new toy or electronic device.

Teach Emphasize the importance of good communication in the design process. Ask: **What might happen if engineers did not communicate their design ideas clearly?** (*The product might not be manufactured correctly or used properly.*)

Creating Data Tables and Graphs

Students can refer to this part of the Skills Handbook whenever they need to review the skills required to create data tables and graphs. You can use the activities provided here to teach or reinforce these skills.

Data Tables

Focus Emphasize the importance of organizing data. Ask: **What might happen if you didn't use a data table for an experiment?** (*Possible answers include that data might not be collected or they might be forgotten.*)

Teach Have students create a data table to show how much time they spend on different activities during one week. Suggest that students first list the main activities they do every week. Then they should determine the amount of time they spend on each activity each day. Remind students to give the data table a title. A sample data table is shown below.

Bar Graphs

Focus Have students compare and contrast the data table and the bar graph on this page. Ask: **Why would you make a bar graph if the data are already organized in a table?** (*The bar graph organizes the data in a visual way that makes them easier to interpret.*)

Teach Students can use the data from the data table they created to make a bar graph that shows the amount of time they spend on different activities during a week. The vertical axis should be divided into units of time, such as hours. Remind students to label both axes and give their graph a title. A sample bar graph is shown below.

Creating Data Tables and Graphs

How can you make sense of the data in a science experiment? The first step is to organize the data to help you understand them. Data tables and graphs are helpful tools for organizing data.

Data Tables

You have gathered your materials and set up your experiment. But before you start, you need to plan a way to record what happens during the experiment. By creating a data table, you can record your observations and measurements in an orderly way.

Suppose, for example, that a scientist conducted an experiment to find out how many Calories people of different body masses burn while doing various activities. The data table shows the results.

Notice in this data table that the manipulated variable (body mass) is the heading of one column. The responding variable (for

Calories Burned in 30 Minutes			
Body Mass	Experiment 1: Bicycling	Experiment 2: Playing Basketball	Experiment 3: Watching Television
30 kg	60 Calories	120 Calories	21 Calories
40 kg	77 Calories	164 Calories	27 Calories
50 kg	95 Calories	206 Calories	33 Calories
60 kg	114 Calories	248 Calories	38 Calories

Experiment 1, the number of Calories burned while bicycling) is the heading of the next column. Additional columns were added for related experiments.

Bar Graphs

To compare how many Calories a person burns doing various activities, you could create a bar graph. A bar graph is used to display data in a number of separate, or distinct, categories. In this example, bicycling, playing basketball, and watching television are the three categories.

To create a bar graph, follow these steps.

1. On graph paper, draw a horizontal, or *x*-, axis and a vertical, or *y*-, axis.

2. Write the names of the categories to be graphed along the horizontal axis. Include an overall label for the axis as well.

3. Label the vertical axis with the name of the responding variable. Include units of measurement. Then create a scale along the axis by marking off equally spaced numbers that cover the range of the data collected.

4. For each category, draw a solid bar using the scale on the vertical axis to determine the height. Make all the bars the same width.

5. Add a title that describes the graph.

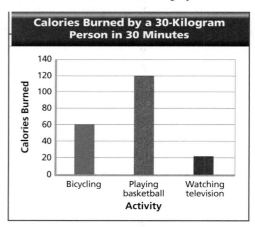

Calories Burned by a 30-Kilogram Person in 30 Minutes

Time Spent on Different Activities in a Week				
	Going to Classes	Eating Meals	Playing Soccer	Watching Television
Monday	6	2	2	0.5
Tuesday	6	1.5	1.5	1.5
Wednesday	6	2	1	2
Thursday	6	2	2	1.5
Friday	6	2	2	0.5
Saturday	0	2.5	2.5	1
Sunday	0	3	1	2

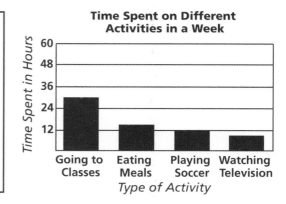

Time Spent on Different Activities in a Week

Line Graphs

To see whether a relationship exists between body mass and the number of Calories burned while bicycling, you could create a line graph. A line graph is used to display data that show how one variable (the responding variable) changes in response to another variable (the manipulated variable). You can use a line graph when your manipulated variable is **continuous,** that is, when there are other points between the ones that you tested. In this example, body mass is a continuous variable because there are other body masses between 30 and 40 kilograms (for example, 31 kilograms). Time is another example of a continuous variable.

Line graphs are powerful tools because they allow you to estimate values for conditions that you did not test in the experiment. For example, you can use the line graph to estimate that a 35-kilogram person would burn 68 Calories while bicycling.

To create a line graph, follow these steps.

1. On graph paper, draw a horizontal, or *x*-, axis and a vertical, or *y*-, axis.

2. Label the horizontal axis with the name of the manipulated variable. Label the vertical axis with the name of the responding variable. Include units of measurement.

3. Create a scale on each axis by marking off equally spaced numbers that cover the range of the data collected.

4. Plot a point on the graph for each piece of data. In the line graph above, the dotted lines show how to plot the first data point (30 kilograms and 60 Calories). Follow an imaginary vertical line extending up from the horizontal axis at the 30-kilogram mark. Then follow an imaginary horizontal line extending across from the vertical axis at the 60-Calorie mark. Plot the point where the two lines intersect.

Effect of Body Mass on Calories Burned While Bicycling

Calories Burned in 30 Minutes (y-axis: 0, 20, 40, 60, 80, 100, 120)
Body Mass (kg) (x-axis: 0, 10, 20, 30, 40, 50, 60, 70)

5. Connect the plotted points with a solid line. (In some cases, it may be more appropriate to draw a line that shows the general trend of the plotted points. In those cases, some of the points may fall above or below the line. Also, not all graphs are linear. It may be more appropriate to draw a curve to connect the points.)

6. Add a title that identifies the variables or relationship in the graph.

Activity

Create line graphs to display the data from Experiment 2 and Experiment 3 in the data table.

Activity

You read in the newspaper that a total of 4 centimeters of rain fell in your area in June, 2.5 centimeters fell in July, and 1.5 centimeters fell in August. What type of graph would you use to display these data? Use graph paper to create the graph.

Line Graphs

Focus Ask: **Would a bar graph show the relationship between body mass and the number of Calories burned in 30 minutes?** *(No. Bar graphs can only show data in distinct categories.)* Explain that line graphs are used to show how one variable changes in response to another variable.

Teach Walk students through the steps involved in creating a line graph using the example illustrated on the page. For example, ask: **What is the label on the horizontal axis? On the vertical axis?** *(Body Mass (kg); Calories Burned in 30 Minutes)* **What scale is used on each axis?** *(10 kg on the x-axis and 20 Calories on the y-axis)* **What does the second data point represent?** *(77 Calories burned for a body mass of 40 kg)* **What trend or pattern does the graph show?** *(The number of Calories burned in 30 minutes of cycling increases with body mass.)*

Activity

Students should make a different graph for each experiment. Each graph should have a different *x*-axis scale that is appropriate for the data. See sample graphs below.

Activity

Students should conclude that a bar graph would be best for displaying the data.

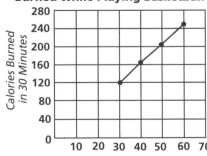

Effect of Body Mass on Calories Burned While Playing Basketball

Calories Burned in 30 Minutes (y-axis: 0, 40, 80, 120, 160, 200, 240, 280)
(x-axis: 10, 20, 30, 40, 50, 60, 70)

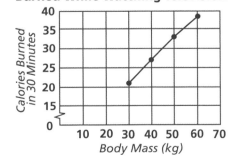

Effect of Body Mass on Calories Burned While Watching Television

Calories Burned in 30 Minutes (y-axis: 0, 15, 20, 25, 30, 35, 40)
Body Mass (kg) (x-axis: 10, 20, 30, 40, 50, 60, 70)

Circle Graphs

Focus Emphasize that a circle graph must include 100 percent of the categories for the topic being graphed. For example, ask: **Could the data in the bar graph titled "Calories Burned by a 30-kilogram Person in Various Activities" (on the previous page) be shown in a circle graph? Why or why not?** *(No. It does not include all the possible ways a 30-kilogram person can burn Calories.)*

Teach Walk students through the steps for making a circle graph. If necessary, help them with the compass and the protractor. Use the protractor to illustrate that a circle has 360 degrees. Make sure students understand the mathematical calculations involved in making a circle graph.

> **Activity**

You might have students work in pairs to complete the activity. Students' circle graphs should look like the graph below.

Ways Students Get to School

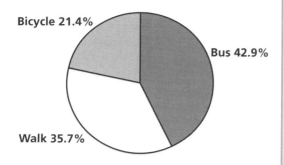

Bicycle 21.4%

Bus 42.9%

Walk 35.7%

Circle Graphs

Like bar graphs, circle graphs can be used to display data in a number of separate categories. Unlike bar graphs, however, circle graphs can only be used when you have data for *all* the categories that make up a given topic. A circle graph is sometimes called a pie chart. The pie represents the entire topic, while the slices represent the individual categories. The size of a slice indicates what percentage of the whole a particular category makes up.

The data table below shows the results of a survey in which 24 teenagers were asked to identify their favorite sport. The data were then used to create the circle graph at the right.

Favorite Sports	
Sport	Students
Soccer	8
Basketball	6
Bicycling	6
Swimming	4

To create a circle graph, follow these steps.

1. Use a compass to draw a circle. Mark the center with a point. Then draw a line from the center point to the top of the circle.

2. Determine the size of each "slice" by setting up a proportion where *x* equals the number of degrees in a slice. (*Note:* A circle contains 360 degrees.) For example, to find the number of degrees in the "soccer" slice, set up the following proportion:

$$\frac{\text{Students who prefer soccer}}{\text{Total number of students}} = \frac{x}{\text{Total number of degrees in a circle}}$$

$$\frac{8}{24} = \frac{x}{360}$$

Cross-multiply and solve for x.

$$24x = 8 \times 360$$
$$x = 120$$

The "soccer" slice should contain 120 degrees.

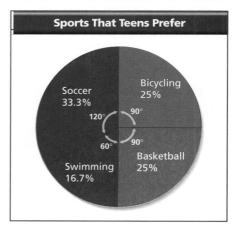

Sports That Teens Prefer

Soccer 33.3%

Bicycling 25%

120° 90°

60° 90°

Swimming 16.7%

Basketball 25%

3. Use a protractor to measure the angle of the first slice, using the line you drew to the top of the circle as the 0° line. Draw a line from the center of the circle to the edge for the angle you measured.

4. Continue around the circle by measuring the size of each slice with the protractor. Start measuring from the edge of the previous slice so the wedges do not overlap. When you are done, the entire circle should be filled in.

5. Determine the percentage of the whole circle that each slice represents. To do this, divide the number of degrees in a slice by the total number of degrees in a circle (360), and multiply by 100%. For the "soccer" slice, you can find the percentage as follows:

$$\frac{120}{360} \times 100\% = 33.3\%$$

6. Use a different color for each slice. Label each slice with the category and with the percentage of the whole it represents.

7. Add a title to the circle graph.

> **Activity**

In a class of 28 students, 12 students take the bus to school, 10 students walk, and 6 students ride their bicycles. Create a circle graph to display these data.

Math Review

Scientists use math to organize, analyze, and present data.
This appendix will help you review some basic math skills.

Mean, Median, and Mode

The **mean** is the average, or the sum of the data divided by the number of data items. The middle number in a set of ordered data is called the **median**. The **mode** is the number that appears most often in a set of data.

Example

A scientist counted the number of distinct songs sung by seven different male birds and collected the data shown below.

Male Bird Songs							
Bird	A	B	C	D	E	F	G
Number of Songs	36	29	40	35	28	36	27

To determine the mean number of songs, add the total number of songs and divide by the number of data items—in this case, the number of male birds.

Mean = $\frac{231}{7}$ = 33 songs

To find the median number of songs, arrange the data in numerical order and find the number in the middle of the series.

27 28 29 35 36 36 40

The number in the middle is 35, so the median number of songs is 35.

The mode is the value that appears most frequently. In the data, 36 appears twice, while each other item appears only once. Therefore, 36 songs is the mode.

Practice

Find out how many minutes it takes each student in your class to get to school. Then find the mean, median, and mode for the data.

Probability

Probability is the chance that an event will occur. Probability can be expressed as a ratio, a fraction, or a percentage. For example, when you flip a coin, the probability that the coin will land heads up is 1 in 2, or $\frac{1}{2}$, or 50 percent.

The probability that an event will happen can be expressed in the following formula.

$$P(\text{event}) = \frac{\text{Number of times the event can occur}}{\text{Total number of possible events}}$$

Example

A paper bag contains 25 blue marbles, 5 green marbles, 5 orange marbles, and 15 yellow marbles. If you close your eyes and pick a marble from the bag, what is the probability that it will be yellow?

$$P(\text{yellow marbles}) = \frac{15 \text{ yellow marbles}}{50 \text{ marbles total}}$$

$$P = \frac{15}{50}, \text{ or } \frac{3}{10}, \text{ or } 30\%$$

Practice

Each side of a cube has a letter on it. Two sides have *A*, three sides have *B*, and one side has *C*. If you roll the cube, what is the probability that *A* will land on top?

Math Review

Students can refer to this part of the Skills Handbook whenever they need to review some basic math skills. You can use the activities provided here to teach or reinforce these skills.

Mean, Median, and Mode

Focus Remind students that data from an experiment might consist of hundreds or thousands of numbers. Unless analyzed, the numbers likely will not be helpful.

Teach Work through the process of determining mean, median, and mode using the example in the book. Make sure students realize that these three numbers do not always equal each other. Point out that taken together, these three numbers give more information about the data than just one of the numbers alone.

Practice

Answers will vary based on class data. The mean should equal the total number of minutes divided by the number of students. The median should equal the number in the middle after arranging the data in numerical order. The mode should equal the number of minutes that is given most frequently.

Probability

Focus Show students a coin and ask: **What is the chance that I will get tails when I flip the coin?** (*Some students might know that there is a 1 in 2, or 50 percent, chance of getting tails.*)

Teach Set up a bag of marbles like the one in the example. Allow students to practice determining the probabilities of picking marbles of different colors. Then, encourage them to actually pick marbles and compare their actual results with those results predicted by probability.

Practice

$P(A) = 2$ sides with $\frac{A}{6}$ sides total

$P = \frac{2}{6}, \text{ or } \frac{1}{3}, \text{ or } 33\%$

Area

Focus Ask: **Who knows what area is?** (*Area is equal to the number of square units needed to cover a certain shape or object.*) On the board, write the formulas for the area of a rectangle and a circle.

Teach Give students various objects of different shapes. Have them measure each object and determine its area based on the measurements. Point out that the units of the answer are squared because they are multiplied together. If students are interested, you might also explain that π is equal to the ratio of the circumference of a circle to its diameter. For circles of all sizes, π is approximately equal to the number 3.14, or $\frac{22}{7}$.

Practice

The area of the circle is equal to $21\text{ m} \times 21\text{ m} \times \frac{22}{7}$, or $1{,}386\text{ m}^2$.

Circumference

Focus Draw a circle on the board. Then trace the outline with your finger and explain that this is the circumference of the circle, or the distance around it.

Teach Show students that the radius is equal to the distance from the center of the circle to any point on it. Point out that the diameter of a circle is equal to two times the radius. Give students paper circles of various sizes, and have them calculate the circumference of each.

Practice

The circumference is equal to $2 \times 28\text{ m} \times \frac{22}{7}$, or 176 m.

Volume

Focus Fill a beaker with 100 milliliters of water. Ask: **What is the volume of water?** (*100 milliliters*) Explain that volume is the amount of space that something takes up. Then point out that one milliliter is equal to one cubic centimeter (cm^3).

Teach Write on the board the formulas for calculating the volumes of a rectangle and a cylinder. Point out that volume is equal to the area of an object multiplied by its height. Then measure the beaker to show students the relationship between liquid volume (100 milliliters) and the number of cubic units it contains (100 cubic centimeters).

Area

The **area** of a surface is the number of square units that cover it. The front cover of your textbook has an area of about 600 cm^2.

Area of a Rectangle and a Square To find the area of a rectangle, multiply its length times its width. The formula for the area of a rectangle is

$$A = \ell \times w, \text{ or } A = \ell w$$

Since all four sides of a square have the same length, the area of a square is the length of one side multiplied by itself, or squared.

$$A = s \times s, \text{ or } A = s^2$$

Example

A scientist is studying the plants in a field that measures 75 m × 45 m. What is the area of the field?

$$A = \ell \times w$$
$$A = 75\text{ m} \times 45\text{ m}$$
$$A = 3{,}375\text{ m}^2$$

Area of a Circle The formula for the area of a circle is

$$A = \pi \times r \times r, \text{ or } A = \pi r^2$$

The length of the radius is represented by r, and the value of π is approximately $\frac{22}{7}$.

Example

Find the area of a circle with a radius of 14 cm.

$$A = \pi r^2$$
$$A = 14 \times 14 \times \frac{22}{7}$$
$$A = 616\text{ cm}^2$$

Practice

Find the area of a circle that has a radius of 21 m.

Circumference

The distance around a circle is called the circumference. The formula for finding the circumference of a circle is

$$C = 2 \times \pi \times r, \text{ or } C = 2\pi r$$

Example

The radius of a circle is 35 cm. What is its circumference?

$$C = 2\pi r$$
$$C = 2 \times 35 \times \frac{22}{7}$$
$$C = 220\text{ cm}$$

Practice

What is the circumference of a circle with a radius of 28 m?

Volume

The volume of an object is the number of cubic units it contains. The volume of a wastebasket, for example, might be about 26,000 cm^3.

Volume of a Rectangular Object To find the volume of a rectangular object, multiply the object's length times its width times its height.

$$V = \ell \times w \times h, \text{ or } V = \ell w h$$

Example

Find the volume of a box with length 24 cm, width 12 cm, and height 9 cm.

$$V = \ell w h$$
$$V = 24\text{ cm} \times 12\text{ cm} \times 9\text{ cm}$$
$$V = 2{,}592\text{ cm}^3$$

Practice

What is the volume of a rectangular object with length 17 cm, width 11 cm, and height 6 cm?

Practice

The volume of the rectangular object is equal to $17\text{ cm} \times 11\text{ cm} \times 6\text{ cm}$, or $1{,}122\text{ cm}^3$.

Fractions

A **fraction** is a way to express a part of a whole. In the fraction $\frac{4}{7}$, 4 is the numerator and 7 is the denominator.

Adding and Subtracting Fractions To add or subtract two or more fractions that have a common denominator, first add or subtract the numerators. Then write the sum or difference over the common denominator.

To find the sum or difference of fractions with different denominators, first find the least common multiple of the denominators. This is known as the least common denominator. Then convert each fraction to equivalent fractions with the least common denominator. Add or subtract the numerators. Then write the sum or difference over the common denominator.

Example
$$\frac{5}{6} - \frac{3}{4} = \frac{10}{12} - \frac{9}{12} = \frac{10-9}{12} = \frac{1}{12}$$

Multiplying Fractions To multiply two fractions, first multiply the two numerators, then multiply the two denominators.

Example
$$\frac{5}{6} \times \frac{2}{3} = \frac{5 \times 2}{6 \times 3} = \frac{10}{18} = \frac{5}{9}$$

Dividing Fractions Dividing by a fraction is the same as multiplying by its reciprocal. Reciprocals are numbers whose numerators and denominators have been switched. To divide one fraction by another, first invert the fraction you are dividing by—in other words, turn it upside down. Then multiply the two fractions.

Example
$$\frac{2}{5} \div \frac{7}{8} = \frac{2}{5} \times \frac{8}{7} = \frac{2 \times 8}{5 \times 7} = \frac{16}{35}$$

Practice
Solve the following: $\frac{3}{7} \div \frac{4}{5}$.

Decimals

Fractions whose denominators are 10, 100, or some other power of 10 are often expressed as decimals. For example, the fraction $\frac{9}{10}$ can be expressed as the decimal 0.9, and the fraction $\frac{7}{100}$ can be written as 0.07.

Adding and Subtracting With Decimals To add or subtract decimals, line up the decimal points before you carry out the operation.

Example

```
  27.4          278.635
+  6.19        - 191.4
 33.59           87.235
```

Multiplying With Decimals When you multiply two numbers with decimals, the number of decimal places in the product is equal to the total number of decimal places in each number being multiplied.

Example

```
  46.2    (one decimal place)
× 2.37    (two decimal places)
109.494   (three decimal places)
```

Dividing With Decimals To divide a decimal by a whole number, put the decimal point in the quotient above the decimal point in the dividend.

Example
$$15.5 \div 5$$
$$5\overline{)15.5} = 3.1$$

To divide a decimal by a decimal, you need to rewrite the divisor as a whole number. Do this by multiplying both the divisor and dividend by the same multiple of 10.

Example
$$1.68 \div 4.2 = 16.8 \div 42$$
$$42\overline{)16.8} = 0.4$$

Practice
Multiply 6.21 by 8.5.

Fractions

Focus Draw a circle on the board, and divide it into eight equal sections. Shade in one of the sections, and explain that one out of eight, or one eighth, of the sections is shaded. Also use the circle to show that four eighths is the same as one half.

Teach Write the fraction $\frac{3}{4}$ on the board. Ask: **What is the numerator?** *(Three)* **What is the denominator?** *(Four)* Emphasize that when adding and subtracting fractions, the denominators of the two fractions must be the same. If necessary, review how to find the least common denominator. Remind students that when multiplying and dividing, the denominators do not have to be the same.

Practice
$$\frac{3}{7} \div \frac{4}{5} = \frac{3}{7} \times \frac{5}{4} = \frac{15}{28}$$

Decimals

Focus Write the number *129.835* on the board. Ask: **What number is in the ones position?** *(9)* **The tenths position?** *(8)* **The hundredths position?** *(3)* Make sure students know that 0.8 is equal to $\frac{8}{10}$ and 0.03 is equal to $\frac{3}{100}$.

Teach Use the examples in the book to review addition, subtraction, multiplication, and division with decimals. Make up a worksheet of similar problems to give students additional practice. Also show students how a fraction is converted to a decimal by dividing the numerator by the denominator. For example, $\frac{1}{2}$ is equal to 0.5.

Practice
$6.21 \times 8.5 = 52.785$

L ● 175

Ratio and Proportion

Focus Differentiate a ratio from a fraction. Remind students that a fraction tells how many parts of the whole. In contrast, a ratio compares two different numbers. For example, $\frac{12}{22}$, or $\frac{6}{11}$, of a class are girls. But the ratio of boys to girls in the class is 10 to 12, or $\frac{5}{6}$.

Teach Use the example in the book to explain how to use a proportion to find an unknown quantity. Provide students with additional practice problems, if needed.

Practice

$6 \times 49 = 7x$
$294 = 7x$
$294 \div 7 = x$
$x = 42$

Percentage

Focus On the board, write $50\% = \frac{50}{100}$. Explain that a percentage is a ratio that compares a number to 100.

Teach Point out that when calculating percentages, you are usually using numbers other than 100. In this case, you set up a proportion. Go over the example in the book. Emphasize that the number representing the total goes on the bottom of the ratio, as does the 100%.

Practice

Students should set up the proportion

$\frac{42 \text{ marbles}}{300 \text{ marbles}} = \frac{x\%}{100\%}$

$42 \times 100 = 300x$

$4200 = 300x$

$4200 \div 300 = 14\%$

Ratio and Proportion

A **ratio** compares two numbers by division. For example, suppose a scientist counts 800 wolves and 1,200 moose on an island. The ratio of wolves to moose can be written as a fraction, $\frac{800}{1,200}$, which can be reduced to $\frac{2}{3}$. The same ratio can also be expressed as 2 to 3 or 2 : 3.

A **proportion** is a mathematical sentence saying that two ratios are equivalent. For example, a proportion could state that $\frac{800 \text{ wolves}}{1,200 \text{ moose}} = \frac{2 \text{ wolves}}{3 \text{ moose}}$. You can sometimes set up a proportion to determine or estimate an unknown quantity. For example, suppose a scientist counts 25 beetles in an area of 10 square meters. The scientist wants to estimate the number of beetles in 100 square meters.

Example

1. Express the relationship between beetles and area as a ratio: $\frac{25}{10}$, simplified to $\frac{5}{2}$.

2. Set up a proportion, with x representing the number of beetles. The proportion can be stated as $\frac{5}{2} = \frac{x}{100}$.

3. Begin by cross-multiplying. In other words, multiply each fraction's numerator by the other fraction's denominator.

   $5 \times 100 = 2 \times x$, or $500 = 2x$

4. To find the value of x, divide both sides by 2. The result is 250, or 250 beetles in 100 square meters.

Practice

Find the value of x in the following proportion: $\frac{6}{7} = \frac{x}{49}$.

Percentage

A **percentage** is a ratio that compares a number to 100. For example, there are 37 granite rocks in a collection that consists of 100 rocks. The ratio $\frac{37}{100}$ can be written as 37%. Granite rocks make up 37% of the rock collection.

You can calculate percentages of numbers other than 100 by setting up a proportion.

Example

Rain falls on 9 days out of 30 in June. What percentage of the days in June were rainy?

$\frac{9 \text{ days}}{30 \text{ days}} = \frac{d\%}{100\%}$

To find the value of d, begin by cross-multiplying, as for any proportion:

$9 \times 100 = 30 \times d$ $d = \frac{900}{30}$ $d = 30$

Practice

There are 300 marbles in a jar, and 42 of those marbles are blue. What percentage of the marbles are blue?

Significant Figures

The **precision** of a measurement depends on the instrument you use to take the measurement. For example, if the smallest unit on the ruler is millimeters, then the most precise measurement you can make will be in millimeters.

The sum or difference of measurements can only be as precise as the least precise measurement being added or subtracted. Round your answer so that it has the same number of digits after the decimal as the least precise measurement. Round up if the last digit is 5 or more, and round down if the last digit is 4 or less.

> **Example**
>
> Subtract a temperature of 5.2°C from the temperature 75.46°C.
>
> $$75.46 - 5.2 = 70.26$$
>
> 5.2 has the fewest digits after the decimal, so it is the least precise measurement. Since the last digit of the answer is 6, round up to 3. The most precise difference between the measurements is 70.3°C.

> **Practice**
>
> Add 26.4 m to 8.37 m. Round your answer according to the precision of the measurements.

Significant figures are the number of nonzero digits in a measurement. Zeroes between nonzero digits are also significant. For example, the measurements 12,500 L, 0.125 cm, and 2.05 kg all have three significant figures. When you multiply and divide measurements, the one with the fewest significant figures determines the number of significant figures in your answer.

> **Example**
>
> Multiply 110 g by 5.75 g.
>
> $$110 \times 5.75 = 632.5$$
>
> Because 110 has only two significant figures, round the answer to 630 g.

Scientific Notation

A **factor** is a number that divides into another number with no remainder. In the example, the number 3 is used as a factor four times.

An **exponent** tells how many times a number is used as a factor. For example, $3 \times 3 \times 3 \times 3$ can be written as 3^4. The exponent ^{4} indicates that the number 3 is used as a factor four times. Another way of expressing this is to say that 81 is equal to 3 to the fourth power.

> **Example**
>
> $$3^4 = 3 \times 3 \times 3 \times 3 = 81$$

Scientific notation uses exponents and powers of ten to write very large or very small numbers in shorter form. When you write a number in scientific notation, you write the number as two factors. The first factor is any number between 1 and 10. The second factor is a power of 10, such as 10^3 or 10^6.

> **Example**
>
> The average distance between the planet Mercury and the sun is 58,000,000 km. To write the first factor in scientific notation, insert a decimal point in the original number so that you have a number between 1 and 10. In the case of 58,000,000, the number is 5.8.
>
> To determine the power of 10, count the number of places that the decimal point moved. In this case, it moved 7 places.
>
> $$58,000,000 \text{ km} = 5.8 \times 10^7 \text{ km}$$

> **Practice**
>
> Express 6,590,000 in scientific notation.

Significant Figures

Focus Measure the length of a paper clip using two different rulers. Use one ruler that is less precise than the other. Compare the two measurements. Ask: **Which measurement is more precise?** *(The ruler with the smallest units will give the more precise measurement.)*

Teach Give students the opportunity to take measurements of an object using tools with different precision. Encourage students to add and subtract their measurements, making sure that they round the answers to reflect the precision of the instruments. Go over the example for significant digits. Check for understanding by asking: **How many significant digits are in the number 324,000?** *(Three)* **In the number 5, 901?** *(Four)* **In the number 0.706?** *(Three)* If students need additional practice, create a worksheet with problems in multiplying and dividing numbers with various significant digits.

> **Practice**
>
> 26.4 m + 8.37 m = 34.77 m
> This answer should be rounded to 34.8 m because the least precise measurement has only one digit after the decimal. This number is rounded up to 8 because the last digit is more than 5.

Scientific Notation

Focus Write a very large number on the board, such as 100 million, using all the zeros. Then, write the number using scientific notation. Ask: **Why do you think scientists prefer to write very large numbers using scientific notation?** *(Possible answers include that it is easier to do calculations, convert units, and make comparisons with other numbers.)*

Teach Go over the examples, and ask: **In the second example, which numbers are the factors?** *(5.8 and 10^7)* **Which number is the exponent?** *(^{7})* Explain that very small numbers have a negative exponent because the decimal point is moved to the right to produce the first factor. For example, 0.00000628 is equal to 6.28×10^{-6}.

> **Practice**
>
> $6,590,000 = 6.59 \times 10^6$

Reading Comprehension Skills

Students can refer to this part of the Skills Handbook whenever they need to review a reading skill. You can use the activities provided here to teach or reinforce these skills.

Learning From Science Textbooks

Reading in a content area presents challenges different from those encountered when reading fiction. Science texts often have more new vocabulary and more unfamiliar concepts that place greater emphasis on inferential reasoning. Students who can apply reading skills and information-organizing strategies will be more successful in reading and understanding a science textbook.

Activity

Turn with students to the first page of any section. Walk through the Reading Preview with students, showing them the Key Concepts that provide a guiding set of questions that students can answer from the text. Next, point out the Key Terms list, which highlights the science vocabulary. Last, have students find the Target Reading Skill with graphic organizer. Make the connection for students to the help in this Skills Handbook.

All in One Teaching Resources

- Target Reading Skills Handbook

Building Vocabulary

Focus Explain to students that knowing the definitions of key concept words can help them understand what they read.

Teach List on the board strategies to learn the definitions of new terms. Also solicit from students strategies that work for them —drawing a picture for the term, acting it out, or using it in conversation. Challenge students to choose a new strategy to learn the Key Terms in your next section.

Using Prior Knowledge

Focus Explain to students that using prior knowledge helps connect what they already know to what they are about to read.

Teach Point out that prior knowledge might not be accurate because memories have faded or perspectives have changed. Encourage students to ask questions

---

Reading Comprehension Skills

Your textbook is an important source of science information. As you read your science textbook, you will find that the book has been written to assist you in understanding the science concepts.

Learning From Science Textbooks

As you study science in school, you will learn science concepts in a variety of ways. Sometimes you will do interesting activities and experiments to explore science ideas. To fully understand what you observe in experiments and activities, you will need to read your science textbook. To help you read, some of the important ideas are highlighted so that you can easily recognize what they are. In addition, a target reading skill in each section will help you understand what you read.

By using the target reading skills, you will improve your reading comprehension—that is, you will improve your ability to understand what you read. As you learn science, you will build knowledge that will help you understand even more of what you read. This knowledge will help you learn about all the topics presented in this textbook.

And—guess what?—these reading skills can be useful whenever you are reading. Reading to learn is important for your entire life. You have an opportunity to begin that process now.

The target reading skills that will improve your reading comprehension are described below.

Building Vocabulary

To understand the science concepts taught in this textbook, you need to remember the meanings of the Key Terms. One strategy consists of writing the definitions of these terms in your own words. You can also practice using the terms in sentences and make lists of words or phrases you associate with each term.

Using Prior Knowledge

Your prior knowledge is what you already know before you begin to read about a topic. Building on what you already know gives you a head start on learning new information. Before you begin a new assignment, think about what you know. You might page through your reading assignment, looking at the headings and the visuals to spark your memory. You can list what you know in the graphic organizer provided in the section opener. Then, as you read, consider questions like the ones below to connect what you learn to what you already know.

- How does what you learn relate to what you know?
- How did something you already know help you learn something new?
- Did your original ideas agree with what you have just learned? If not, how would you revise your original ideas?

Asking Questions

Asking yourself questions is an excellent way to focus on and remember new information in your textbook. You can learn how to ask good questions.

One way is to turn the text headings into questions. Then your questions can guide you to identify and remember the important information as you read. Look at these examples:

Heading: Using Seismographic Data
Question: How are seismographic data used?
Heading: Kinds of Faults
Question: What are the kinds of faults?

---

to resolve discrepancies between their prior knowledge and what they have learned.

Asking Questions

Focus Demonstrate to students how to change a text heading into a question to help them anticipate the concepts, facts, and events they will read about.

Teach Encourage students to use this reading skill for the next section they read. Instruct them to turn the text headings into questions. Also challenge students to write at least four *what, how, why, who, when,* or *where* questions. Then, have students evaluate the skill. Ask: **Did asking questions about the text help you focus on the reading and remember what you read?** (*Answers will vary, but encourage honesty.*) If this reading skill didn't help, challenge them to assess why not.

You do not have to limit your questions to the text headings. Ask questions about anything that you need to clarify or that will help you understand the content. *What* and *how* are probably the most common question words, but you may also ask *why*, *who*, *when*, or *where* questions. Here is an example:

Properties of Waves

Question	Answer
What is amplitude?	Amplitude is . . .

Previewing Visuals

Visuals are photographs, graphs, tables, diagrams, and illustrations. Visuals, such as this diagram of a normal fault, contain important information. Look at visuals and their captions before you read. This will help you prepare for what you will be reading about.

Often you will be asked what you want to learn about a visual. For example, after you look at the normal fault diagram, you might ask: What is the movement along a normal fault? Questions about visuals give you a purpose for reading—to answer your questions. Previewing visuals also helps you see what you already know.

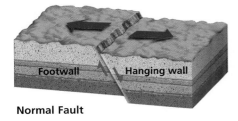

Footwall   Hanging wall

Normal Fault

Outlining

An outline shows the relationship between main ideas and supporting ideas. An outline has a formal structure. You write the main ideas, called topics, next to Roman numerals. The supporting ideas, sometimes called subtopics, are written under the main ideas and labeled A, B, C, and so on. An outline looks like this:

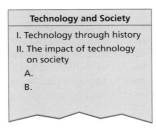

Technology and Society

I. Technology through history
II. The impact of technology on society
   A.
   B.

When you have completed an outline like this, you can see at a glance the structure of the section. You can use this outline as a study tool.

Identifying Main Ideas

When you are reading, it is important to try to understand the ideas and concepts that are in a passage. As you read science material, you will recognize that each paragraph has a lot of information and detail. Good readers try to identify the most important—or biggest—idea in every paragraph or section. That's the main idea. The other information in the paragraph supports or further explains the main idea.

Sometimes main ideas are stated directly. In this book, some main ideas are identified for you as key concepts. These are printed in boldface type. However, you must identify other main ideas yourself. In order to do this, you must identify all the ideas within a paragraph or section. Then ask yourself which idea is big enough to include all the other ideas.

Skills Handbook ♦ 179

Previewing Visuals

Focus Explain to students that looking at the visuals before reading will help them activate prior knowledge and predict what they are about to read.

Teach Assign a section for students to preview the visuals. First, instruct them to write a sentence describing what the section will be about. Then, encourage them to write one or two questions for each visual to give purpose to their reading. Also have them list any prior knowledge about the subject.

Outlining

Focus Explain that using an outline format helps organize information by main topic, subtopic, and details.

Teach Choose a section in the book, and demonstrate how to make an outline for it. Make sure students understand the structure of the outline by asking: **Is this a topic or a subtopic? Where does this information go in the outline? Would I write this heading next to a Roman numeral or a capital letter?** *(Answers depend on the section being outlined.)* Also show them how to indent and add details to the outline using numerals and lowercase letters.

Identifying Main Ideas

Focus Explain that identifying main ideas and details helps sort the facts from the information into groups. Each group can have a main topic, subtopics, and details.

Teach Tell students that paragraphs are often written so that the main idea is in the first or second sentence, or in the last sentence. Assign students a page in the book. Instruct them to write the main idea for each paragraph on that page. If students have difficulty finding the main idea, suggest that they list all of the ideas given in the paragraph, and then choose the idea that is big enough to include all the others.

Comparing and Contrasting

Focus Explain that comparing and contrasting information shows how concepts, facts, and events are similar or different. The results of the comparison can have importance.

Teach Point out that Venn diagrams work best when comparing two things. To compare more than two things, students should use a compare/contrast table. Have students make a Venn diagram or compare/contrast table using two or more different sports or other activities, such as playing musical instruments. Emphasize that students should select characteristics that highlight the similarities and differences in the activities.

Sequencing

Focus Tell students that organizing information from beginning to end will help them understand a step-by-step process.

Teach Encourage students to create a flowchart to show the things they did this morning to get ready for school. Remind students that a flowchart should show the correct order in which events occur. *(A typical flowchart might include: got up ➤ took a shower ➤ got dressed ➤ ate breakfast ➤ brushed teeth ➤ gathered books and homework ➤ put on jacket.)* Then explain that a cycle diagram shows a sequence of events that is continuous. Challenge students to create a cycle diagram that shows how the weather changes with the seasons where they live. *(Most cycle diagrams will include four steps, one for each season.)*

Comparing and Contrasting

When you compare and contrast, you examine the similarities and differences between things. You can compare and contrast in a Venn diagram or in a table. Your completed diagram or table shows you how the items are alike and how they are different.

Venn Diagram A Venn diagram consists of two overlapping circles. In the space where the circles overlap, you write the characteristics that the two items have in common. In one of the circles outside the area of overlap, you write the differing features or characteristics of one of the items. In the other circle outside the area of overlap, you write the differing characteristics of the other item.

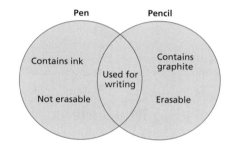

Table In a compare/contrast table, you list the items to be compared across the top of the table. Then list the characteristics or features to be compared in the left column. Complete the table by filling in information about each characteristic or feature.

Blood Vessel	Function	Structure of Wall
Artery	Carries blood away from heart	
Capillary		
Vein		

Sequencing

A sequence is the order in which a series of events occurs. Recognizing and remembering the sequence of events is important to understanding many processes in science. Sometimes the text uses words like *first, next, during,* and *after* to signal a sequence. A flowchart or a cycle diagram can help you visualize a sequence.

Flowchart To make a flowchart, write a brief description of each step or event in a box. Place the boxes in order, with the first event at the top of the page. Then draw an arrow to connect each step or event to the next.

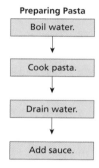

Cycle Diagram A cycle diagram shows a sequence that is continuous, or cyclical. A continuous sequence does not have an end because when the final event is over, the first event begins again. To create a cycle diagram, write the starting event in a box placed at the top of a page in the center. Then, moving in a clockwise direction around an imaginary circle, write each event in a box in its proper sequence. Draw arrows that connect each event to the one that occurs next, forming a continuous circle.

Identifying Supporting Evidence

A hypothesis is a possible explanation for observations made by scientists or an answer to a scientific question. A hypothesis is tested over and over again. The tests may produce evidence that supports the hypothesis. When enough supporting evidence is collected, a hypothesis may become a theory.

Identifying the supporting evidence for a hypothesis or theory can help you understand the hypothesis or theory. Evidence consists of facts—information whose accuracy can be confirmed by testing or observation.

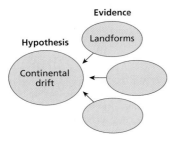

Relating Cause and Effect

Identifying causes and effects helps you understand relationships among events. A cause makes something happen. An effect is what happens. When you recognize that one event causes another, you are relating cause and effect. Words like *cause, because, effect, affect,* and *result* often signal a cause or an effect.

Sometimes an effect can have more than one cause, or a cause can produce several effects. For example, car exhaust and smoke from industrial plants are two causes of air pollution. Some effects of air pollution include breathing difficulties for some people, death of plants along some highways, and damage to some building surfaces.

Science involves many cause-and-effect relationships. Seeing and understanding these relationships helps you understand science processes.

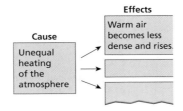

Concept Mapping

Concept maps are useful tools for organizing information on any topic. A concept map begins with a main idea or core concept and shows how the idea can be subdivided into related subconcepts or smaller ideas. In this way, relationships between concepts become clearer and easier to understand.

You construct a concept map by placing concepts (usually nouns) in ovals and connecting them with linking words. The biggest concept or idea is placed in an oval at the top of the map. Related concepts are arranged in ovals below the big idea. The linking words are often verbs and verb phrases and are written on the lines that connect the ovals.

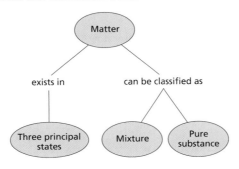

Identifying Supporting Evidence

Focus Explain to students that identifying the supporting evidence will help them to understand the relationship between the facts and the hypothesis.

Teach Remind students that a hypothesis is neither right nor wrong, but it is either supported or not supported by the evidence from testing or observation. If evidence is found that does not support a hypothesis, the hypothesis can be changed to accommodate the new evidence, or it can be dropped.

Relating Cause and Effect

Focus Explain to students that cause is the reason for what happens. The effect is what happens in response to the cause. Relating cause and effect helps students relate the reason for what happens to what happens as a result.

Teach Emphasize that not all events that occur together have a cause-and-effect relationship. For example, tell students that you went to the grocery store and your car stalled. Ask: **Is there a cause-and-effect relationship in this situation? Explain.** (*No. Going to the grocery store could not cause a car to stall. There must be another cause to make the car stall.*)

Concept Mapping

Focus Elicit from students how a map shows the relationship of one geographic area to another. Connect this idea to how a concept map shows the relationship between terms and concepts.

Teach Challenge students to make a concept map with at least three levels of concepts to organize information about types of transportation. All students should start with the phrase *Types of transportation* at the top of the concept map. After that point, their concepts may vary. (*For example, some students might place* private transportation *and* public transportation *at the next level, while other students might choose* human-powered *and* gas-powered.) Make sure students connect the concepts with linking words.

Interactive Textbook

- Complete student edition
- Video and audio
- Simulations and activities
- Section and chapter activities

Laboratory Safety

Laboratory safety is an essential element of a successful science class. Students need to understand exactly what is safe and unsafe behavior and what the rationale is behind each safety rule.

All in One Teaching Resources

- Laboratory Safety Teacher Notes
- Laboratory Safety Rules
- Laboratory Safety Symbols
- Laboratory Safety Contract

General Precautions

- Post safety rules in the classroom, and review them regularly with students before beginning every science activity.
- Familiarize yourself with the safety procedures for each activity before introducing it to your students.
- For open-ended activities like Chapter Projects, have students submit their procedures or design plans in writing and check them for safety considerations.
- Always act as an exemplary role model by displaying safe behavior.
- Know how to use safety equipment, such as fire extinguishers and fire blankets, and always have it accessible.
- Have students practice leaving the classroom quickly and orderly to prepare them for emergencies.
- Explain to students how to use the intercom or other available means of communication to get help during an emergency.
- Never leave students unattended while they are engaged in science activities.
- Provide enough space for students to safely carry out science activities.
- Instruct students to report all accidents and injuries to you immediately.

Safety Symbols

These symbols warn of possible dangers in the laboratory and remind you to work carefully.

 Safety Goggles Wear safety goggles to protect your eyes in any activity involving chemicals, flames or heating, or glassware.

 Lab Apron Wear a laboratory apron to protect your skin and clothing from damage.

 Breakage Handle breakable materials, such as glassware, with care. Do not touch broken glassware.

 Heat-Resistant Gloves Use an oven mitt or other hand protection when handling hot materials such as hot plates or hot glassware.

 Plastic Gloves Wear disposable plastic gloves when working with harmful chemicals and organisms. Keep your hands away from your face, and dispose of the gloves according to your teacher's instructions.

 Heating Use a clamp or tongs to pick up hot glassware. Do not touch hot objects with your bare hands.

 Flames Before you work with flames, tie back loose hair and clothing. Follow instructions from your teacher about lighting and extinguishing flames.

 No Flames When using flammable materials, make sure there are no flames, sparks, or other exposed heat sources present.

 Corrosive Chemical Avoid getting acid or other corrosive chemicals on your skin or clothing or in your eyes. Do not inhale the vapors. Wash your hands after the activity.

 Poison Do not let any poisonous chemical come into contact with your skin, and do not inhale its vapors. Wash your hands when you are finished with the activity.

 Fumes Work in a ventilated area when harmful vapors may be involved. Avoid inhaling vapors directly. Only test an odor when directed to do so by your teacher, and use a wafting motion to direct the vapor toward your nose.

 Sharp Object Scissors, scalpels, knives, needles, pins, and tacks can cut your skin. Always direct a sharp edge or point away from yourself and others.

 Animal Safety Treat live or preserved animals or animal parts with care to avoid harming the animals or yourself. Wash your hands when you are finished with the activity.

 Plant Safety Handle plants only as directed by your teacher. If you are allergic to certain plants, tell your teacher; do not do an activity involving those plants. Avoid touching harmful plants such as poison ivy. Wash your hands when you are finished with the activity.

 Electric Shock To avoid electric shock, never use electrical equipment around water, or when the equipment is wet or your hands are wet. Be sure cords are untangled and cannot trip anyone. Unplug equipment not in use.

 Physical Safety When an experiment involves physical activity, avoid injuring yourself or others. Alert your teacher if there is any reason you should not participate.

 Disposal Dispose of chemicals and other laboratory materials safely. Follow the instructions from your teacher.

 Hand Washing Wash your hands thoroughly when finished with the activity. Use antibacterial soap and warm water. Rinse well.

 General Safety Awareness When this symbol appears, follow the instructions provided. When you are asked to develop your own procedure in a lab, have your teacher approve your plan before you go further.

End-of-Experiment Rules

- Always have students use warm water and soap for washing their hands.

Heating and Fire Safety

- No flammable substances should be in use around hot plates, light bulbs, or open flames.
- Test tubes should be heated only in water baths.

- Students should be permitted to strike matches to light candles or burners *only* with strict supervision. When possible, you should light the flames, especially when working with younger students.
- Be sure to have proper ventilation when fumes are produced during a procedure.
- All electrical equipment used in the lab should have GFI (Ground Fault Interrupter) switches.

Science Safety Rules

General Precautions

Follow all instructions. Never perform activities without the approval and supervision of your teacher. Do not engage in horseplay. Never eat or drink in the laboratory. Keep work areas clean and uncluttered.

Dress Code

Wear safety goggles whenever you work with chemicals, glassware, heat sources such as burners, or any substance that might get into your eyes. If you wear contact lenses, notify your teacher.

Wear a lab apron or coat whenever you work with corrosive chemicals or substances that can stain. Wear disposable plastic gloves when working with organisms and harmful chemicals. Tie back long hair. Remove or tie back any article of clothing or jewelry that can hang down and touch chemicals, flames, or equipment. Roll up long sleeves. Never wear open shoes or sandals.

First Aid

Report all accidents, injuries, or fires to your teacher, no matter how minor. Be aware of the location of the first-aid kit, emergency equipment such as the fire extinguisher and fire blanket, and the nearest telephone. Know whom to contact in an emergency.

Heating and Fire Safety

Keep all combustible materials away from flames. When heating a substance in a test tube, make sure that the mouth of the tube is not pointed at you or anyone else. Never heat a liquid in a closed container. Use an oven mitt to pick up a container that has been heated.

Using Chemicals Safely

Never put your face near the mouth of a container that holds chemicals. Never touch, taste, or smell a chemical unless your teacher tells you to.

Use only those chemicals needed in the activity. Keep all containers closed when chemicals are not being used. Pour all chemicals over the sink or a container, not over your work surface. Dispose of excess chemicals as instructed by your teacher.

Be extra careful when working with acids or bases. When mixing an acid and water, always pour the water into the container first and then add the acid to the water. Never pour water into an acid. Wash chemical spills and splashes immediately with plenty of water.

Using Glassware Safely

If glassware is broken or chipped, notify your teacher immediately. Never handle broken or chipped glass with your bare hands.

Never force glass tubing or thermometers into a rubber stopper or rubber tubing. Have your teacher insert the glass tubing or thermometer if required for an activity.

Using Sharp Instruments

Handle sharp instruments with extreme care. Never cut material toward you; cut away from you.

Animal and Plant Safety

Never perform experiments that cause pain, discomfort, or harm to animals. Only handle animals if absolutely necessary. If you know that you are allergic to certain plants, molds, or animals, tell your teacher before doing an activity in which these are used. Wash your hands thoroughly after any activity involving animals, animal parts, plants, plant parts, or soil.

During field work, wear long pants, long sleeves, socks, and closed shoes. Avoid poisonous plants and fungi as well as plants with thorns.

End-of-Experiment Rules

Unplug all electrical equipment. Clean up your work area. Dispose of waste materials as instructed by your teacher. Wash your hands after every experiment.

Handling Organisms Safely

- In an activity where students are directed to taste something, be sure to store the material in clean, *nonscience* containers. Distribute the material to students in *new* plastic or paper dispensables, which should be discarded after the tasting. Tasting or eating should never be done in a lab classroom.

- When growing bacterial cultures, use only disposable petri dishes. After streaking, the dishes should be sealed and not opened again by students. After the lab, students should return the unopened dishes to you.

- Two methods are recommended for the safe disposal of bacterial cultures. *First method:* Autoclave the petri dishes and discard them without opening. *Second method:* If no autoclave is available, carefully open the dishes (never have a student do this), pour full-strength bleach into the dishes, and let them stand for a day. Then pour the bleach from the petri dishes down a drain, and flush the drain with lots of water. Tape the petri dishes back together, and place them in a sealed plastic bag. Wrap the plastic bag with a brown paper bag or newspaper, and tape securely. Throw the sealed package in the trash. Thoroughly disinfect the work area with bleach.

- To grow mold, use a new, sealable plastic bag that is two to three times larger than the material to be placed inside. Seal the bag and tape it shut. After the bag is sealed, students should not open it. To dispose of the bag and mold culture, make a small cut near an edge of the bag, and cook the bag in a microwave oven on a high setting for at least one minute. Discard the bag according to local ordinance, usually in the trash.

- Students should wear disposable nitrile, latex, or food-handling gloves when handling live animals or nonliving specimens.

Using Glassware Safely

- Use plastic containers, graduated cylinders, and beakers whenever possible. If using glass, students should wear safety goggles.
- Use only nonmercury thermometers with anti-roll protectors.

Using Chemicals Safely

- When students use both chemicals and microscopes in one activity, microscopes should be in a separate part of the room from the chemicals so that when students remove their goggles to use the microscopes, their eyes are not at risk.

The laboratory balance is an important tool in scientific investigations. You can use a balance to determine the masses of materials that you study or experiment with in the laboratory.

Different kinds of balances are used in the laboratory. One kind of balance is the triple-beam balance. The balance that you may use in your science class is probably similar to the balance illustrated in this Appendix. To use the balance properly, you should learn the name, location, and function of each part of the balance you are using. What kind of balance do you have in your science class?

The Triple-Beam Balance

The triple-beam balance is a single-pan balance with three beams calibrated in grams. The back, or 100-gram, beam is divided into ten units of 10 grams each. The middle, or 500-gram, beam is divided into five units of 100 grams each. The front, or 10-gram, beam is divided into ten major units of 1 gram each. Each of these units is further divided into units of 0.1 gram. What is the largest mass you could find with a triple-beam balance?

The following procedure can be used to find the mass of an object with a triple-beam balance:

1. Place the object on the pan.

2. Move the rider on the middle beam notch by notch until the horizontal pointer drops below zero. Move the rider back one notch.

3. Move the rider on the back beam notch by notch until the pointer again drops below zero. Move the rider back one notch.

4. Slowly slide the rider along the front beam until the pointer stops at the zero point.

5. The mass of the object is equal to the sum of the readings on the three beams.

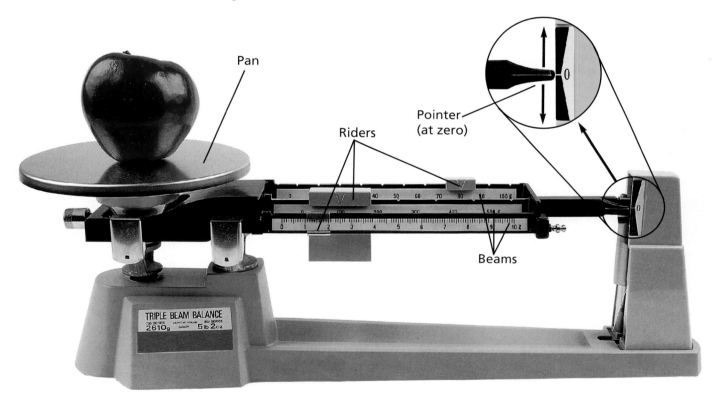

Triple-Beam Balance

Name	Symbol	Atomic Number	Atomic Mass[†]
Actinium	Ac	89	(227)
Aluminum	Al	13	26.982
Americium	Am	95	(243)
Antimony	Sb	51	121.75
Argon	Ar	18	39.948
Arsenic	As	33	74.922
Astatine	At	85	(210)
Barium	Ba	56	137.33
Berkelium	Bk	97	(247)
Beryllium	Be	4	9.0122
Bismuth	Bi	83	208.98
Bohrium	Bh	107	(264)
Boron	B	5	10.81
Bromine	Br	35	79.904
Cadmium	Cd	48	112.41
Calcium	Ca	20	40.08
Californium	Cf	98	(251)
Carbon	C	6	12.011
Cerium	Ce	58	140.12
Cesium	Cs	55	132.91
Chlorine	Cl	17	35.453
Chromium	Cr	24	51.996
Cobalt	Co	27	58.933
Copper	Cu	29	63.546
Curium	Cm	96	(247)
Darmstadtium	Ds	110	(269)
Dubnium	Db	105	(262)
Dysprosium	Dy	66	162.50
Einsteinium	Es	99	(252)
Erbium	Er	68	167.26
Europium	Eu	63	151.96
Fermium	Fm	100	(257)
Fluorine	F	9	18.998
Francium	Fr	87	(223)
Gadolinium	Gd	64	157.25
Gallium	Ga	31	69.72
Germanium	Ge	32	72.59
Gold	Au	79	196.97
Hafnium	Hf	72	178.49
Hassium	Hs	108	(265)
Helium	He	2	4.0026
Holmium	Ho	67	164.93
Hydrogen	H	1	1.0079
Indium	In	49	114.82
Iodine	I	53	126.90
Iridium	Ir	77	192.22
Iron	Fe	26	55.847
Krypton	Kr	36	83.80
Lanthanum	La	57	138.91
Lawrencium	Lr	103	(262)
Lead	Pb	82	207.2
Lithium	Li	3	6.941
Lutetium	Lu	71	174.97
Magnesium	Mg	12	24.305
Manganese	Mn	25	54.938
Meitnerium	Mt	109	(268)
Mendelevium	Md	101	(258)
Mercury	Hg	80	200.59
Molybdenum	Mo	42	95.94
Neodymium	Nd	60	144.24
Neon	Ne	10	20.179
Neptunium	Np	93	(237)
Nickel	Ni	28	58.71
Niobium	Nb	41	92.906
Nitrogen	N	7	14.007
Nobelium	No	102	(259)
Osmium	Os	76	190.2
Oxygen	O	8	15.999
Palladium	Pd	46	106.4
Phosphorus	P	15	30.974
Platinum	Pt	78	195.09
Plutonium	Pu	94	(244)
Polonium	Po	84	(209)
Potassium	K	19	39.098
Praseodymium	Pr	59	140.91
Promethium	Pm	61	(145)
Protactinium	Pa	91	231.04
Radium	Ra	88	(226)
Radon	Rn	86	(222)
Rhenium	Re	75	186.21
Rhodium	Rh	45	102.91
Rubidium	Rb	37	85.468
Ruthenium	Ru	44	101.07
Rutherfordium	Rf	104	(261)
Samarium	Sm	62	150.4
Scandium	Sc	21	44.956
Seaborgium	Sg	106	(263)
Selenium	Se	34	78.96
Silicon	Si	14	28.086
Silver	Ag	47	107.87
Sodium	Na	11	22.990
Strontium	Sr	38	87.62
Sulfur	S	16	32.06
Tantalum	Ta	73	180.95
Technetium	Tc	43	(98)
Tellurium	Te	52	127.60
Terbium	Tb	65	158.93
Thallium	Tl	81	204.37
Thorium	Th	90	232.04
Thulium	Tm	69	168.93
Tin	Sn	50	118.69
Titanium	Ti	22	47.90
Tungsten	W	74	183.85
Ununbium	Uub	112	(277)
Ununquadium	Uuq	114	*
Unununium	Uuu	111	(272)
Uranium	U	92	238.03
Vanadium	V	23	50.941
Xenon	Xe	54	131.30
Ytterbium	Yb	70	173.04
Yttrium	Y	39	88.906
Zinc	Zn	30	65.38
Zirconium	Zr	40	91.22

[†]Numbers in parentheses give the mass number of the most stable isotope.

*Newly discovered

Appendix C ◆ 185

Key

C	Solid
Br	Liquid
H	Gas
Tc	Not found in nature

1

1
1
H
Hydrogen
1.0079

2

3	4
Li	**Be**
Lithium	Beryllium
6.941	9.0122

11	12
Na	**Mg**
Sodium	Magnesium
22.990	24.305

3	**4**	**5**	**6**	**7**	**8**	**9**
21	22	23	24	25	26	27
Sc	**Ti**	**V**	**Cr**	**Mn**	**Fe**	**Co**
Scandium	Titanium	Vanadium	Chromium	Manganese	Iron	Cobalt
44.956	47.90	50.941	51.996	54.938	55.847	58.933

19	20
K	**Ca**
Potassium	Calcium
39.098	40.08

37	38	39	40	41	42	43	44	45
Rb	**Sr**	**Y**	**Zr**	**Nb**	**Mo**	**Tc**	**Ru**	**Rh**
Rubidium	Strontium	Yttrium	Zirconium	Niobium	Molybdenum	Technetium	Ruthenium	Rhodium
85.468	87.62	88.906	91.22	92.906	95.94	(98)	101.07	102.91

55	56	71	72	73	74	75	76	77
Cs	**Ba**	**Lu**	**Hf**	**Ta**	**W**	**Re**	**Os**	**Ir**
Cesium	Barium	Lutetium	Hafnium	Tantalum	Tungsten	Rhenium	Osmium	Iridium
132.91	137.33	174.97	178.49	180.95	183.85	186.21	190.2	192.22

87	88	103	104	105	106	107	108	109
Fr	**Ra**	**Lr**	**Rf**	**Db**	**Sg**	**Bh**	**Hs**	**Mt**
Francium	Radium	Lawrencium	Rutherfordium	Dubnium	Seaborgium	Bohrium	Hassium	Meitnerium
(223)	(226)	(262)	(261)	(262)	(263)	(264)	(265)	(268)

Lanthanides

57	58	59	60	61	62
La	**Ce**	**Pr**	**Nd**	**Pm**	**Sm**
Lanthanum	Cerium	Praseodymium	Neodymium	Promethium	Samarium
138.91	140.12	140.91	144.24	(145)	150.4

Actinides

89	90	91	92	93	94
Ac	**Th**	**Pa**	**U**	**Np**	**Pu**
Actinium	Thorium	Protactinium	Uranium	Neptunium	Plutonium
(227)	232.04	231.04	238.03	(237)	(244)

Key

Metal

Metalloid

Nonmetal

Properties not established

18
2 **He** Helium 4.0026

13	14	15	16	17
5 **B** Boron 10.81	6 **C** Carbon 12.011	7 **N** Nitrogen 14.007	8 **O** Oxygen 15.999	9 **F** Fluorine 18.998	10 **Ne** Neon 20.179

| 13 **Al** Aluminum 26.982 | 14 **Si** Silicon 28.086 | 15 **P** Phosphorus 30.974 | 16 **S** Sulfur 32.06 | 17 **Cl** Chlorine 35.453 | 18 **Ar** Argon 39.948 |

10	11	12

| 28 **Ni** Nickel 58.71 | 29 **Cu** Copper 63.546 | 30 **Zn** Zinc 65.38 | 31 **Ga** Gallium 69.72 | 32 **Ge** Germanium 72.59 | 33 **As** Arsenic 74.922 | 34 **Se** Selenium 78.96 | 35 **Br** Bromine 79.904 | 36 **Kr** Krypton 83.80 |

| 46 **Pd** Palladium 106.4 | 47 **Ag** Silver 107.87 | 48 **Cd** Cadmium 112.41 | 49 **In** Indium 114.82 | 50 **Sn** Tin 118.69 | 51 **Sb** Antimony 121.75 | 52 **Te** Tellurium 127.60 | 53 **I** Iodine 126.90 | 54 **Xe** Xenon 131.30 |

| 78 **Pt** Platinum 195.09 | 79 **Au** Gold 196.97 | 80 **Hg** Mercury 200.59 | 81 **Tl** Thallium 204.37 | 82 **Pb** Lead 207.2 | 83 **Bi** Bismuth 208.98 | 84 **Po** Polonium (209) | 85 **At** Astatine (210) | 86 **Rn** Radon (222) |

| 110 **Ds** Darmstadtium (269) | 111 ***Uuu** Unununium (272) | 112 ***Uub** Ununbium (277) | | 114 ***Uuq** Ununquadium |

*Name not officially assigned
(Atomic masses in parentheses are those of the most stable isotope.)

| 63 **Eu** Europium 151.96 | 64 **Gd** Gadolinium 157.25 | 65 **Tb** Terbium 158.93 | 66 **Dy** Dysprosium 162.50 | 67 **Ho** Holmium 164.93 | 68 **Er** Erbium 167.26 | 69 **Tm** Thulium 168.93 | 70 **Yb** Ytterbium 173.04 |

| 95 **Am** Americium (243) | 96 **Cm** Curium (247) | 97 **Bk** Berkelium (247) | 98 **Cf** Californium (251) | 99 **Es** Einsteinium (252) | 100 **Fm** Fermium (257) | 101 **Md** Mendelevium (258) | 102 **No** Nobelium (259) |

English and Spanish Glossary

A

acid A substance that tastes sour, reacts with metals and carbonates, and turns blue litmus red. (p. 98)
ácido Sustancia de sabor agrio que reacciona con metales y carbonatos, y que vuelve rojo el papel de tornasol azul.

activation energy The minimum amount of energy needed to get a chemical reaction started. (p. 67)
energía de activación Cantidad mínima de energía que se necesita para que empiece una reacción química.

alcohol A substituted hydrocarbon that contains one or more hydroxyl groups. (p. 132)
alcohol Hidrocarburo sustituto que contiene uno o más grupos hidroxilos.

alkali metal An element belonging to Group 1 of the periodic table. (p. 17)
metal alcalino Elemento que pertenece al Grupo 1 de la tabla periódica.

alloy A material made of two or more elements that has the properties of a metal. (p. 37)
aleación Material hecho de dos o más elementos que tiene las propiedades de un metal.

amino acid One of 20 kinds of organic compounds that are the monomers of proteins. (p. 140)
aminoácido Uno de 20 tipos de compuestos orgánicos que son los monómeros de las proteínas.

atom The smallest particle of an element. (p. 7)
átomo Partícula más pequeña de un elemento.

atomic number The number of protons in the nucleus of an atom. (p. 14)
número atómico Número de protones en el núcleo de un átomo.

B

base A substance that tastes bitter, feels slippery, and turns red litmus paper blue. (p. 100)
base Sustancia de sabor amargo, escurridiza y que vuelve azul el papel de tornasol rojo.

C

carbohydrate An energy-rich organic compound made of the elements carbon, hydrogen, and oxygen. (p. 137)
carbohidrato Compuesto orgánico altamente energético hecho de elementos de carbono, hidrógeno y oxígeno.

carboxyl group A —COOH group, found in organic acids. (p. 133)
grupo carboxilo Grupo —COOH, que se haya en los ácidos orgánicos.

catalyst A material that increases the rate of a reaction by lowering the activation energy. (p. 71)
catalítico Material que aumenta la velocidad de una reacción al disminuir la energía de activación.

cellulose A complex carbohydrate found in plant structures. (p. 140)
celulosa Carbohidrato complejo que se haya en las estructuras vegetales.

chemical bond The force that holds atoms together.
enlace químico Fuerza que mantiene unidos a los átomos. (p. 13)

chemical digestion The process that breaks large molecules in food into smaller molecules. (p. 113)
digestión química Proceso que rompe las moléculas grandes en la comida en moléculas más pequeñas.

chemical equation A short, easy way to show a chemical reaction, using symbols. (p. 57)
ecuación química Forma corta y sencilla de mostrar una reacción química, usando símbolos.

chemical formula A combination of symbols that represents the elements in a compound. (p. 25)
fórmula química Combinación de símbolos que representan a los elementos de un compuesto.

chemical property A characteristic of a substance that describes its ability to change into different substances. (p. 47)
propiedad química Característica de una sustancia que describe su capacidad de convertirse en sustancias diferentes.

chemical reaction The process in which substances undergo chemical changes that result in the formation of new substances. (p. 48)
reacción química Proceso por el que las sustancias sufren cambios químicos que dan como resultado la formación de nuevas sustancias.

chemistry The study of the properties of matter and how matter changes. (p. 46)
química Estudio de las propiedades de la materia y de sus cambios.

cholesterol A waxy lipid in animal cells. (p. 142)
colesterol Lípido ceroso que se haya en las células animales.

closed system A system in which no matter is allowed to enter or leave. (p. 59)
sistema cerrado Sistema en el cual la materia no puede entrar ni salir.

coefficient A number in front of a chemical formula in an equation that indicates how many molecules or atoms of each reactant and product are involved in a reaction. (p. 60)
coeficiente En un ecuación, número delante de una fórmula química que indica cuántas moléculas o átomos de cada reactivo y producto participan en una reacción.

colloid A mixture containing small, undissolved particles that do not settle out. (p. 86)
coloide Mezcla que contiene partículas pequeñas y sin disolver que no se depositan.

combustion A rapid reaction between oxygen and fuel that results in fire. (p. 75)
combustión Reacción rápida entre el oxígeno y el combustible que produce fuego.

complex carbohydrate A long chain, or polymer, of simple carbohydrates. (p. 138)
carbohidrato complejo Cadena larga, o polímero, de carbohidratos simples.

compound A substance made of two or more elements chemically combined in a specific ratio, or proportion. (p. 7)
compuesto Sustancia hecha de dos o más elementos combinados químicamente en una razón o proporción específica.

concentrated solution A mixture that has a lot of solute dissolved in it. (p. 92)
solución concentrada Mezcla que tiene muchos solutos disueltos en ella.

concentration The amount of one material in a certain volume of another material. (p. 70)
concentración Cantidad de un material en un cierto volumen de otro material.

conservation of mass The principle stating that matter is not created or destroyed during a chemical reaction. (p. 58)
conservación de la masa Principio que enuncia que la materia no se crea ni se destruye durante una reacción química.

corrosive The way in which acids react with some metals so as to eat away the metal. (p. 99)
corrosivo Forma en que reaccionan los ácidos con algunos metales, como si se comieran el metal.

covalent bond A chemical bond formed when two atoms share electrons. (p. 31)
enlace covalente Enlace químico que se forma cuando dos átomos comparten electrones.

crystal An orderly, three-dimensional pattern of ions or atoms in a solid. (p. 26)
cristal Patrón ordenado tridimensional de iones o átomos en un sólido.

decomposition A chemical reaction that breaks down compounds into simpler products. (p. 62)
descomposición Reacción química que descompone los compuestos en productos más simples.

diamond A form of the element carbon in which the atoms are arranged in a crystal structure. (p. 124)
diamante Forma del elemento del carbono en la cual los átomos de carbono están dispuestos en una estructura de cristal.

digestion The process that breaks down complex molecules of food into smaller molecules. (p. 113)
digestión Proceso que rompe las moléculas complejas de comida en moléculas más pequeñas.

dilute solution A mixture that has only a little solute dissolved in it. (p. 92)
solución diluida Mezcla que sólo tiene un poco de soluto disuelto en ella.

DNA Deoxyribonucleic acid, one type of nucleic acid.
ADN Ácido desoxirribonucleico, un tipo de ácido nucleico. (p. 143)

double bond A chemical bond formed when atoms share two pairs of electrons. (p. 32)
enlace doble Enlace químico formado cuando los átomos comparten dos pares de electrones.

ductile A term used to describe a material that can be pulled out into a long wire. (p. 38)
dúctil Término usado para describir un material que se puede estirar hasta crear un alambre largo.

electron dot diagram A representation of the valence electrons in an atom, using dots. (p. 13)
esquema de puntos por electrones Representación del número de electrones de valencia en un átomo, usando puntos.

electrons Negatively charged particles that move around outside the nucleus of an atom. (p. 8)
electrones Partículas de cargadas negativamente que se mueven alrededor del núcleo de un átomo.

element A substance that cannot be broken down into any other substances by chemical or physical means. (p. 6)
elemento Sustancia que no se puede descomponer en otras sustancias por medios químicos o físicos.

endothermic reaction A reaction that absorbs energy in the form of heat. (p. 52)
reacción endotérmica Reacción que absorbe energía en forma de calor.

energy level A region of an atom in which electrons of the same energy are likely to be found. (p. 10)
nivel de energía Región alrededor del núcleo en la cual es probable que se encuentren los electrones con la misma energía.

enzyme A biological catalyst that lowers the activation energy of reactions in cells. (p. 71)
enzima Catalítico biológico que disminuye la energía de activación de las reacciones en las células.

ester An organic compound made by chemically combining an alcohol and an organic acid. (p. 133)
ester Compuesto orgánico formado químicamente al combinar un alcohol y un ácido orgánico.

exothermic reaction A reaction that releases energy in the form of heat. (p. 53)
reacción exotérmica Reacción que libera energía en forma de calor.

family Elements in the same vertical column of the periodic table; also called a group. (p. 15)
familia Elementos en la misma columna vertical de la tabla periódica; también llamado grupo.

fatty acid An organic compound that is a monomer of a fat or oil. (p. 142)
ácido graso Compuesto orgánico que es un monómero de una grasa o aceite.

fuel A material that releases energy when it burns.
combustible Material que libera energía cuando se quema. (p. 75)

fullerene A form of carbon that consists of atoms arranged in the shape of a hollow sphere. (p. 125)
fullereno Forma del elemento del carbono que consiste en átomos de carbono colocados en forma de esfera hueca.

glucose A simple carbohydrate; the monomer of many complex carbohydrates. (p. 137)
glucosa Carbohidrato simple; monómero de muchos carbohidratos complejos.

graphite A form of the element carbon in which a carbon atom is bonded tightly to three other carbon atoms in flat layers. (p. 124)
grafito Forma del elemento del carbono en el cual un átomo de carbono se une estrechamente a otros tres átomos de carbono en capas llanas.

group Elements in the same vertical column of the periodic table; also called a family. (p. 15)
grupo Elementos en la misma columna vertical de la tabla periódica; también llamado familia.

halogen An element belonging to Group 17 of the periodic table. (p. 17)
halógeno Elemento que pertenece al Grupo 17 de la tabla periódica.

hydrocarbon An organic compound that contains only carbon and hydrogen. (p. 128)
hidrocarburo Compuesto orgánico que contiene sólo carbono e hidrógeno.

hydrogen ion A positively charged ion (H^+) formed of a hydrogen atom that has lost its electron. (p. 104)
ión hidrógeno Ión cargado positivamente (H^+) formado por un átomo de hidrógeno que ha perdido su electrón.

hydroxide ion A negatively charged ion made of oxygen and hydrogen (OH^-). (p. 105)
ión hidróxido Ión cargado negativamente formado de oxígeno e hidrógeno (OH^-).

hydroxyl group An —OH group, found in alcohols.
grupo hidroxilo Grupo —OH, que se haya en los alcoholes. (p. 132)

indicator A compound that changes color in the presence of an acid or a base. (p. 100)
indicador Compuesto que cambia de color en presencia de un ácido o una base.

inhibitor A material that decreases the rate of a reaction. (p. 71)
inhibidor Material que disminuye la velocidad de una reacción.

ion An atom or group of atoms that has become electrically charged. (p. 23)
ión Átomo o grupo de átomos que está cargado eléctricamente.

ionic bond The attraction between oppositely charged ions. (p. 24)
enlace iónico Atracción entre iones con cargas opuestas.

ionic compound A compound that consists of positive and negative ions. (p. 24)
compuesto iónico Compuesto que tiene iones positivos y negativos.

isomers Compounds that have the same chemical formula but different structures. (p. 130)
isómeros Compuestos que tienen la misma fórmula química pero diferentes estructuras.

 L

lipid An energy-rich organic compound made of carbon, oxygen, and hydrogen. Fats, oils, waxes, and cholesterol are lipids. (p. 141)
lípido Compuesto orgánico rico en energía hecho de carbono, oxígeno e hidrógeno; grasas, aceites, ceras y colesterol son lípidos.

 M

malleable A term used to describe material that can be hammered or rolled into shape. (p. 38)
maleable Término usado para describir el material que se puede golpear o enrollar para darle forma.

matter Anything that has mass and occupies space.
materia Cualquier cosa que tiene masa y ocupa espacio. (p. 6, 46)

mechanical digestion The physical process that tears, grinds, and mashes large pieces of food into smaller ones. (p. 113)
digestión mecánica Proceso físico que rompe, tritura y muele grandes pedazos de comida en pedazos más pequeños.

metallic bond An attraction between a positive metal ion and the electrons surrounding it. (p. 37)
enlace metálico Atracción entre un ión metálico positivo y los electrones que lo rodean.

mixture Two or more substances that are mixed together but not chemically combined. (p. 7)
mezcla Dos o más sustancias que se mezclan, pero que no se combinan químicamente.

model Physical, mental, visual, and other representations of an idea to help people understand a concept that they cannot observe directly. (p. 8)
modelo Representaciones físicas, mentales o visuales de una idea que ayudan a la gente a entender un concepto que no se puede observar directamente.

molecular compound A compound that is composed of molecules. (p. 32)
compuesto molecular Compuesto que contiene moléculas.

molecule A neutral particle made of two or more atoms joined by covalent bonds. (p. 31)
molécula Partícula neutral hecha de dos o más átomos que se unen por enlaces covalentes.

monomer One molecule that makes up the links in a polymer chain. (p. 134)
monómero Molécula que forma los enlaces en una cadena polímera.

 N

nanotube A form of carbon that consists of atoms in the form of a long, hollow cylinder. (p. 125)
nanotubo Forma del carbono que consiste en átomos en forma de un cilindro largo y hueco.

neutralization A reaction of an acid with a base, yielding a solution that is not as acidic or basic as the starting solutions were. (p. 108)
neutralización Reacción de un ácido con una base, que produce una solución que no es ácida ni básica, como lo eran las soluciones originales.

neutrons Small, uncharged particles that are found in the nucleus of an atom. (p. 10)
neutrones Partículas pequeñas sin carga que se encuentran en el núcleo de un átomo.

noble gas An element of Group 18 of the periodic table. (p. 16)
gas noble Elemento del Grupo 18 de la tabla periódica.

nonpolar bond A covalent bond in which electrons are shared equally. (p. 34)
enlace no polar Enlace covalente en el que los electrones se comparte por igual.

nucleic acid A very large organic compound made up of carbon, oxygen, hydrogen, nitrogen, and phosphorus; examples are DNA and RNA. (p. 143)
ácido nucleico Compuesto orgánico muy grande hecho de carbono, oxígeno, hidrógeno, nitrógeno y fósforo; ejemplos son ADN and ARN.

nucleotide An organic compound that is one of the monomers of nucleic acids. (p. 144)
nucleótido Compuesto orgánico que es uno de los monómeros de los ácidos nucleicos.

nucleus The central core of the atom, containing protons and usually neutrons. (p. 9)
núcleo Parte central del átomo que contiene protones y normalmente neutrones.

 O

open system A system in which matter can enter from or escape to the surroundings. (p. 59)
sistema abierto Sistema en el que la materia puede entrar desde el medio que la rodea o salir hacia él.

organic acid A substituted hydrocarbon with one or more of the —COOH group of atoms. (p. 133)
ácido orgánico Hidrocarburo sustituto que tiene uno o más grupos de átomos —COOH.

organic compound Most compounds that contain carbon. (p. 127)
compuesto orgánico La mayoría de los compuestos que contienen carbono.

P

period Elements in the same horizontal row of the periodic table. (p. 15)
período Elementos en la misma fila horizontal de la tabla periódica.

pH scale A range of values used to express the concentration of hydrogen ions in a solution. (p. 106)
escala pH Rango de valores usados para expresar la concentración de iones de hidrógeno que hay en una solución.

physical change A change that alters the form or appearance of a material but does not make the material into another substance. (p. 48)
cambio físico Cambio que altera la forma o apariencia de un material, pero que no convierte el material en otra sustancia.

physical property A characteristic of a substance that can be observed without changing the substance into another substance. (p. 47)
propiedad física Característica de una sustancia que se puede observar sin convertir la sustancia en otra sustancia.

polar bond A covalent bond in which electrons are shared unequally. (p. 34)
enlace polar Enlace covalente en el que los electrones se comparten de forma desigual.

polyatomic ion An ion that is made of more than one atom. (p. 23)
ión poliatómico Ión que está hecho de más de un átomo.

polymer A large molecule in which many smaller molecules are bonded together. (p. 134)
polímero Molécula grande en la que muchas moléculas más pequeñas están unidas.

precipitate A solid that forms from a solution during a chemical reaction. (p. 50)
precipitado Sólido que se forma de una solución durante una reacción química.

product A substance formed as a result of a chemical reaction. (p. 57)
producto Sustancia formada como resultado de una reacción química.

protein An organic compound that is a polymer of amino acids. (p. 140)
proteína Compuesto orgánico que es un polímero de aminoácidos.

protons Small, positively charged particles that are found in the nucleus of an atom. (p. 9)
protones Partículas pequeñas cargadas positivamente que se encuentran en el núcleo de un átomo.

R

reactant A substance that enters into a chemical reaction. (p. 57)
reactante Sustancia que participa en una reacción química.

replacement A reaction in which one element replaces another in a compound or when two elements in different compounds trade places. (p. 62)
sustitución Reacción en la que un elemento reemplaza a otro en un compuesto o dos elementos de diferentes compuestos se intercambian.

RNA Ribonucleic acid, a type of nucleic acid. (p. 143)
ARN Ácido ribonucleico; un tipo de ácido nucleico.

S

salt An ionic compound made from the neutralization of an acid with a base. (p. 109)
sal Compuesto iónico formado por la neutralización de un ácido con una base.

saturated hydrocarbon A hydrocarbon in which all the bonds between carbon atoms are single bonds. (p. 131)
hidrocarburo saturado Hidrocarburo en el que todos los enlaces entre los átomos de carbono son enlaces simples.

saturated solution A mixture that contains as much dissolved solute as is possible at a given temperature. (p. 93)
solución saturada Mezcla que contiene la mayor cantidad posible de soluto disuelto a una temperatura determinada.

scientific theory A well-tested idea that explains and connects a wide range of observations. (p. 8)
teoría científica Idea bien comprobada que explica y conecta una amplia gama de observaciones.

solubility A measure of how much solute can dissolve in a given solvent at a given temperature.
solubilidad Medida de cuánto soluto se puede disolver en un solvente dada una temperatura determinada. (p. 93)

solute The part of a solution present in a lesser amount and dissolved by the solvent. (p. 84)
soluto Parte de una solución presente en menor cantidad y disuelta por el solvente.

solution A well-mixed mixture containing a solvent and at least one solute that has the same properties throughout. (p. 84)
solución Mezcla homogénea que contiene un solvente y al menos un soluto que tiene las mismas propiedades en toda la solución.

solvent The part of a solution that is present in the largest amount and dissolves a solute. (p. 84)
solvente Parte de una solución que está presente en la mayor cantidad y que disuelve un soluto.

starch A complex carbohydrate in which plants store energy. (p. 139)
almidón Carbohidrato complejo en la que las plantas almacenan la energía.

structural formula A description of a molecule that shows the kind, number, and arrangement of atoms. (p. 129)
fórmula estructural Descripción de una molécula que muestra el tipo, número y posición de los átomos.

Methane CH_4

Propane C_3H_8

subscript A number in a chemical formula that tells the number of atoms in a molecule or the ratio of elements in a compound. (p. 25)
subíndice Número en una fórmula química que indica el número de átomos que tiene una molécula o la razón de elementos en un compuesto.

substituted hydrocarbon A hydrocarbon in which one or more hydrogen atoms have been replaced by atoms of other elements. (p. 132)
hidrocarburo sustituido Hidrocarburo en el cual uno o más átomos de hidrógeno han sido sustituidos por átomos de otros elementos.

supersaturated solution A mixture that has more dissolved solute than is predicted by its solubility at a given temperature. (p. 97)
solución supersaturada Mezcla que tiene más soluto disuelto de lo que se predice por su solubilidad a una temperatura determinada.

suspension A mixture in which particles can be seen and easily separated by settling or filtration. (p. 86)
suspensión Mezcla en la cual las partículas se pueden ver y separar fácilmente por fijación o por filtración.

symbol A one- or two-letter set of characters that is used to identify an element. (p. 14)
símbolo Grupo de caracteres de una o dos letras que se usa para identificar un elemento.

synthesis A chemical reaction in which two or more simple substances combine to form a new, more complex substance. (p. 62)
síntesis Reacción química en la que dos o más sustancias simples se combinan para formar una sustancia nueva más compleja.

T

triple bond A chemical bond formed when atoms share three pairs of electrons. (p. 32)
enlace triple Enlace químico formado cuando los átomos comparten tres pares de electrones.

U

unsaturated hydrocarbon A hydrocarbon in which one or more of the bonds between carbon atoms is double or triple. (p. 131)
hidrocarburo no saturado Hidrocarburo en el que uno o más de los enlaces entre átomos de carbono es doble o triple.

unsaturated solution A mixture that contains less dissolved solute than is possible at a given temperature. (p. 93)
solución no saturada Mezcla que contiene menos soluto disuelto de lo que es posible a una temperatura determinada.

V

valence electrons The electrons that are in the highest energy level of an atom and that are involved in chemical reactions. (p. 12)
electrones de valencia Electrones que tienen el más alto nivel de energía de un átomo y participan en reacciones químicas.

Index

Index

Index

Page numbers for key terms are printed in **boldface** type.
Page numbers for illustrations, maps, and charts are printed in *italics*.

Acknowledgments

Acknowledgment for page 159: Excerpt from *The Iron Peacock* by Mary Stetson Clarke. Copyright © 1966 by Mary Stetson Clarke. Reprinted with permission from The Estate of Mary Stetson Clarke.

Staff Credits

Scott Andrews, Jennifer Angel, Laura Baselice, Carolyn Belanger, Barbara A. Bertell, Suzanne Biron, Peggy Bliss, Stephanie Bradley, James Brady, Anne M. Bray, Kerry Cashman, Jonathan Cheney, Joshua D. Clapper, Lisa J. Clark, Bob Craton, Patricia Cully, Patricia M. Dambry, Kathy Dempsey, Emily Ellen, Thomas Ferreira, Jonathan Fisher, Patricia Fromkin, Paul Gagnon, Robert Graham, Ellen Granter, Barbara Hollingdale, Etta Jacobs, Linda Johnson, Anne Jones, John Judge, Kevin Keane, Kelly Kelliher, Toby Klang, Russ Lappa, Carolyn Lock, Rebecca Loveys, Constance J. McCarty, Carolyn B. McGuire, Ranida Touranont McKneally, Anne McLaughlin, Eve Melnechuk, Tania Mlawer, Janet Morris, Francine Neumann, Marie Opera, Jill Ort, Joan Paley, Dorothy Preston, Rashid Ross, Siri Schwartzman, Laurel Smith, Emily Soltanoff, Jennifer A. Teece, Diane Walsh, Amanda M. Watters, Merce Wilczek, Amy Winchester, Char Lyn Yeakley. **Additional Credits** Tara Allamilla, Terence Hegarty, Louise Gachet, Andrea Golden, Stephanie Rogers, Kim Schmidt, Joan Tobin, Pat Williams.

Illustration

All art development by Morgan Cain and Associates unless otherwise noted. Annie Bissett: 155–157; **Kerry Cashman:** 143; **John Edwards:** 64, 107; **Barbara Hollingdale:** 16; **Rich McMahon:** 18–19, 138; **Fran Milner:** 114; **All charts and graphs by Matt Mayerchak.**

Photography

Photo Research John Judge

Cover Image top, Jeff Hunter/Getty Images, Inc.; **bottom,** Phil Degginger/Color-Pic, Inc.

Page vi, Russ Lappa; **vii l,** LWA-Dann Tardif/Corbis; **vii r,** Richard Haynes; **viii l,** 2004 Estate of Alexander Calder/Artists Rights Society (ARS), New York/Art Resource, NY; **viii r,** Russ Lappa; **ix,** Richard Haynes; **x t,** George D. Lepp/Corbis; **x b,** Ken O'Donoghue; **1,** Leonard Lessin/Peter Arnold, Inc.; **2 all,** NASA/Goddard Space Flight Center Scientific Visualization Studio; **3,** Ken O'Donoghue.

Chapter 1
Pages 4–5, Kenneth Eward/BioGrafx/Photo Researchers, Inc; **5r,** Richard Haynes; **7,** Andre Jenny/Focus Group/PictureQuest; **8t,** Royalty-Free/Corbis; **8b,** Russ Lappa; **9,** Dorling Kindersley; **10t,** ©Stockbyte; **10b,** Frank Cezus/Getty Images, Inc.; **11,** Paul Johnson/Index Stock Imagery, Inc.; **12–13,** Jump Run Productions/Getty Images, Inc.; **16,** Terry W. Eggers/Corbis; **17l,** Richard Megna/Fundamental Photographs; **17m,** Fundamental Photographs; **17r,** Andrew Lambert Photography/SPL/ Photo Researchers, Inc.; **18l,** Lester V. Bergman/Corbis; **18m,** Cecile Brunswick/Peter Arnold, Inc.; **18r,** The Granger Collection, NY; **19t,** Alexander Tsiaras/Stock Boston; **19b,** AP/Wide World Photos; **20l,** George Payne; **20r,** Sheila Terry/SPL/Photo Researchers, Inc.; **21,** Russ Lappa; **22t,** Russ Lappa; **22b,** Richard Haynes; **22b inset,** Russ Lappa; **24tl,** Lawrence Migdale/Photo Researchers, Inc.; **24tr,** Stephen Frisch/Stock Boston; **24b,** Barry Runk/Grant Heilman Photography; **25,** Ric Ergenbright/Corbis; **26,** M. Claye/Jacana/Photo Researchers, Inc.; **27,** Richard Megna/Fundamental Photographs; **28,** Richard Haynes; **29,** Richard Haynes; **30,** Richard Haynes; **35,** Richard Hutchings/Photo Researchers, Inc.; **36,** Andrea Pistolesi/Getty Images, Inc.; **37,** Russ Lappa; **38bl,** Helene Rogers/Art Directors; **38br,** 2004 Estate of Alexander Calder/Artists Rights Society (ARS), New York/Art Resource, NY; **38–39t,** NASA; **39r,** Dorling Kindersley; **40,** Jump Run Productions/Getty Images, Inc.

Chapter 2
Pages 44–45, Richard Megna/Fundamental Photographs; **45r,** Russ Lappa; **46,** Ariel Skelley/Corbis; **47,** Tim Hauf/Visuals Unlimited; **48l,** Richard Haynes; **48r,** Russ Lappa; **49 both,** Richard Megna/Fundamental Photographs; **50tl,** John Serrao/Photo Researchers, Inc.; **50tm,** Charles D. Winters/Photo Researchers, Inc.; **50tr,** Russ Lappa; **50b,** Michael P. Gadomski/Photo Researchers, Inc.; **51 both,** Russ Lappa; **52,** David Young-Wolff/PhotoEdit; **53,** Aero Graphics, Inc./Corbis; **55,** Richard Haynes; **56,** Russ Lappa; **58 all,** Russ Lappa; **59t,** John D. Cunningham/Visuals Unlimited; **59 both,** Dorling Kindersley; **66,** Aaron Horowitz/Corbis; **69,** Charlie Neibergall/AP/Wide World Photos; **70 both,** Richard Megna/Fundamental Photographs; **72,** Russ Lappa; **73,** Russ Lappa; **74t,** Richard Haynes; **74b,** Melanie Duncan Thortis/The Vicksburg Post/AP/Wide World Photos; **75,** Kevin Keane; **77 all,** Russ Lappa; **78t,** John Serrao/Photo Researchers, Inc.; **78b both,** Richard Megna/Fundamental Photographs.

Chapter 3
Pages 82–83, Richard Megna/Fundamental Photographs; **83r,** Richard Haynes; **85,** Digital Vision/Getty Images, Inc.; **86,** Richard Haynes; **88t,** Layne Kennedy/Corbis; **88b,** Onne van der Wal/Corbis; **89,** Paul Barton/Corbis; **90,** Russ Lappa; **91,** Richard Haynes; **92l,** Tim Laman/Index Stock Imagery, Inc.; **92m,** Randy Ury/Corbis; **92r,** Mike & Carol Werner/Stock Boston; **93,** Richard Haynes; **94,** Russ Lappa; **95 all,** Richard Haynes; **96,** Tony Freeman/PhotoEdit; **97 all,** Russ Lappa; **98t,** Russ Lappa; **98b,** Lawrence Migdale/Photo Researchers, Inc.; **99 both,** Russ Lappa; **100 both,** Russ Lappa; **101,** LWA-Dann Tardif/Corbis; **102t,** Mark C. Burnett/Stock Boston; **102bl,** Russ Lappa; **102br,** Russ Lappa; **103tl,** B. Daemmrich/The Image Works; **103tr,** Russ Lappa; **103b,** Russ Lappa; **104,** Russ Lappa; **105,** Tom Pantages; **107,** Richard Haynes; **110,** Russ Lappa; **111,** Richard Haynes; **112,** Cleo Photography/Photo Researchers, Inc.; **113,** Russ Lappa; **114,** Richard Haynes; **116,** Richard Haynes.

Chapter 4
Pages 120–121, Gerald D. Tang; **121r,** Richard Haynes; **122l,** Volker Steger/SPL/Photo Researchers, Inc.; **122r,** SIU/Peter Arnold, Inc.; **124l,** Cary Wolinsky/carywolinksy.com; **124r,** Barry Runk/Grant Heilman Photography; **125,** Richard Pasley/Stock Boston; **126,** Richard Haynes; **127tl,** Tom Vezo/Minden Pictures; **127tr,** Russ Lappa; **127b,** Getty Images, Inc.; **128t,** Amana America, Inc.; **128b,** Tony Craddock/SPL/Photo Researchers, Inc.; **130t,** Russ Lappa; **130b,** Richard Haynes; **131l,** Michael J. Doolittle/The Image Works; **131r,** Grant Heilman Photography, Inc.; **132,** Roberto Borea/AP/Wide World Photos; **133t,** R.J. Erwin/Photo Researchers, Inc.; **133b,** Russ Lappa; **134,** Richard Haynes; **135t,** Russ Lappa; **135b,** Russ Lappa; **136t,** Russ Lappa; **136–137b,** Richard Haynes; **137t,** E.S. Ross/Visuals Unlimited; **138l,** Library of Congress; **138m,** Science Museum/Science & Society Picture Library; **138r,** Gim Media/Gemological Institute of America; **139t,** Mauro Fermariello/SPL/Photo Researchers, Inc.; **139b,** Richard Haynes; **140 both,** Richard Haynes; **141,** Richard Haynes; **142,** ISM/Phototake; **144,** Erich Lessing/Art Resource, NY; **146–147,** Richard Haynes; **148,** Richard Haynes; **149,** Russ Lappa; **150,** Erich Lessing/Art Resource, NY.

Page 154, Robert Llewellyn/Corbis; **155t,** Spencer Grant/PhotoEdit; **155b,** PhotoDisc/Getty Images, Inc.; **157,** Russell Gordon/Aurora; **158t,** Mary Evans Picture Library; **158b,** Corbis; **159t,** Bettmann/Corbis; **159b,** PhotoDisc/Getty Images, Inc.; **160–161,** Russ Lappa; **161l,** LWA-Dann Tardif/Corbis; **162,** Tony Freeman/PhotoEdit; **163t,** Russ Lappa; **163m,** Richard Haynes; **163b,** Russ Lappa; **164,** Richard Haynes; **166,** Richard Haynes; **168,** Tanton Yachts; **169,** Richard Haynes; **171t,** Dorling Kindersley; **171b,** Richard Haynes; **173,** Image Stop/Phototake; **176,** Richard Haynes; **183,** Richard Haynes; **192,** Richard Haynes.